FUNDAMENTALS OF REINFORCED CONCRETE

To my wife, Patricia,
and daughters, Kathleen, Judith
and Alice.

D1131299

This book is in the ADDISON-WESLEY SERIES IN CIVIL ENGINEERING

FUNDAMENTALS OF REINFORCED CONCRETE

JOHN N. CERNICA, PH.D.

Professor and Chairman
Department of Civil Engineering, Youngstown University

 ADDISON-WESLEY PUBLISHING COMPANY, INC.

READING, MASSACHUSETTS · PALO ALTO · LONDON

PREFACE

The content of this textbook and the presentation of the material are geared toward the following objectives: (1) To give the reader basic information which, once mastered, will serve him as foundations on which he can "build." (2) To emphasize an orderly and systematic procedure of solving problems. (3) To present the most recent design practices, and to show the interplay of physical testing, research, and latest ACI Code requirements regarding design practices. (4) To emphasize the need for good judgment and practical considerations in the choice, design, and erection of a concrete structure.

In striving to reach the first objective, the author has devoted appreciable effort to a detailed discussion of the basic material, its manufacture, its behavior, and the function of the components of a structure. Chapter 1 covers the subject of reinforced concrete from the standpoint of the material involved, whereas the remaining chapters discuss the behavior of the various components under load and present fundamental expressions for analysis and design. Wherever feasible, the equations are derived and explained—not merely used. Numerous sketches, photographs, and explanations are provided throughout the text to help the reader visualize, rather than memorize, the various techniques used in presenting the material.

To attain the second objective, the author has presented the example problems in "component" form: *Given:—To find:—Solution*. This manner of presentation, which leads the reader in systematic steps toward the final answer, provides an efficient and easy-to-understand procedure for solving problems. The reader who has adopted this method of problem solving will benefit from it in two ways: he will make fewer computational errors and he will have acquired a desirable form of presenting his data to those who check, approve, or "just look" at his work.

To meet the third objective, the author refers throughout to the most recent version of the ACI Code (June 1963) specifications governing the design under discussion, and cites the reasons for the existence of the requirements stated in the Code. Since the ultimate-load theory is being used more and more frequently, appreciable emphasis is placed on this method of analysis. Whenever feasible, and in conjunction with the design practice and ACI Code requirements, the elastic-stress approach is followed by one based on the ultimate-strength theory. Although these two methods represent two totally different design concepts, their merits are quite comparable. Thus a knowledge of both methods may indeed prove helpful to the future designer.

Finally, the last objective of the text is to emphasize that common sense, rather than the unquestioned use of some available form, method, specification, or procedure is the most important factor in design decisions. Without a sense of imagination, curiosity, and a look to the future, there would be no progress. No specification is intended to eliminate the "thinking" part of the design process.

In writing this text, the author has drawn on material presented by many writers in the field, and on his own notes accumulated while teaching the subject for many years. The author is particularly indebted to the American Concrete Institute, the Portland Cement Association, and the Concrete Reinforcing Steel Institute for their generous permission to reproduce many illustrations and tabular material in this text. He also wishes to express his gratitude to Dr. Hubert Howard, Dr. Frank D'Isa, and Professor Gus Mavrigan of the faculty of Youngstown University for their constructive criticism of the text, and to Mrs. Ralph Morell and Miss Gerri Sfara for the care and patience with which they typed a difficult manuscript.

Youngstown, Ohio   J.N.C.
June 1964

ACKNOWLEDGMENTS

The author wishes to thank the following organizations for permission to reproduce the material listed below:

AMERICAN CONCRETE INSTITUTE: 1963 ACI Standard Building Code Requirements for Reinforced Concrete (ACI 318–63).

AMERICAN INSTITUTE OF STEEL CONSTRUCTION: The tables appearing in Appendix A.

PORTLAND CEMENT ASSOCIATION: All the photographs appearing in the text with the exception of those mentioned below.

RAYMOND CONCRETE PILE COMPANY: The photograph at the beginning of Chapter 1.

STATE DEPARTMENT OF HIGHWAYS, HARRISBURG, PENNSYLVANIA: The photograph opening Chapter 4, as well as Figs. 6–2 and 6–6.

U.S. ARMY CORPS OF ENGINEERS, PITTSBURGH DISTRICT: Fig. 6–21.

CONTENTS

4   Axially Loaded Columns

5   Eccentrically Loaded Columns

6   Retaining Walls

7   Footings

Strength, firesafety, economy, weather resistance, durability, ease of fabrication, and natural beauty are some characteristics of concrete which make it a rather unique and desirable building material. The beauty of concrete is well exemplified by this single-arch bridge located in Arizona on the access road to Glen Canyon Dam from Kanob, Utah. The relative slenderness, and yet sturdy appearance, coupled with the bright reflection of the concrete in this rather sunny part of the country, gives the bridge a rare beauty, and demonstrates the accomplishments achieved in the technology of concrete.

1 REINFORCED CONCRETE

Matanzas Bridge over Canimar River, Cuba. Triple parabolic concrete-arch design 973 ft long and 115 ft high.

1–1 THE MATERIAL CONCRETE

Concrete is an artificial stone consisting of a mixture of cementing material and a mineral aggregate which is combined with water and cast in place in a plastic condition. This semifluid then hardens to a strong and durable substance. The strength, firesafety, economy, weather resistance, durability, and ease of fabrication are some of the characteristics of concrete which make it rather unique and certainly a very desirable building material.

Unlike steel or other structural materials, which are prefabricated in factories by machines and skilled workmen under closely controlled conditions of fabrication, concrete is often manufactured at the job site by unskilled workers and under adverse weather conditions. The proportioning and quality of the materials used and the process of mixing, placing, and curing are indeed important in the production, or manufacture, of concrete. However, to the laborer producing concrete, these aspects may not mean very much. Therefore supervision and inspection are significant factors in concrete constructions.

Complete control, however, is not possible; hence it is up to the designer to know the practical limitations of the materials and his design. It is up to him to study and control these factors so as to produce desirable results. Although there is no real substitute for sound engineering judgment, local building codes and *The American Concrete Institute (ACI) Building Code* are invaluable tools to the designer to ensure proper design and construction of concrete structures. The 1963 revision of the *ACI Building Code* (Appendix D) will be adhered to closely in this text. For the quality of some of the materials used, and for some tests to be performed, references will be made to *The American Society of Testing Materials (ASTM) Specifications,* obtainable at the Society's headquarters.

1–2   CEMENTS

The binding agents used in the fabrication of concrete are known as cements. They can be divided into two classifications: *bituminous* and *nonbituminous.* Asphalts and tars are bituminous cements. Natural cements, alumina cement, and portland cement are nonbituminous and are sometimes classified as *hydraulic* cements because they "set" (solidify) under water.

Because of the wide use of portland cement in this country, the term is frequently used as a synonym for concrete. Unless specified otherwise, the discussion of concrete in this text will be based on the assumption that portland cement is the cementing material and that it conforms to the *Specifications for Portland Cement (ASTM C 150)* or *Specifications for Air-Entraining Portland Cement (ASTM C 175).*

The use of cements dates back over two thousand years. Although no data are available concerning the composition or means of manufacturing cement, the ruins of some structures built by the Romans and Egyptians show that the mortars and the quality of the mortar-making material were good. Portland cement was first made in England about 140 years ago, and the credit for being the first to produce it goes to a bricklayer named Joseph Aspdin from Leeds, England. It was not until about 1860 that portland cement was brought to this country.

Portland cement is manufactured from raw materials containing lime, silica, and alumina in appropriate proportions. For the most part, limestone and shale compose the raw material.

The materials are ground separately to a fine grade and are then blended under carefully controlled proportioning either in a dry form or by a wet process.

Fig. 1–1. Set of laboratory standard sieves.

TABLE 1–1.   Calculated Compound Composition of Portland Cements*

Type of cement	Compound composition, %				Fineness	
	C_3S	C_2S	C_3A	C_4AF	cm²/gm†	% passing 325-mesh sieve
1. Normal	45	27	11	8	1710	90.7
2. Modified	44	31	5	13	1990	94.7
3. High-early-strength	53	19	10	10	2730	99.5
4. Low-heat	28	49	4	12	1880	93.1
5. Sulfate-resistant	38	43	4	8	1960	93.2

Tricalcium silicate	$3CaO \cdot SiO_2 = C_3S$
Dicalcium silicate	$2CaO \cdot SiO_2 = C_2S$
Tricalcium aluminate	$3CaO \cdot Al_2O_3 = C_3A$
Tetracalcium aluminoferrite	$4CaO \cdot Al_2O_3 \cdot Fe_2O_3 = C_4AF$

* Courtesy Portland Cement Association.
† Surface area as determined by Wagner turbidimeter test.

The blended mixture is then placed in a rotary kiln, essentially a cylindrical shell from 150 to 450 ft long and 8 to 13 ft in diameter, rotating about an axis slightly inclined to the horizontal. The temperature inside the kiln is approximately 2700°F.

The immediate product emerging from the kiln is clinkers which are cooled and then ground so fine that the majority will pass through a sieve having 200 meshes to the lineal inch, or 40,000 openings in one square inch (Fig. 1–1). A small amount of plaster of paris (or gypsum) is added to regulate the setting time of the cement. At this stage the cement is ready to be shipped for use.

There are five basic types of portland cement. In addition, special cements are also available. Table 1–2 complemented by the descriptions given in Table 1–3

TABLE 1–2.   Approximate Relative Strengths of Concrete
as Affected by Type of Cement

Type of portland cement	Compressive strength, % of strength of normal portland cement concrete		
	3 days	28 days	3 months
1. Normal	100	100	100
2. Modified	80	85	100
3. High-early-strength	190	130	115
4. Low-heat	50	65	90
5. Sulfate-resistant	65	65	85

TABLE 1–3.   Water-cement Ratios for Various Types of Construction and Exposure Conditions*

Type or location of structure	Severe or moderate climate, wide range of temperature, rain, and long freezing spells or frequent freezing and thawing, gal/sack of cement			Mild climate, rain or semi-arid; rarely snow or frost, gal/sack of cement		
	Thin sections	Moderate sections	Mass sections	Thin sections	Moderate sections	Mass sections
A. At the water line in hydraulic or waterfront structures or portions of such structures where complete saturation or intermittent saturation is possible, but not where the structure is continuously submerged in water	5	5½	6	5	5½	6
B. Portions of hydraulic or waterfront structures some distance from water line, but subject to frequent wetting by water	5½	6	6	5½	6½	7
C. Ordinary exposed structures, buildings and portions of bridges not coming under above groups	6	6½	7	6	7	7½
D. Complete continuous submergence in water	6	6½	7	6	6½	7
E. Concrete deposited through water	†	5½	5½	†	5½	5½
F. Pavement slabs directly on ground: Wearing slabs Base slabs	5½ 6½	† †	† †	6 7	† †	† †
G. Special case: For concrete not exposed to the weather, such as interiors of buildings and portions of structures entirely below ground, no exposure hazard is involved and the water-cement ratio should be selected on the basis of the strength and workability requirements.						

* Courtesy Portland Cement Association.
† These sections not practicable for the purpose intended.

should prove helpful to the engineer in deciding the type of cement most suitable for a particular job.

Type 1. Normal portland cement.   This is a general-purpose cement suitable for all uses that do not require the special properties of the other types. It is used in pavement and sidewalk construction, reinforced concrete buildings and bridges, railway structures, tanks and reservoirs, sewers, culverts, water pipe, masonry units, soil-cement mixtures, and whenever cement or concrete is not subject to special sulfate hazards or the heat generated by the hydration of the cement will not cause an objectionable rise in temperature.

Type 2. Modified portland cement.   This cement has a lower heat of hydration than Type 1 and generates heat at a slower rate. It also has improved resistance to sulfate attack. It is intended for use in structures of considerable size where a moderate heat of hardening is desirable to minimize the rise in temperature, as in large piers, heavy abutments, and heavy retaining walls built in warm weather. In cold weather, when the heat generated is of advantage, Type 1 may be preferable for these purposes. Type 2 is also used when added precaution against sulfate attack is important, as in drainage structures, where the sulfate concentrations are higher than normal but are not unusually severe.

Type 3. High-early-strength portland cement.   This type is used (a) when it is desired that cement develop high strength in a very short time so that forms may be removed as soon as possible or the concrete put into service as quickly as possible; (b) in cold-weather construction to reduce the usual period of protection against low temperatures; and (c) when the rapid development of high strengths can be secured more satisfactorily or more economically than by using richer mixes of cement of Type 1. It is produced from materials of high lime content, and the clinkers are ground more finely than for normal cements. The production of Type 3 is more costly than that of normal cement. Due to the greater shrinkage of the concrete mass subjected to drying, high-early-strength cements often cause extensive cracking and hence require intensive inspection.

Type 4. Low-heat portland cement.   This is a special cement to be used where the amount and rate of heat generated must be kept to a minimum. The development of strength also proceeds at a slower rate. It is intended for use only in large masses of concrete, such as large gravity dams where temperature rise resulting from the heat generated during hardening is a critical factor.

Type 5. Sulfate-resistant portland cement.   This is a special cement intended for use only in structures exposed to severe sulfate action, such as is encountered in some western states having soils or waters of high alkali content. It has a slower rate of hardening than normal portland cement.

1–3 AGGREGATES

The aggregates are the inner filler materials, usually particles of rock that are naturally or artificially crushed and added to the cement paste to increase its bulk. Approximately three-fourths of the total volume of a concrete mass is occupied by the aggregates.

In general, the aggregates fall into two categories: *fine* and *coarse*. The fine aggregate, which is usually designated as sand, is the filler material that will pass through a No. 4 sieve (approximately ¼-in. opening). Anything retained by this sieve, up to as much as 6 in., is usually classified as coarse aggregate.

A good aggregate, whether fine or coarse, is one that is clean, hard, strong, resistant to weathering action, contains no impurities which affect the strength of the concrete, and is well graded. The latter factor is particularly important in that it controls, to some extent, the workability of the plastic mass.

Since aggregate is cheaper than cement, it follows that an increase in the percentage of aggregates in the mix increases the economy of the mix. The quantity of water required to make the mass workable, however, is about proportional to the quantity of aggregate used. As we shall see later, the lower the water content, the greater the strength of the concrete. There is a practical limitation, therefore, to aggregate size and content.

The size, or grading, of the aggregate has some influence on the mix. For example, for one 1-in. cube the surface area to be wetted is only one-half of that of eight ½-in. cubes (same volume). Therefore, one way of cutting the water content is to increase the size of the aggregate. However, remember that the large aggregate creates voids which must be filled with smaller particles.

Of the coarse aggregates, crushed stone and blast-furnace slag are the two most predominantly used in concrete mixes. Crushed stone is produced by crushing or breaking up large solid rocks. Blast-furnace slag is a hard, relatively light, porous material produced during the melting of iron in a blast furnace.

1-4 CONCRETE PROPORTIONING

The strength of concrete depends on many factors, such as thoroughness of mixing, care in curing, and, perhaps most, on the quality and relative amounts of materials used in the mix. The proportioning, as well as the quality, of the cement, water, and aggregate used is dictated to a large extent by economy and the desired quality of the finished product (Fig. 1-2).

It is not always necessary or feasible to develop concrete of the highest possible quality. The quality of the concrete in a footing might be quite different from that in a building floor or that of a dam. Although there are methods of proportioning based on experimental data, there is no mathematical formula that can be used to predict the strength of the concrete for various mixes and conditions.

A satisfactory, and perhaps the oldest, method of proportioning is the trial, or empirical, method. As the name suggests, one proceeds by selecting two or three water-cement ratios, and knowing the consistency or slump desired on the job, one varies the ratio of fine to coarse aggregate for each water-cement ratio (Table 1-3). From each mix, cast at least two, but preferably three, 6-in. by 12-in. cylinders in the standard manner explained by ASTM C 39. Basically, the specimens are formed by placing the concrete in three layers of approximately equal volume, each layer being rodded with 25 strokes of a ⅝-in. round rod, approxi-

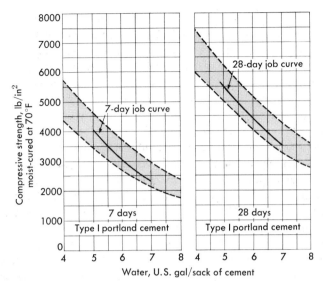

Fig. 1–2. For important work, the job materials should be tested and the data used to construct job curves. These curves suggest the water content which will produce specified strengths.

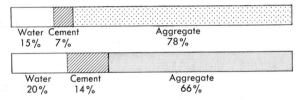

Fig. 1–3. Range in proportion of materials usually used in concrete. Upper bar represents lean mix of stiff consistency with large aggregate. Lower bar represents rich mix of wet consistency with small aggregate.

mately 2 ft long. The curing of these cylinders should be the same for all mixes and should simulate the conditions of the structure in the field. After testing the cylinders, the desired mix is that which most satisfies both strength requirements and economy. In many cases it is not necessary to run these trial tests because such tests have been run, and data giving the proportions which satisfy certain slump and strength conditions may be profitably applied to various other situations. For example, the National Slag Association is one source of much information of this sort.

The proportions are usually designated as a ratio of cement, fine aggregate, and coarse aggregate, in that order. For example, a 1:2:3 ratio designates one part of cement, two parts of fine aggregate, and three parts of coarse aggregate. This can be expressed in terms of volume or weight. To prevent confusion, volume or weight should be included in the description. For example, the water-cement ratio is commonly expressed in gallons of water per sack of cement, but it may also be expressed as pounds of water to pounds of cement. Figure 1–3 shows the common range in proportions of materials usually used in concrete.

1–5 ADMIXTURES

An admixture is a substance other than the cement, water, and aggregate which is added to the concrete mix for the purpose of achieving one or more of the following objectives: improve the workability of the plastic mass, provide air entrainment, accelerate setting and hardening, improve the dispersion of cement particles, the curing, and the water-repellent characteristics, modify chemical reactions and color, or to produce some other desirable effects.

When the quantity of cement and fine aggregate is relatively small, the resulting concrete is a poorly workable plastic mass. *Hydrated lime, diatomaceous silica, fly ash,* and *bentonite* are some of the admixtures used to correct this condition. These substances act as separators of the coarse aggregate particles, thus reducing friction and increasing the *workability* of the plastic mass. Although the above are generally classed as workability admixtures because they improve the workable features of a mix, they also serve as fillers of small voids. Their presence helps to reduce the amount of "bleeding." They complement the fine particles necessary for the formation of a film of water which creates cohesion among the particles and helps stiffen and add total form to the mix. One should note, however, that the presence of large quantities of these mixtures provides more surface area to be wetted and therefore requires a higher water-cement ratio to yield a prescribed consistency. In this connection the effect of the increased water-cement ratio on the quality of the concrete must be kept in mind since water affects the strength of the concrete (Fig. 1–2).

For various reasons, it might be desirable to speed up the setting and hardening time of the concrete. Such reasons might include: detrimental effects of low temperature, earlier use of the structure, economy in one form or another, etc. *Calcium chloride* is the only material approved for use as an *accelerator* in general concrete work (it is also a good antifreeze admixture), but the quantity used should be limited to not more than 2% by weight of the cement. It is added either in the form of a solution considered as part of the mixing water, or in dry crystalline form. In the latter case, it should be added to the aggregates and kept away from contact with the cement until the materials are put in the mixer. When it is used in combination with heated materials, as for winter construction, care must be taken to avoid overly rapid stiffening that might interfere with proper placing. It should not be used to prevent freezing of the concrete; this should be done by protective covers and by heating the surrounding air. Such protection can be eliminated sooner, however, when the admixture is used.

Introducing air into the concrete mix generally results in a small decrease in strength and weight, but the workability of the mix and the life of the concrete usually increase. The voids formed by the entrained air serve as a cushion to the deformation resulting from freezing or thawing, and thus increase the durability of the concrete. Air entraining is effectively, and most frequently, accomplished either by using air-entrained portland cement, or by adding an agent at the mixer. In general, the compressive-strength effect of the air-entrained portland cement concrete is about the same as or slightly less than that of the standard portland cement. *Sulfonated soaps* or *oils* and *natural resins* are examples of compounds which can be used to produce air entrainment.

The above-mentioned effects are perhaps the most commonly sought special advantages of using an admixture. Other agents used for the purposes of reducing the clustering effect of the cement particles, aiding the curing process, repelling water, and modifying chemical reaction or color might be important, depending on the conditions desired. For the effect they create and for the description of their use, refer to a text on plain concrete.

1–6   MORTAR MIXTURES

Mortars are mixtures of cement, sand, and water. As in the case of the concrete mix, the proportions of the mortar mix are governed by the quality desired, which is dictated by the type of use, by economy, and by other factors, and the quantity of mixing water per quantity of cement notably influences the strength of a mortar—the larger the amount of water, the weaker the mortar.

Assuming no air voids in a wet mortar, we find that the volume of the mortar is approximately equal to the sum of the absolute volumes of sand, cement, and water. The absolute volume of one cubic foot of sand generally varies from 0.6 to 0.7 ft³ of solids. The volume of solids in a 94-lb sack of cement (standard sack) amounts to approximately 0.49 ft³.

1–7   COMPRESSIVE STRENGTH OF CONCRETE

The most significant characteristic of concrete is its great compressive strength, which is so much greater than its tensile strength that just about all concrete structures are designed with the assumption that the concrete resists compressive forces but not tensile forces. To take care of tensile forces, steel is embedded in the concrete, in a manner described in the following chapters.

The ultimate compressive strength is the basis on which the specification codes prescribe the unit stress that is assumed in the design. The ultimate strength most frequently used as a basis is that exhibited 28 days after pouring, but strengths at ages of 3 and 7 days are sometimes used as a basis, especially for high-early-strength concretes. Therefore the age used as base line should be stated. Depending on the type of mix and the curing conditions, the ultimate strength of concrete at an age of 28 days may exceed even 8000 lb/in².

In most instances, the compressive strength is determined by testing molded cylindrical specimens 6 in. in diameter and 12 in. long at a specific rate of load until rupture occurs (see "Method of Test for Compressive Strength of Molded Concrete Cylinders," *ASTM Specifications*). In determining the strength of any

Fig. 1–4. Placing test specimen in testing machine. The spherical bearing block on the machine head prevents bending of the specimen.

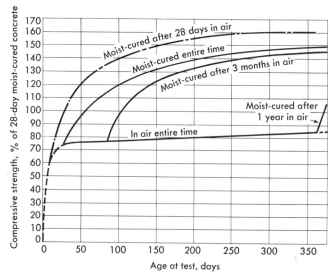

Fig. 1–5. Strength of concrete continues to increase so long as moisture is present to promote hydration of the cement. Note that resumption of moist curing after a drying period also increases strength. The test specimens were relatively small compared to most concrete construction members. Hence in practice it would be difficult to obtain resaturation, and moist curing should therefore be continuous.

one mix, one should note that no two cylinders from that mix will have exactly the same ultimate strength. Sometimes the difference may be quite great; deviations of perhaps 15% or more from an average mean may occur. It follows therefore that for a relatively dependable average of strength, at least three cylinders should be tested (Fig. 1–4).

It should be noted that the ultimate strength for a prescribed age refers to the rupture strength of the concrete at that age. The ultimate strength at different ages varies, the relative difference being quite great per unit time at first but much less after a few weeks (Fig. 1–5). For about the first month, the strength increases quite rapidly with time. The increase continues indefinitely but at a much lower rate.

1–8   TENSILE STRENGTH OF CONCRETE

Compared with the compressive strength, the tensile strength of concrete is relatively low, averaging about 10% of the compressive strength. It ranges from 7% to a little over 10%. For this reason it is seldom expected to resist tensile load and, in most cases, such as in the design of reinforced concrete beams, the tensile strength is completely ignored. In such instances, the tensile forces are supplied by the steel reinforcement. The tensile strength does, however, help to combat cracking due to thermal and shrinkage stresses and that due to horizontal shearing stresses in a beam.

Mounting a specimen for tensile tests is more difficult than it is for a compressive test. Also, the holding vices may induce secondary stresses in the specimen, thus making the reliability of the results questionable. These factors, coupled with the fact that tensile tests are in most cases of little importance, make such tests uncommon.

1–9   SHEARING STRENGTH OF CONCRETE

The sliding of two adjacent planes, one upon the other, creates two equal and opposite parallel forces on those planes. The cohesion of the concrete material and the interlocking action of the components (stone against stone) tend to resist such sliding action, allowing the concrete a certain shearing strength.

Tests to determine the ability of the concrete to resist direct shear are difficult to perform. The effects of bending, friction, bearing, diagonal tension, or of other stresses which are often difficult to eliminate, tend to make the results inconclusive. Perhaps the best practical means of applying pure shear is through torsion of a cylindrical specimen. Although the results of tests seem to vary widely, the shearing strength is generally assumed to range from about one-sixth to one-fourth of the compressive strength. Like the compressive strength, the shearing strength is also influenced, both qualitatively and quantitatively, by the contents of the mix. For example, a concrete composed of a "rich" paste (higher cement-aggregate ratio) and a better aggregate generally gives a higher shear strength than that consisting of a lean mix.

1–10 MODULUS OF ELASTICITY OF CONCRETE

For most structural materials, it has been established by direct experimentation that, within certain limits, the deformation of the material is proportional to the applied force. The ratio of the stress up to the proportional limit to the strain in the direction of this force and caused by this force is known as the modulus of elasticity. There are three points at which the modulus of elasticity is taken (Fig. 1–6): one, called the *initial modulus,* is computed by taking the tangent at the origin of the graph; the second, called the *secant modulus,* is the slope of the line connecting the origin to the point on the curve representing an arbitrary stress; the third, called the *tangent modulus,* is the slope of the tangent to the stress-strain curve at the working stress. There seems to be some disagreement as to which is the best. The secant modulus is perhaps the one most commonly used in design. The *ACI Code* gives an expression for determining the modulus of elasticity of concrete:

$$E_c = w^{1.5}33\sqrt{f_c'},$$

where w is the unit weight of concrete. Likewise, the code assumes the modulus of elasticity of steel to be 29 million pounds per square inch ($E_s = 29 \times 10^6$ psi).

Influenced by several factors, the modulus varies quite widely, perhaps from 1 to 5 million psi at, say, 28 days. Cement content, curing conditions, age, density, quality of ingredients, especially aggregates, and the water-cement ratio all tend to affect the modulus. Although time consuming, a common method of determining the secant modulus of elasticity is by testing a 6 in. by 12 in. molded, cylindrical specimen in compression. The stress-strain relationship is then plotted and the modulus determined as described above. The modulus of elasticity is expressed in pounds per square inch.

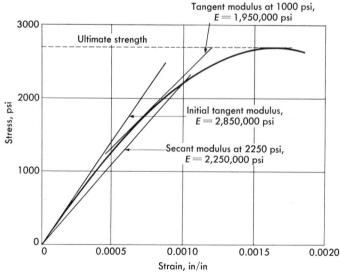

Fig. 1–6. Three moduli of elasticity for a concrete specimen tested at an age of 28 days.

1–11   CREEP OR PLASTIC FLOW OF CONCRETE

In designing reinforced concrete structures by the straight-line theory, one assumes that concrete is an elastic material. This assumption is usually safe and practical, although basically incorrect. Concrete is actually a very rigid plastic which is subject to progressive and cumulative deformation under load at common temperatures. This property, called *plastic strain,* will here be defined as the time yield of concrete under prolonged constant load or, in the case of repeated load, as the strain obtained beyond that of the first instance of loading.

The plastic strain may cause (a) a shifting of load from the concrete to the steel reinforcement in compression members, (b) a reduction of prestress in pre- or post-tensioned beams, (c) a change of inflection points in continuous beams, and (d) an increase in the deflection of a simple beam. All these are points that may be important in the design and use of concrete.

An illustrative explanation of plastic flow can be given by considering a simple static load P applied axially to a concrete cylinder, as shown in Fig. 1–7. The initial elastic deformation is Δ_e; if the load is maintained over a long period of time, an increase in the deflection can be observed. This added deflection, Δ_p, is known as the plastic strain.

Previous investigations show that in the case of sustained loading, the amount of plastic deformation is a function of time and of load. In the case of repeated loading, the plastic deformation is also a function of the number of load applications.

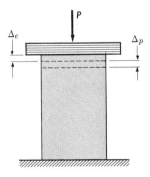

Figure 1–7

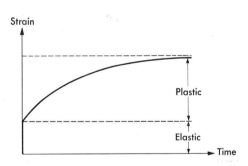

Fig. 1–8. Typical strain-versus-time relationship; sustained load.

There is no conclusive experimental evidence concerning the exact mechanism of creep. Figure 1–8 serves as a general explanation of plastic strain, in that it shows a typical graph which represents a time vs. plastic strain relationship. It can be seen that the rate of change of plastic strain is different from that of the elastic strain. At the end of 6 months, about three-fourths of the total plastic strain has occurred; at the end of one year 90% has occurred, and the rest is spread out over a longer period of time.

1–12 OTHER PROPERTIES

Changes in temperature, loads, water-cement ratio, chemical composition of the cement, moisture content, and settlement of the fresh mass influence the change of the volume of concrete. Concrete shrinks when exposed to air and expands when immersed in water; it expands with increasing and contracts with decreasing temperature. Loads may cause temporary and/or permanent deformation.

The change of volume of concrete is relatively small. The thermal coefficient of expansion of concrete is commonly accepted to be approximately 0.000006 in./in./°F. The shrinkage caused by the escape of water or drying may vary from 0.0002 to 0.005 of the volume. It is evident that were the concrete free to deform, the magnitudes of these changes would be of little importance. Therefore, provisions must be made in the design to compensate for this condition. In most reinforced concrete members, deformation is counteracted by the individual or combined effort of steel reinforcement, adjacent structures, foundation, or other means.

The weight of concrete may vary from less than 100 lb/ft^3 to as high as 160 lb/ft^3, except in relatively rare cases where it is even higher. Most ordinary stone or gravel concretes will range from 140 lb to 160 lb/ft^3. The reinforced concretes are about 3 to 5 lb heavier than similar plain concrete. For estimates, an average value of 150 lb/ft^3 is commonly assumed. The proportions of the ingredients, the water content, and the entrained-air content influence the weight of the concrete. But perhaps the most significant factor is the weight of the aggregate used. Concretes with lightweight aggregates have been reported to weigh as little as 80 lb/ft^3. For special projects where iron ore and steel punchings were used in the mix, concretes weighing over 250 lb/ft^3 have been made.

Concrete is not a good conductor of heat. Unlike steel, the strength of the concrete and its ability to carry load are not extensively affected by heat. Thickness, voids, cement, water content, and type and size of aggregate (different types have different effects) influence the thermal conductivity of the concrete.

The durability of the concrete as a structure is to some extent influenced by its weathering qualities, i.e., its ability to combat the effects of freezing and thawing, of wind and rain, and of variation in moisture content. Temperature changes may cause small cracks. Volumetric changes due to moisture contribute further to this cracking tendency, the result being a gradual deterioration of the surface. It is difficult to determine the weathering resistance of a concrete in a laboratory. Tests have shown, however, that concretes of high moisture content failed at fewer cycles of freezing and thawing. It is generally assumed that the ice in the cracks is one of the main causes leading to fast deterioration of the concrete.

1–13 MIXING CONCRETE

The process of interfolding or incorporating the cement paste in the aggregate to produce a uniformly consistent mix of cement, water, and aggregate is called *mixing*. The ingredients are placed in a mixing chamber known as a *drum*.

Fig. 1–9. Concrete batch plant.

Fig. 1–10. Truck mixer discharging concrete mass.

These drums are equipped with blades so arranged that when the drum rotates, the blades lift the ingredients up to the top of the drum and then drop it to the bottom. Depending on the mixer, these blades also aid in the discharge of the plastic mass.

Mixers vary in design and size. They might vary in capacity from 1 ft^3 to 8 yd^3. Most job mixers have a capacity of at least 1 yd^3. The mixers that are mounted on trucks which deliver concrete from a central mixing plant, or batch plant (Fig. 1–9), to the job usually have a capacity of 2 to 5 yd³. These mixers are known as *transit* mixers (Fig. 1–10). They have a bowl-shaped drum for which the ratio of length to diameter, for best efficiency, is a little over one to one.

All concrete should be mixed thoroughly until it is uniform in appearance and all ingredients are uniformly distributed. The time required for thorough mixing depends on several factors. Specifications usually require a minimum of one minute for mixers up to 1-yd³ capacity, with an increase of 15 seconds for each additional ½ cubic yard or fraction thereof. The mixing period should be measured from the time all solid materials are in the mixer drum, provided that all the water is added before one-fourth the mixing time has elapsed.

For best results, the larger mixers rotate slower than the smaller. The circumferential speed should be approximately 200 ft/min. For most mixers this amounts to approximately 20 rpm.

1–14 PLACING AND CURING CONCRETE

Poor placing and curing operations may do a great deal of harm to the most thorough and careful design. Placing is the movement of the concrete mass from the mixer to the final place in the structure. Curing entails the control and adjustment of conditions which affect the process of hardening and the strength of the concrete.

Needless to say, segregation of the concrete is undesirable. Therefore care should be taken to avoid it, or to correct the situation should segregation occur. Chuting of the concrete into a form at an angle, horizontal flow of the concrete within a form, or dropping of the plastic mass from great heights usually results in undesirable segregation. To reduce the height of the fall, it is advisable to let the concrete drop into an outside pocket or baffle from which it flows over into the lower forms. Such an arrangement is shown in Fig. 1–11. Discharge through steep chutes usually makes the concrete strike against the form faces and thus leads to separation and honeycombing of the plastic mass at the bottom. Likewise, lateral movement of the concrete causes the coarse aggregate and the mortar to flow separately through forms, the result being a porous and honeycombed structure. Figure 1–11 shows correct and incorrect methods of placing the concrete.

Concrete should be deposited vertically in horizontal, even layers; it should not be dumped in large quantities at any one point and then spread throughout the form by vibrators or other means (Fig. 1–12). The depth of the layers should not, in most instances, exceed one foot. Greater depths usually result in the segregation of the coarse aggregate and sedimentation of the finer ingredients of the mixture.

To eliminate the danger of damaging a layer already placed during further operations, it is advisable to place a new layer either when the one previously laid is still in the plastic state or when it is thoroughly hardened.

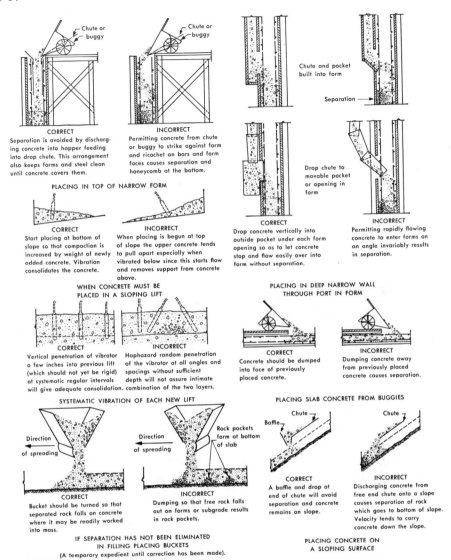

Fig. 1–11. Correct and incorrect methods of placing concrete. Adapted from *Recommended Practice for Measuring, Mixing, and Placing Concrete* (ACI 614–42) of the American Concrete Institute.

Except when immersed in water, concrete should be compacted by tamping, rodding, spading, or vibrating to assure complete encasement of the reinforcing bars and other embedded fixtures, to eliminate large voids, and to bring it in contact with the forms. Vibrating the concrete with power-driven vibrators is perhaps the most widely used means of compaction. The use of mechanically

Fig. 1–12. Pouring buckets transport the plastic mass from truck to form.

Fig. 1–13. Workman using mechanical vibrator.

driven vibrators is beneficial and is recommended, but caution should be exercised in their operation (Fig. 1–13).

Workmen find that vibrators can be used to move concrete from one place to another within the form and hence tend to substitute this method for shoveling. As previously mentioned, this vibration tends to segregate the aggregate. Moreover, the consistency of the concrete, the time of vibration, and the speed of the vibrator are important factors.

With a given amount of cement paste, more aggregate is used in stiff mixes than in fluid ones; consequently, the stiff mixes are more economical from the standpoint of cost of materials. Stiff mixes require more labor in placing, however, and when the mixture is too stiff for the given placing conditions, the additional cost of placing may offset any saving that is made in materials. Concrete mixtures should always be of a consistency and workability suitable for the conditions of the job. Thin members and heavily reinforced members require mixtures that are more fluid than large members containing little reinforcement. Mixtures of plastic consistency are required for the majority of concrete work, since concrete of such consistency does not crumble, but flows sluggishly without segregation. Thus neither very stiff, crumbly mixes nor very fluid, watery mixes are regarded to be of plastic consistency.

The slump test, ASTM C 143, is used as a measure of consistency. Briefly, this test is carried out by filling a slump cone in three layers of about one-third the volume of the mold, and rodding each layer with 25 strokes of a $\frac{5}{8}$-in. round rod. The mold is then removed from the concrete by raising it carefully in the vertical direction. The slump is the difference between the height of the mold and the axis of the specimen. The slump test should not be used to compare proportions or the water content. To avoid mixes too stiff or too fluid, slumps falling within the limits given in Table 1–4 are recommended.

After the concrete has been placed, it is permitted to harden and gain strength, a process known as curing. This is considered as the last but certainly not the

TABLE 1–4. Recommended Slumps for Various Types of Construction*

Type of construction	Slump, in.	
	Maximum	Minimum
Reinforced foundation walls and footings	5	2
Plain footings, caissons and substructure walls	4	1
Slabs, beams and reinforced walls	6	3
Building columns	6	3
Pavements	3	2
Heavy mass construction	3	1

* Adapted from the 1940 Joint Committee Report on "Recommended Practice and Standard Specifications for Concrete and Reinforced Concrete." When high-frequency vibrators are used, the values given should be reduced about one-third.

least step of importance in the manufacture of concrete—as a matter of fact, it might be considered one of the most important steps.

Water is necessary for the hydration of the cement, and therefore for maximum strength, the fresh concrete must not be permitted to dry prematurely for at least several days. The time depends, to some extent, on the temperature. Usually the lower the temperature the longer the time that the concrete should be kept wet. Temperatures below freezing are undesirable, the most favorable normal range being between 55°F and 100°F. Temperature affects the speed with which the chemical reaction takes place. Increasing the temperature speeds up the chemical reaction in the concrete, as well as the hardening and setting process. A typical relationship between temperature and strength is shown in Fig. 1–14.

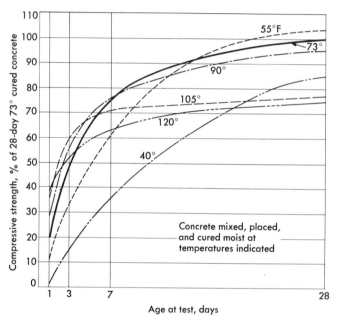

Fig. 1–14. The strength and other properties of concrete are affected by the temperature.

In a sense, the curing process may be defined as the process of retaining in the concrete all the mixing water. Most of the concrete strength is developed in the first 28 days, increasing quite rapidly during the first few days. In these early stages, premature and rapid drying is most dangerous. Fast drying may result in cracking or crazing of the surface, and in a very significant reduction of the strength. For the first few days, at least, it is advisable to keep the surface constantly protected against drying either by preventing the moisture already in the concrete from escaping or by applying new moisture to it. The latter process, which often is the most economical, involves the use of sprinkling, covering the surface with burlap or straw which is kept moist by sprinkling, or by ponding with earth banks, or other means.

It was found that concretes cured at temperatures around 300°F, a temperature commonly used in prestressed concrete manufacture, reached a strength in one day equivalent to that of a strength gained in 30 days under normal temperature. It should be noted, however, that at a higher temperature the rate of evaporation increases, and therefore the amount of water supplied to the concrete should be adjusted accordingly.

1–15 STEEL REINFORCEMENT

As previously stated, the tensile strength of concrete is only about 10% of its compressive strength. Hence concrete cannot be relied upon to take a high tensile load. To overcome this deficiency, steel bars are embedded in the concrete to form a composite unit such that the concrete withstands compression and steel, tension.

It should be noted that this combination, known as reinforced concrete, is an efficient unit. As mentioned above, concrete has high compressive strength. Steel has very desirable tensile properties, as well as good compressive strength, although care must be taken to avoid buckling. Concrete is less affected by heat than is steel, and is more resistant to normal atmospheric conditions. Used as a composite unit, the concrete protects the steel from heat and corrosion while the steel supplies the tensile, and often compressive, force necessary for a most efficient and economical design.

To develop tensile force in the steel, there must be sufficient bond between the concrete and the steel. Originally the reinforcing rods consisted primarily of plain round and square bars. These, however, furnish a relatively poor resistance to slippage and are therefore seldom employed in present-day construction. Instead so-called deformed bars (Fig. 1–15) with surface irregularities (deformations) are almost universally used.

Fig. 1–15. Types of deformed bars.

The bars are manufactured from three grades of steel: *structural, intermediate,* and *hard*. From a structural viewpoint, only the yield point of these different grades is important. Ductility and other properties may be significant in certain instances, such as for structures subjected to shock loads. For the three types mentioned, the yield point is highest for the hard grade and lowest for the structural grade. The grade used may be governed by specific situations, code requirements, or it may be a matter of choice on the part of the engineer. The cross-sectional areas of the reinforcing bars, plain or deformed, vary from a size equivalent to that of a round bar with diameter $\frac{1}{4}$ in. to that of a round bar with diameter 2.25 in., i.e., they vary from a No. 2 to a No. 18 bar inclusive. The larger bars, from No. 11 to No. 18, are used primarily for "special" jobs. Each of these numbers implies an $\frac{1}{8}$-in. increment in the diameter of round bars. Because of the stated equivalence, a No. 4 deformed bar, for example, has a cross-sectional area and a unit weight that are equivalent to those of a round bar whose diameter is four times $\frac{1}{8}$ in., or $\frac{1}{2}$ in. Likewise a No. 7 bar is $\frac{7}{8}$ in. in diameter, etc.

Wire and wire mesh are other forms of steel reinforcement extensively used in slabs, walls, and other thin concrete sections for the purpose of taking the tensile effects of bending, shrinkage, and thermal stress. Wire mesh is steel wire woven in various patterns.

1–16 FORMS

In concrete construction, the term "forms" is taken to mean the formwork into which concrete in the plastic condition is poured to give a structure, or part of a structure, a definite size and shape and a certain relative alignment. The form must be designed to withstand the pressure that the concrete exerts. It must be braced against bulging or movement in any direction. It must be capable of preventing leakage of the mortar before setting occurs. Its surface must be prepared such as to not only produce a certain finish on the concrete but also preserve the life of the form which is to be used again.

A fluid in a container exerts a pressure on the bottom due to its own weight, as well as a pressure on the walls of the container due to the hydrostatic head of the fluid. As a semifluid, concrete acts in a similar manner. When floors or slabs are to be poured, the forms must be designed to prevent the excessive deflection or settlement that would otherwise occur due to the weight of the concrete. For walls and columns, lateral pressure is encountered. This pressure varies with depth and depends to a large extent on the temperature, placement, and the method of compacting the concrete. To determine the lateral pressure, one usually assumes that the concrete is a liquid weighing 145 lb/ft³. Actually the weight is almost always less than that. The assumption of 145 lb/ft³ is perhaps most correct for structures such as columns which are usually poured very rapidly. For a certain temperature, different rates of pouring result in different maximum pressures. Interestingly enough, it seems that in all cases a maximum pressure is reached at some depth, then decreases with further increases in depth. Concrete sets faster at high temperatures than at low ones, i.e., at low temperature it remains a semifluid longer. Therefore, it follows that the lateral pressure of the concrete on the forms is greater at lower temperatures. Vibrating the concrete tends to increase its fluidity, which in turn increases the lateral pressure.

The forms should be cleaned and oiled before the concrete is poured. This improves the surface of the finished concrete, facilitates the removal of the forms, and helps preserve the life of the forms. Care must be taken to ensure that no oil gets on the reinforcement, since this contact would be harmful to the bond between steel and concrete. There are many types of oils that serve the above-mentioned purpose. However, remember that it should never be applied so thick that it will have a detrimental effect on the concrete.

1–17 SAFETY FACTORS

Since one will rarely find a structure which does not, in some way, either directly or indirectly affect the safety and welfare of the people about it, and since unsafe structures are in the long run uneconomical, every precaution must be taken to eliminate the building of unsafe structures that may fail under loads exceeding the design load. One such precaution is the use of conservative values of steel and concrete stresses in the design. The unit stresses used in the design are not the ultimate stresses for concrete or steel, but fractions of those values. The ratio of the ultimate stress in the case of concrete, or the elastic limit in the case of steel, to that used in the design is called the safety factor.

It should be noted that the safety factor is not the same for all structures. It varies with conditions and, to some degree, with the designer. In general, the design engineer has to comply with certain regulations and specifications both in the design and building of a structure. The *American Concrete Institute Building Code* requirements for reinforced concrete list the unit stresses permissible for safe design (Table 1–5). These specifications are considered complete, reliable, and authoritative. They are based, to a great extent, on the practical experience and good judgment of many engineers working with reinforced concrete, and on many tests and investigations. These specifications are widely used and closely adhered to. But it must be remembered that they are a good guide, but cannot take the place of good judgment. Good judgment is irreplaceable. To acquaint the students with their use, reference to these specifications shall be made throughout this text.

1–18 WORKMANSHIP AND INSPECTION

The quality of concrete depends to a large extent on good workmanship during its fabrication. Mechanized equipment helps in concrete construction, but it is the workman who controls and operates this equipment and properly arranges the material as called for in the design. A good design might be severely damaged by poor workmanship in construction. It is not sufficient to merely present the

TABLE 1–5. Allowable Stresses in Concrete

Description		For any strength of concrete in accordance with Section 502	Allowable stresses			
			For strength of concrete shown below			
			$f_c' = 2500$ psi	$f_c' = 3000$ psi	$f_c' = 4000$ psi	$f_c' = 5000$ psi
Modulus of elasticity ratio: n For concrete weighing 145 lb/ft³ (see Section 1102 of ACI Code)	n	$\dfrac{29{,}000{,}000}{w^{1.5}33\sqrt{f_c'}}$	10	9	8	7
Flexure: f_c Extreme fiber stress in compression	f_c	$0.45f_c'$	1125	1350	1800	2250
Extreme fiber stress in tension in plain concrete footings and walls	f_c	$1.6\sqrt{f_c'}$	80	88	102	113
Shear: v (as a measure of diagonal tension at a distance d from the face of the support) Beams with no web reinforcement*	v_c	$1.1\sqrt{f_c'}$	55*	60*	70*	78*
Joists with no web reinforcement	v_c	$1.2\sqrt{f_c'}$	61	66	77	86
Members with vertical or inclined web reinforcement or properly combined bent bars and vertical stirrups	v	$5\sqrt{f_c'}$	250	274	316	354
Slabs and footings (peripheral shear, Section 1207)*	v_c	$2\sqrt{f_c'}$	100*	110*	126*	141*
Bearing: f_c On full area			625	750	1000	1250
On one-third area or less†		$0.25f_c'$ $0.375f_c'$	938	1125	1500	1875

   * For shear values for lightweight aggregate concrete see Section 1208 ACI Code.
   † This increase shall be permitted only when the least distance between the edges of the loaded and unloaded areas is a minimum of one-fourth of the parallel side dimension of the loaded area. The allowable bearing stress on a reasonably concentric area greater than one-third but less than the full area shall be interpolated between the values given.

specifications to the contractor. They must be enforced and followed to ensure quality and to prevent mistakes. In other words, the work must be inspected by men who are familiar with the design, with the function of the structure, and with the characteristics and purposes of the materials used. The materials must be checked and the production scheme closely supervised. It might be remembered that the selection of a reliable contractor is an important factor to be considered in the production of good-quality concrete.

REFERENCES

1. PORTLAND CEMENT ASSOCIATION, *Design and Control of Concrete Mixtures,* 10th ed.
2. R. C. REESE, *CRSI Design Handbook,* Concrete Reinforcing Steel Institute, 1962.
3. HARLAN H. EDWARDS, "Progress in Determining the Relation Between Test Cylinders and Concrete in the Structure," *ACI Journal,* Nov. 1929.
4. J. R. SHANK, "The Mechanics of Plastic Flow of Concrete," *ACI Journal,* Nov.–Dec. 1935.
5. COMMITTEE 212, "Admixtures for Concrete," *ACI Journal,* Nov. 1944.
6. W. T. MORAN, F. H. JACKSON, BRUCE E. FOSTER, T. C. POWERS, "Admixtures in Concrete," *ACI Journal,* Sept. 1950.
7. H. F. GONNERMAN, "Study of Methods of Curing Concrete," *ACI Journal,* Feb. 1930.
8. R. C. REESE, *Recommended Practice for Placing Reinforcing Bars,* Concrete Reinforcing Steel Institute, 1959.
9. AMERICAN CONCRETE INSTITUTE, *Manual of Standard Practice for Detailing Reinforced Concrete Structures* (ACI 315–57), June 1957.
10. HENRY L. KENNEDY, "The Function of Entrained Air in Concrete," *ACI Journal,* June 1943.
11. COMMITTEE 614, "Recommended Practice for Measuring, Mixing, and Placing Concrete," *ACI Journal,* Nov. 1941.
12. JOHN H. BANKER, "Vibration Practices in Structural Work," *ACI Journal,* June 1953.
13. LEWIS H. TUTHILL, "Vibration of Mass Concrete," *ACI Journal,* June 1953.
14. WALTER O. CRAWLEY, "Effect of Vibration on Air Content of Mass Concrete," *ACI Journal,* June 1953.
15. H. S. MEISSNER, "Compacting Concrete by Vibration," *ACI Journal,* June 1953.
16. SAM COMESS, "Practical Applications of Vibration for Placing Concrete," *ACI Journal,* Sept.–Oct. 1935.
17. W. R. JOHNSON, "Vibration of Concrete," *ACI Journal,* Mar.–Apr. 1935.
18. S. I. COLLIER, "Bond Characteristics of Commercial and Prepared Reinforcing Bars," *ACI Journal,* June 1947.

2 BEAMS IN BENDING

Highway Bridge, Spartanburg, South Carolina. This highway-separation structure over U.S. 29 at Shop Road has 10 prestressed beams, each 60 ft long, and 10 beams, each 65 ft long. Piles and pile caps were cast in place.

2–1 INTRODUCTION

A beam may be generally defined as a structural member subjected to bending. Structural members may be subjected to direct stress, i.e., tension or compression, to bending stress, or to a combination of direct and bending stresses. A column carrying a compressive load may be subjected to a direct stress, or to both a direct and a bending stress, depending upon the location of the load with respect to the center line of the column. An arch or a prestressed beam may also be subjected to both compressive and bending stresses simultaneously. In this chapter we shall discuss only straight beams and transverse loads, i.e., loads which cause bending.

As mentioned in Chapter 1, concrete does not have good tensile-strength properties and to overcome this deficiency, steel bars are embedded in the concrete beam. Hence a reinforced concrete beam is not homogeneous, and it follows that the methods of analyzing reinforced beams must differ from those used to analyze homogeneous beams.

Two theories are available for determining the stresses in a reinforced concrete beam. One is called the *elastic-load theory,* the other the *plastic- or ultimate-strength theory.* The latter is discussed at the end of this chapter.

When the elastic-load theory is used to analyze a reinforced concrete beam, one begins with the assumption that plane sections remain plane and normal to the longitudinal fiber before and after bending; that both materials are elastic and stress is proportional to strain; that the modulus of elasticity in each material is constant and that the ratio of modulus of elasticity of steel to modulus of elasticity of concrete is also a constant.

2–2   STRESSES IN A REINFORCED CONCRETE BEAM

Since the tensile strength of concrete is only about 10% of the compressive strength, it is customary to omit the former in the analysis or design of beams. Therefore, a beam subjected to an external bending moment will be assumed to resist this moment internally by a couple composed of the compressive forces in the concrete and the tensile forces in the steel (see Fig. 2–1).

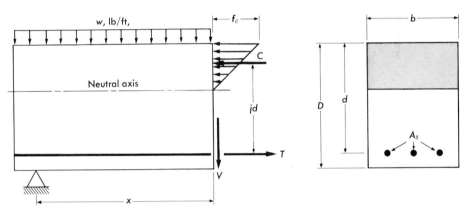

Figure 2–1

The tensile force, T, acts through the center of gravity of the group of reinforcing bars. For equilibrium, T must be equal to C, the compressive force in concrete. To find the vertical shear force, denoted by V, one has to take only the sum of the forces acting in the vertical direction. The result is

$$\sum M = 0, \qquad \sum F_x = 0, \qquad \sum F_y = 0.$$

Besides the vertical shear, horizontal shear is also present in the beam. This can be readily seen if one imagines the beam to be composed of two layers of concrete glued at, say, the neutral axis (Fig. 2–1). By taking the sum of the forces acting in the horizontal direction, it becomes obvious that the resisting force of the "glue" will be equal to the force C.

A similar analysis shows that the force created by the bond of the concrete to the steel must be equal to the tensile force in the bars. This force per unit area is called the *bond stress*. Shear and bond stresses will be discussed further in Chapter 3.

2–3 THEORY OF FLEXURE

As previously mentioned, for purposes of design and analysis, it is assumed that all the tension in the reinforced concrete beam is taken by the steel reinforcement. The compression may be taken solely by the concrete or, where compressive reinforcement is present, by both the concrete and the compression steel. For small loads, the tension may be taken by both the reinforcement and the concrete. However, as bending increases, the concrete on the tensile face may be subjected to a tensile stress which causes it to crack. This crack may extend almost to the neutral axis. Since no tensile forces can be transmitted across a crack, they must be provided by the steel reinforcement alone. It is therefore reasonable to neglect entirely all the concrete below the neutral axis so that only the concrete above the neutral axis and the steel reinforcement are considered effective.

Because of our somewhat limited knowledge of the stress distribution in the concrete above the neutral axis, one has made an assumption regarding the shape of this distribution which, although admittedly imperfect, has proved to be satisfactory and reliable up to the elastic limit of the material. Under gradual load application, the stress is assumed to be proportional to the distance from the neutral axis, as indicated by the sequence of sketches shown in Fig. 2–2. As the load increases, the linearity seems to be lost, and beyond this load it might not be even detectable. For elastic design and analysis, it is usually assumed that linearity holds up to the yield point of the concrete. This is the basis of the straight-line or elastic-load theory. Beyond this point, the stress distribution approaches a shape like that shown in Fig. 2–2(c). The ultimate-strength theory is based on the assumption that this shape is a rectangular one.

Compression tests of standard 6 in. × 12 in. concrete cylinders give an indication of the quality of concrete in a member, and although experiments seem to indicate that for beams of reasonably large cross sections, the unit compressive stress would exceed that of a 6 in. × 12 in. cylinder for the same mix, the stresses used in designing beams are frequently based solely on the results of these tests. It might be worth repeating that experience has proved the assumption mentioned above to be not only reliable but also practical.

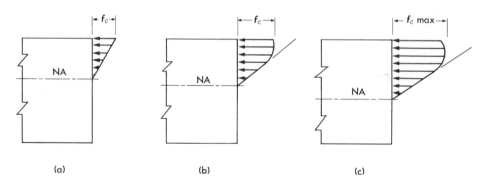

Fig. 2–2. (a) Early elastic range. (b) Yield point. (c) Plastic range.

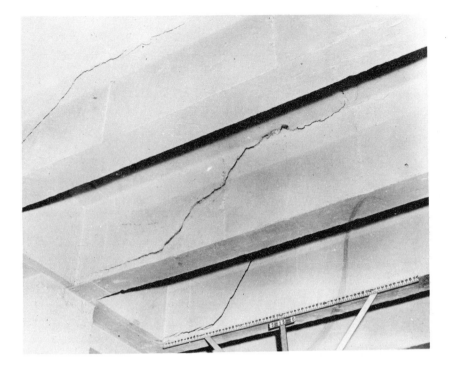

Fig. 2–3. Diagonal tension over the web causes a beam to crack as shown. Diagonal reinforcement, either stirrup bars or bent-up bars (Chapter 3), are used to take up the excessive diagonal tension over the web.

2–4 STRAIGHT-LINE OR ELASTIC-LOAD THEORY

The assumptions that plane sections remain plane and normal to the longitudinal fiber stress before and after bending and that both materials, i.e., steel and concrete, are elastic serve as the basis for the straight-line theory. The concrete stress varies from f_c in the extreme fiber to zero at the neutral axis, as shown in Fig. 2–4.

Assuming that the modulus of the elasticity of each material is constant, and denoting the strains in the concrete and the steel by e_c and e_s, respectively, we have

$$E_c = \frac{f_c}{e_c}, \qquad E_s = \frac{f_s}{e_s}.$$

Let

$$n = \frac{E_s}{E_c} = \frac{f_s e_c}{f_c e_s}.$$

Referring to the *strain* distribution of Fig. 2–4, we find

$$e_c/kd = e_s/(d - kd),$$

from which

$$\frac{e_c}{e_s} = \frac{kd}{d - kd} = \frac{k}{1 - k}.$$

Substituting for e_c/e_s, we get

$$n = \frac{f_s}{f_c}\left(\frac{k}{1 - k}\right).$$

Solving, we obtain

$$k = \frac{1}{1 + f_s/nf_c}. \tag{2–1}$$

Table 3 Appendix B Design

Equation (2–1) determines the value for k if the factors f_s and f_c are known or assumed. This equation is, therefore, primarily a *design* rather than an analysis equation.

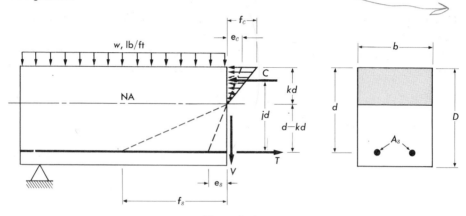

Figure 2–4

Referring to Fig. 2–4 again, we see that the total compressive force in the concrete, C, is equal to the area of the concrete under compression times the average stress, i.e., it is equal to the volume of the stress diagram. Therefore

$$C = \tfrac{1}{2}f_c bkd. \tag{2–2}$$

The tensile force T is equal to the area of the steel times the stress of the steel, and it must equal C to satisfy equilibrium. Note that it is assumed that all the tension is taken by the steel. Therefore

$$A_s f_s = \tfrac{1}{2}f_c bkd. \tag{2–3}$$

The resultant force, C, acts at a distance $\frac{1}{3}kd$ from the top:

$$jd = d - \frac{kd}{3} \quad \text{or} \quad j = 1 - \frac{k}{3}. \tag{2–4}$$

Let p denote the ratio of the area of steel to the effective area of concrete, i.e.,

$p = A_s/bd.$ Substituting in Eq. (2–3), we get

$$\frac{f_s}{f_c} = \frac{\frac{1}{2}kbd}{pbd} = \frac{k}{2p}. \tag{2-5}$$

Substituting this expression in Eq. (2–1) gives

$$k = \frac{1}{1 + k/2pn},$$

$$k = \frac{2pn}{2pn + k} \quad \text{or} \quad k^2 + 2pnk - 2pn = 0.$$

$n = \frac{E_s}{E_c}$

Solving for k ($k > 0$), we obtain the *analysis* equation

$$k = \sqrt{2np + (np)^2} - np. \tag{2-6}$$

Analysis

This expression is useful for the analysis of beams for which n is known and the ratio of the steel to the concrete, p, can be determined.

It is readily evident from Fig. 2–4 that the moment the concrete can withstand is equal to the compressive force C times the moment arm, or

$$M_c = Cjd = \tfrac{1}{2}f_c kbd\,jd = \tfrac{1}{2}f_c jkbd^2. \tag{2-7}$$

Similarly, for the steel, the moment is equal to

$$M_s = Tjd = A_s f_s jd = f_s jpbd^2, \tag{2-8}$$

or

$$A_s = \frac{M_s}{f_s jd}. \tag{2-8a}$$

Now assume a balanced design, i.e., assume that the moment which the concrete can resist is equal to the moment that the steel can resist. Then set Eq. (2–7) equal to Eq. (2–8):

$$\frac{f_c}{2}\,jkbd^2 = f_s jpbd^2,$$

and let

$$\frac{f_c}{2}\,jk = f_s jp = K.$$

Thus,

$$M_s = M_c = Kbd^2. \tag{2-9}$$

$A_s = p\,bd$

This is a convenient form used for *balanced design*.

It must be borne in mind that the previous expressions were derived for beams containing tensile reinforcement only and that alterations have to be made if compressive reinforcement is included. Such a case is discussed in the following article.

Example 2–1. *Analysis*

Given: Bending moment $= 500$ k-in., $n = 12$.

Find: Stresses in steel, f_s, and concrete, f_c, due to bending.

SOLUTION: (The student should be familiar with the basis and derivation of any equation before he uses it.) It is assumed that units are expressed to slide rule accuracy.

From Eq. (2–7)

$$f_c = \frac{2M_c}{kjbd^2},$$

and from Eq. (2–8)

$$f_s = \frac{M_s}{A_s jd}$$

and,

$$A_s = 3 \times 0.6 = 1.80 \text{ in}^2.$$

(See Table 2, Appendix B.) Then

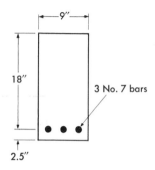

Figure 2–5

$$p = \frac{A_s}{bd} = \frac{1.8}{9 \times 18} = 0.0111,$$

$$k = \sqrt{2pn + (pn)^2} - pn = \sqrt{2(0.0111 \times 12) + (0.0111 \times 12)^2} - 0.0111 \times 12$$
$$= 0.403,$$

$$j = 1 - \frac{k}{3} = 1 - \frac{0.403}{3} = 0.866,$$

$$f_c = \frac{2M_c}{kjbd^2} = \frac{2 \times 500,000}{0.403 \times 0.866 \times 9 \times (18)^2} = 990 \text{ psi},$$

$$f_s = \frac{M_s}{A_s jd} = \frac{500,000}{1.8 \times 0.866 \times 18} = 17,700 \text{ psi}.$$

Example 2–2. *Analysis*

Given: A simply supported one-way slab, with a 10-ft span, and the cross section shown in Fig. 2–6. Assume that $n = 10$; allowable $f_c = 900$ psi; and $f_s = 18,000$ psi.

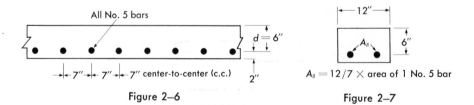

Figure 2–6   Figure 2–7

Find: The maximum uniform live load that the slab can carry.

SOLUTION: Assume that the slab is composed of rectangular beams 12 in. wide (Fig. 2–7). Such an assumption is typical in the analysis of simply supported slabs.

Then

$$A_s = \tfrac{12}{7} \times 0.31 = 0.531 \text{ in}^2 /12 \text{ in. width} \qquad \text{(for No. 5 bars, } A_s = 0.31 \text{in}^2, \text{ Table 2,}$$
Appendix B),

$$p = \frac{A_s}{bd} = \frac{0.531}{12 \times 6} = 0.0074,$$

$$k = \sqrt{2pn + (pn)^2} - pn = \sqrt{2(0.0074) \times (10) + (0.0074 \times 10)^2} - 0.0074 \times 10$$
$$= 0.318$$

$$j = 1 - \frac{k}{3} = 1 - \frac{0.318}{3} = 0.894,$$

$$M_s = A_s f_s jd = 0.531 \times 18,000 \times 0.894 \times 6 = 51,300 \text{ in-lb},$$

$$M_c = \tfrac{1}{2} f_c k jbd^2 = \tfrac{1}{2} \times 900 \times 0.318 \times 0.894 \times 12 \times 6^2 = 55,260 \text{ in-lb}.$$

The strength of the steel in our case limits the bending moment to 51,300 in-lb. Therefore

$$M = 51,300 \text{ in-lb} = 4278 \text{ ft-lb} = \frac{wl^2}{8},$$

$$w = \frac{8M}{l^2} = \frac{8 \times 4278}{(10)^2} = 342 \text{ lb/lin. ft},$$

$$\text{Dead load (DL)} = 150 \text{ lb/ft}^3 \times \frac{6 \text{ in} + 2 \text{ in}}{12 \text{ in}} \times 1\text{-ft width} = 100 \text{ lb/lin. ft/ft width}.$$

Hence the permissible live load is

$$342 - 100 = \boxed{242 \text{ lb/lin. ft/ft width.}}$$

Example 2–3. Design

Given: Allowable f_c and $f_s = 1000$ psi and 20,000 psi, respectively; $E_c = 2.5 \times 10^6$ psi and $E_s = 30 \times 10^6$ psi.

Find: Suitable design for a beam which is to withstand a bending moment of 250 k-in. (Note the units for the bending moment.)

SOLUTION:

$$n = \frac{E_s}{E_c} = \frac{30 \times 10^6}{2.5 \times 10^6} = 12.$$

From Eq. (2–1), or Table 3, Appendix B, we find that for a balanced design, $f_c = 1000$ psi, $f_s = 20,000$ psi, $n = 12$, $k = 0.40$, $j = 0.866$. From Eq. (2–7),

$$bd^2 = \frac{2 \times M_c}{f_c k j} = \frac{2 \times 250,000}{1000 \times 0.40 \times 0.866} = 1440 \text{ in}^3.$$

Now let us make an assumption for one dimension and solve for the other. One possible approach is to take a value for b and then solve for d, trying several values until a *reasonable* ratio of d/b is obtained. As a guide, use a ratio in the range from

1.75 to 2. For our case, assume that $d/b = 1.75$. Then

$$\frac{d^3}{1.75} = 1440 \quad \text{or} \quad d = (2530)^{1/3} = 13.7 \text{ in.}, \quad \text{say } 13.75 \text{ in.,}$$

and

$$b = \frac{13.75}{1.75} = 7.86 \text{ in}, \quad \text{say } 8 \text{ in.}$$

Let us assume that there is a 2-in. cover for the steel. Then the overall dimensions are $15\frac{3}{4}$ in. $\times$ 8 in. The quantity of steel required is

$$A_s = \frac{M_s}{f_s jd} = \frac{250,000}{20,000 \times 0.866 \times 13.75} = 1.17 \text{ in}^2.$$

From Table 2, Appendix B, we see that $A_s = 1.20$ for two No. 7 bars. Next we check the recommended width of the beam from Tables 4 and 5 of Appendix B. Assuming that the aggregate is $\frac{3}{4}$ in., we find that the width is $6\frac{1}{2}$ to 8 in. Since we have a width of 8 in., the design is considered to be satisfactory.

2–5   TRANSFORMED-SECTION METHOD

Up to this point we had no means of analyzing or designing a beam with compressive reinforcement although such a structure might not only be desirable but in some cases necessary. The transformed-section method makes such analysis possible and practical. (This should not be taken to mean that beams with only tensile reinforcement may not be advantageously analyzed by this method.) It is based on the assumptions that plane sections remain plane after bending, that stress varies linearly, and that each material has a constant modulus of elasticity throughout the beam.

So far, we have treated the concrete and the steel as two separate materials which act together to form a reinforced concrete beam. According to the assumptions mentioned above, the deformation in the steel at a certain level will be the same as that of the concrete at the same level. However, since the moduli of elasticity of the two materials are different, it follows that the stresses will also be different; i.e., if the modulus of elasticity of steel is n times that of the concrete, the stress in the steel will be n times that of the concrete. Let C_c and C_s' represent the force of the stress block for concrete and compression steel, respectively. The resultant of C_c and C_s' will be C, as shown in Fig. 2–8(a). The ACI Code, Article 1102(c), states that "in doubly reinforced beams and slabs, an effective modular ratio of $2n$ shall be used to transform the compression reinforcement and compute its stress, which shall not be taken as greater than the allowable tensile stress." On this basis, the steel beam may be replaced by an equivalent area of concrete acting at the same elevation with respect to the neutral axis, to form an imaginary beam composed of concrete only (Fig. 2–8c). This is then referred to as the *transformed section*, i.e., transformed from steel and concrete to concrete only. One should note that this substitution, or transformation, yields

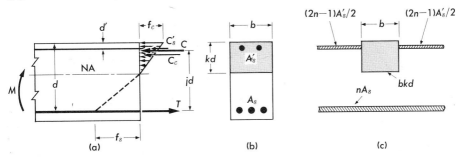

Fig. 2–8. (b) Actual cross section. (c) Transformed cross section.

a definite location for the neutral axis and a definite moment of inertia for the cross section of this imaginary beam. It follows, therefore, that the stress in the concrete in the extreme fiber is equal to the moment divided by the *section modulus, S,* or

$$f_c = \frac{M_c}{S_c} = \frac{M_c}{I_c/kd} = \frac{M_c(kd)}{I_c}. \tag{2–10}$$

Similarly, the stress in the tensile steel is equal to the moment divided by the section modulus of the steel, or

$$f_s = \frac{M}{S_s} = \frac{M}{I_c/n(d-kd)} = \frac{nM(d-kd)}{I_c}. \tag{2–11}$$

The expressions kd and $(d - kd)$ correspond to the y in the familiar formula

$$\sigma = \frac{My}{I}.$$

The stress in the compressive reinforcing steel is

$$f_s' = \frac{kd - d'}{d - kd} 2f_s. \tag{2–12}$$

To find the value for k, remember that the static moment of the cross section about the neutral axis is zero. Referring to Fig. 2–8(c) and *neglecting the concrete displaced by A_s'*, we find that

$$bkd\frac{kd}{2} + n2A_s'(kd - d') = nA_s(d - kd),$$

$$\frac{b(kd)^2}{2} + nkd(2A_s' + A_s) = n(2A_s'd' + A_sd),$$

but

$$A_s' = p'bd; \quad \text{and} \quad A_s = pbd.$$

Therefore

$$\frac{b(kd)^2}{2} + nkd(2p'bd + pbd) = n(2p'bdd' + pbd^2).$$

Solving for k $(k > 0)$, we have

$$\frac{k^2 d}{2} + nkd(2p' + p) - n(2p'd' + pd) = 0,$$

$$k = \sqrt{n^2(2p' + p)^2 + 2n[p + 2p'(d'/d)]} - n(2p' + p). \quad (2\text{-}13)$$

Comparing Eq. (2–13) with Eq. (2–6), we clearly see that if there is no compressive reinforcement, that is, $p' = 0$, Eq. (2–13) is exactly the same as Eq. (2–6). It is thus evident that *the transformed-section method works equally well for beams which have only tensile reinforcement as it does for beams that have compressive and tensile reinforcement.* Like Eq. (2–6), Eq. (2–13) is very useful for analyzing or checking existing designs. For design purposes the value of k is essentially that expressed by Eq. (2–1), since the same assumption holds true in Eq. (2–13) that held for that derivation, i.e., that plane sections remain plane after bending takes place.

As previously mentioned, in the derivation of Eq. (2–13), the area of the concrete under compression was assumed to be bkd. Actually, the area is bkd minus the area of the compressive reinforcement $(bkd - A_s')$. However, since the ratio of the area of the steel to that of the concrete was very small, the error involved was negligible, and hence for practical value and simplicity, the area of the concrete was assumed to be bkd.

Recall the *parallel-axis theorem* from statics, i.e., the moment of inertia of an area with respect to any axis is equal to the moment of inertia with respect to a parallel axis through the centroid of the area plus the product of the area and the square of the distance between the two axes. The moment of inertia of the transformed section is

$$I_c = \frac{b(kd)^3}{3} + nA_s(d - kd)^2 + 2nA_s'(kd - d')^2, \quad (2\text{-}14)$$

or substituting pbd and $p'bd$ for A_s and A_s', respectively, we obtain

$$I_c = \frac{b(kd)^3}{3} + nbd[p(d - kd)^2 + 2p'(kd - d')^2]. \quad (2\text{-}14a)$$

The first term in Eq. (2–14) is the moment of inertia of the rectangular cross section above the neutral axis with respect to the neutral axis. The second and third terms are the moments of inertia of the steel with respect to the neutral axis. One should note that the moment of inertia of the steel with respect to its own centroidal axis is neglected because it is very small.

The transformed-section method is, then, more a tool of analysis than one of design. But, one may make an assumption regarding a section of the beam and then analyze it. In this sense the method may be thought of as a tool of design. It is simple, easy to understand, and very useful and versatile, applying both to beams with tension reinforcement only, as well as to beams with tension and compression reinforcement.

Example 2–4. *Analysis*

Given: The cross section shown in Fig. 2–9 is subjected to a bending moment of 500,000 in-lb.

Find: f_s and f_c by the transformed-section method. Assume that $n = 12$.

SOLUTION: The problem is the same as that given in Example 2–1. Compare the final results. Note that

$$A_s' = 0, \qquad A_s = 1.8 \text{ in}^2, \qquad nA_s = 21.6 \text{ in}^2.$$

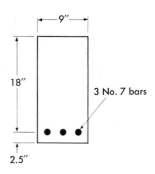

Figure 2–9

Equation (2–13) applies in our case (should we choose to use it), where p' and d' are equal to zero. Instead of using it, let us derive the expression for kd. The static moment of the cross section about the neutral axis is zero (Fig. 2–10). Therefore

$$\frac{bkd(kd)}{2} = nA_s(d - kd)$$

[see the derivation of Eq. (2–13)],

$$\frac{9(kd)^2}{2} = 21.6(18 - kd).$$

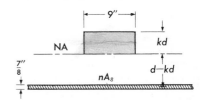

Fig. 2–10. Transformed cross section.

Solving the quadratic equation for kd, we obtain

$$kd = 7.26 \text{ in.} \qquad \text{and} \qquad (d - kd) = 18 - 7.26 = 10.74 \text{ in.}$$

Then

$$I_c = \frac{b(kd)^3}{3} + nA_s(d - kd)^2$$

[see Eq. (2–14), $A_s' = 0$].

Again note that the moment of inertia of the steel with respect to its own neutral axis is negligible. Thus

$$I_c = \tfrac{9}{3}(7.26)^3 + 21.6(10.74)^2 = 3650 \text{ in}^4,$$

$$f_c = \frac{Mkd}{I_c} = \frac{500{,}000 \times 7.26}{3650} = 990 \text{ psi},$$

$$f_s = \frac{Mn(d - kd)}{I_c} = \frac{500{,}000 \times 12 \times 10.74}{3650} = 17{,}700 \text{ psi}.$$

Comparison of these results with those of Example 2–1 shows that they are the same (as they should be) for both methods.

Example 2–5. *Analysis*

Given: $n = 12$. Allowable f_s and $f_c = 20{,}000$ psi and 1000 psi, respectively (Fig. 2–11).

Find: The allowable moment the beam can carry.

SOLUTION: We have from Table 2, Appendix B:

$$A_s' = 1.20 \text{ in}^2, \quad A_s = 2.40 \text{ in}^2; \quad \text{then} \quad 2nA_s' = 28.8 \text{ in}^2, \quad nA_s = 28.8 \text{ in}^2.$$

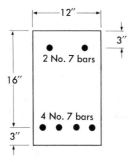

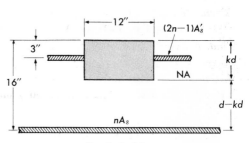

Figure 2–11   Figure 2–12

Taking the moment of the transformed area about the neutral axis (Fig. 2–12), we obtain

$$bkd(kd/2) + 2nA_s'(kd - d') = nA_s(d - kd),$$
$$\tfrac{12}{2}(kd)^2 + 28.8(kd - 3) = 28.8(16 - kd).$$

Solving the quadratic gives

$$kd = 6.23 \text{ in.,} \quad d - kd = 9.77 \text{ in.,} \quad kd - d' = 3.23 \text{ in.,}$$

$$I_c = \frac{b(kd)^3}{3} + nA_s(d - kd)^2 + 2nA_s'(kd - d')^2$$

$$= \frac{12(6.23)^3}{3} + 28.8(9.77)^2 + 28.8(3.23)^2 = 4150 \text{ in}^4,$$

$$f_s = 20,000 = \frac{M_s n(d - kd)}{I_c} = \frac{M_s \cdot 12(9.77)}{4150},$$

$$M_s = \frac{20,000 \times 4150}{12 \times 9.77} = 707,000 \text{ in-lb,}$$

$$f_c = 1000 = \frac{M_c(kd)}{I_c},$$

$$M_c = \frac{1000 \times 4150}{6.23} = 666,000 \text{ in-lb.}$$

The concrete thus governs the maximum bending moment. Hence

$$f_c = 1000 \text{ psi,}$$

$$f_s = \frac{Mn(d - kd)}{I_c} = \frac{666,000 \times 12 \times 9.77}{4150} = 18,800 \text{ psi.}$$

Note that for a more correct analysis, $(2n - 1)A_s'$ should have been used instead of $2nA_s'$. However, the substitution has little effect on the value of kd.

$$f_s' = \frac{M2n(kd - d')}{4150} = 11{,}550 \text{ psi.}$$

Example 2–6. *Design*

Given: Allowable f_s and $f_c = 20{,}000$ psi and 1000 psi, respectively; $n = 12$. The cross section of the beam is limited to an overall width of 12 in. and depth of 19 in.

Find: A suitable design to carry a bending moment of 685,000 in-lb.

SOLUTION: Note the similarity of this and the previous example. Let us assume that there is a 3-in. cover over the rods and that $k = 0.38$ and $j = 0.88$. (We need not calculate exact values for k and j until the reinforcement has been decided upon.) Thus

$$kd = 0.38(19 - 3) = 6.08 \text{ in.}$$

The area of steel required to take the tension is A_s. From Eq. (2–8a),

$$A_s = \frac{M}{f_s jd} = \frac{685{,}000}{20{,}000 \times 0.88 \times 16} = 2.43 \text{ in.}^2.$$

According to Eq. (2–7), the stress in the concrete can be expressed as

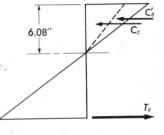

Figure 2–13

$$f_c = \frac{2M}{kjbd^2} = 1330 \text{ psi.}$$

The excess stress (over 1000 psi allowable) has to be assumed by the compressive reinforcement. From Fig. 2–13, the total force that the compression reinforcement takes is $\frac{1}{2} \times 330 \times 12$-in. width $\times 6.08$. Hence the force is 11,800 lb. The stress in the compression steel may be approximated by the property of similar triangles, that is,

$$f_s' : (kd - d') = f_s : (d - kd),$$

or, from Article 1102(c) of the ACI Code,

$$f_s' = 2f_s \frac{(kd - d')}{(d - kd)} = 2(20{,}000)\left(\frac{6.08 - 3}{16 - 6.08}\right) = 12{,}400 \text{ psi,}$$

$$A_s' = \frac{11{,}800}{12{,}400} = 0.981 \text{ in.}^2.$$

We will assume that for A_s, four No. 7 bars, and for A_s', two No. 7 bars will be satisfactory. (Others might have been chosen.) Hence we have $kd = 6.23$ in., $d - kd = 9.77$ in., $kd - d' = 3.23$ in., and $I_c = 3864$ in⁴. The actual values are: $f_c = 967$ psi, $f_s = 18{,}198$ psi, and $f_s' = 12{,}000$ psi. Note that f_s' determined by the similar-triangle approach, above, would have only half the value of that determined on the basis of Article 1102(c) of the Code. However, since an effective modular ratio of $2n$ was assumed in determining the beam's section modulus, this assumption is also preferred when determining the stress f_s'.

2–6 PRACTICAL CONSIDERATION OF RECTANGULAR SECTIONS; SIMPLE BENDING

Although all the derivations in this chapter are based on beams of rectangular cross section, nothing has been said about the practical limitations imposed on the design of such beams. For example, a beam might have a constant cross section along its whole length, even though the cross section is governed by the maximum moment existing at only one point along its span.

There may be many beams of different sizes which can safely carry a given load, but factors such as economy and effective use of material, lateral stiffness, strength, or deflections might eliminate quite a few of these. For example, the ACI Code (Article 908) specifies that the clear distance between lateral supports of a beam shall not exceed 50 times the smallest width of the compression flange. Similarly, many sizes may be eliminated by the specifications pertaining to the placing of steel or to the sizes of aggregate used.

To further guide a designer and help to reduce his work, tables and charts were developed and are available from various sources. Remember that the techniques presented here are mostly methods of analysis which are not primarily concerned with the practical side of the design phase, whereas tables and charts are not only useful time-saving devices but are also guides to practical considerations.

2–7 T-SECTIONS IN SIMPLE BENDING; STRESS IN STEM NEGLECTED

For concrete-floor construction, it is customary to pour the beams and the slab monolithically, or, if they are poured separately, to bond them together by stirrups and bent-up bars to form a unit. A slab and a beam acting as a unit form a T-beam. Figure 2–14 shows a T-beam (shaded area) as part of a floor system. The slab portion of the T-beam is called a *flange* and the lower portion, the "beam" portion, is called a *stem*.

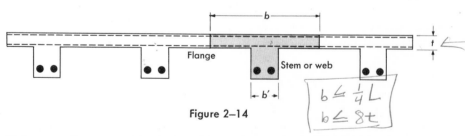

Figure 2–14

It is generally accepted in design that the flange takes most of the compressive force, but it is questionable what the exact width of the slab should be to resist compression. The ACI Code (Article 906) specifies that the flange width for symmetrical beams shall not exceed one-fourth the span length of the beam; also, that the overhanging width of the flange on either side of the stem or web shall not exceed eight times the thickness of the slab, or one-half the clear distance between any adjacent beams.

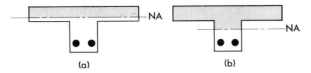

Figure 2–15

The neutral axis of a reinforced T-beam may lie either in the flange, as illustrated in Fig. 2–15(a), or in the stem, as shown in Fig. 2–15(b), depending upon the dimensions of the flange and stem, as well as upon the steel. The compressive area in the flange is usually large enough to make the steel the controlling factor for the bending moment.

For design purposes, it is practical to neglect the area in the stem above the neutral axis. In most instances, the neutral axis will fall very near the bottom edge of the flange or within the flange itself. In the latter case, no portion of the stem is in compression, and for such a beam, the analysis is precisely that given in Section 2–4, and is exact within the limits of the assumptions.

Let us assume that the concrete area in compression is that shown in Fig. 2–15(b). As in the case of the straight-line theory, it then follows that if the factors f_s and f_c are known, k is exactly as given in Eq. (2–1).

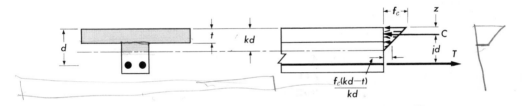

Figure 2–16

Assuming a linear stress distribution, we find that the stress at the bottom of the flange has the value indicated in Fig. 2–16. When *the stress in the stem is neglected,* the compressive force C is

$$C = \frac{f_c + f_c(kd - t)/kd}{2} tb$$

$$= \frac{f_c bt}{2kd} (2kd - t). \tag{2–15}$$

Taking the summation of forces in the horizontal direction, we find that C equals T and therefore

$$\frac{f_c bt}{2kd} (2kd - t) = A_s f_s. \tag{2–16}$$

As derived in Section 2–4,

$$\frac{f_s}{f_c} = \frac{E_s e_s}{E_c e_c} = n \frac{e_s}{e_c} = n \frac{(d - kd)}{kd}. \tag{2–17}$$

Substituting in (2–16), we get

$$\frac{bt}{2kd}\frac{(2kd - t)}{A_s} = n\left(\frac{d - kd}{kd}\right),$$

$$2btkd + 2nA_skd = bt^2 + 2ndA_s,$$

$$kd(2bt + 2nA_s) = bt^2 + 2nA_sd,$$

$$kd = \frac{bt^2/2 + nA_sd}{bt + nA_s}. \tag{2-18}$$

Having obtained kd, we determine the moment of inertia of the section (neglecting the portion of the stem which takes the compression). Now Eqs. (2–10) and (2–11) can be used to find the unknown quantity (i.e., stress or moment).

For a comparative approach to the analysis, let us look at Fig. 2–16. For the internal-moment arm of jd, the moment taken by the steel is

$$M_s = Tjd = A_sf_sjd. \tag{2-19}$$

For several rows of bars, d is measured to the resultant of the force systems of the bars. In most instances, it is sufficient to assume that d is at the *centroid* of the bar areas. Also note that f_s is the stress in the steel at depth d, and that jd is not equal to $d - kd/3$ as it is for rectangular beams (see Example 2–8).

Likewise, the moment the concrete takes is equal to

$$M_c = Cjd = \frac{f_cbt}{2kd}(2kd - t)jd, \tag{2-20}$$

where C is given by Eq. (2–15).

From Fig. 2–16, we see that $jd = d - z$, where z equals the centroidal distance of the trapezoid from the top of the beam. The value for jd can be determined by first finding the centroidal distance of C from the top of the beam; that is, when $\sum M_{top} = 0$,

$$z = \frac{f_c[(kd - t)/kd](bt^2/2) + (f_c/2)[1 - (kd - t)/kd](bt^2/3)}{C}.$$

From Eq. (2–15), $C = (f_cbt/2kd)(2kd - t)$, and thus

$$z = \left(\frac{3kd - 2t}{2kd - t}\right)\frac{t}{3}. \tag{2-21}$$

It is suggested that the student not memorize equations, but rather derive them for every problem. In this manner he can acquire a greater familiarity with the structural analysis of concrete.

Example 2–7. *Analysis*

Given: The T-beam shown in Fig. 2–17. Allowable $f_s = 18{,}000$ psi, $f_c = 1000$ psi, $n = 10$, $t = 4$ in.

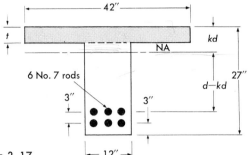

Figure 2–17

Find: The resisting bending moment that the T-beam carries. Neglect the effect of the portion of the stem above the neutral axis.

SOLUTION: $\sum M_{NA} = 0$. The average depth of the 6 rods from the neutral axis equals $(27 - 4.5 - kd) = 22.5 - kd$.

$$bt(kd - t/2) = nA_s(d_{\text{ave}} - kd),$$

$$42 \times 4(kd - 2) = 10 \times 3.6(22.5 - kd),$$

$$kd = 5.62 \text{ in.}$$

We check the results by using Eq. (2–18):

$$kd = \frac{(42 \times 4^2/2) + 10 \times 3.6 \times 22.5}{42 \times 4 + 10 \times 3.6} = 5.62 \text{ in.,}$$

$$I_c = I_{NA}$$

$$= \frac{42 \times 4^3}{12} + (42 \times 4)(5.62 - \tfrac{4}{2})^2 + \frac{nA_s}{2}[(24 - 5.62)^2 + (21 - 5.62)^2]$$

$$= 12,760 \text{ in}^4,$$

$$M_s = \frac{f_s I_c}{n(d - kd)} = \frac{18,000 \times 12,760}{10(24 - 5.62)} = 1,249,900 \text{ in-lb} \qquad \text{(lower row of bars),}$$

$$M_c = \frac{f_c I_c}{kd} = \frac{1000 \times 12,760}{5.62} = 2,270,000 \text{ in-lb.}$$

$f_s = \dfrac{nMc}{I}$

We further check by using Eqs. (2–19) and (2–20):

$$M_s = A_s f_s jd; \qquad M_c = \frac{f_c bt}{2kd}(2kd - t)jd,$$

$$jd = d - z, \qquad \text{where} \qquad z = \left(\frac{3kd - 2t}{2kd - t}\right)\frac{t}{3}, \qquad (2\text{–}21)$$

$$z = \frac{(3 \times 5.62 - 2 \times 4)}{(2 \times 5.62 - 4)}\frac{4}{3} = 1.63 \text{ in.}$$

We then have (Fig. 2–18a)

$$f_{s1} = \frac{(21 - 5.62)}{(24 - 5.62)} f_{s2} = 15,060 \text{ psi,}$$

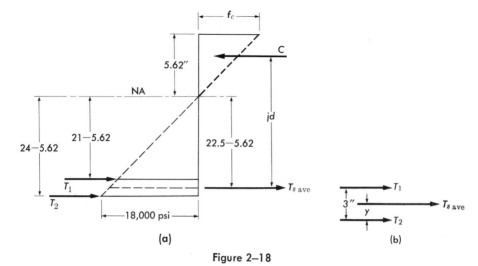

Figure 2–18

where $f_{s2} = 18,000$ psi. The resultant of the tensile forces is found to be at

$$y = \frac{15,060A \cdot 3}{(15,060A + 18,000A)} = 1.366 \text{ in.}$$

from the lower row of bars. From Fig. 2–18(b), which is a magnified detail of the tensile steel, we find d:

$$d = 27 - 3 - 1.366 = 22.63 \text{ in.,}$$

$$jd = 22.63 - 1.63 = 21 \text{ in.,}$$

$$f_s = \frac{24 - 1.366 - 5.62}{24 - 5.62} \times 18,000 = 16,600 \text{ psi,}$$

$$M_s = A_s f_s jd = 3.6 \times 16,658 \times 21 = 1,259,000 \text{ in-lb,}$$

$$M_c = \frac{1000 \times 42 \times 4}{2 \times 5.62} (2 \times 5.62 - 4) \times 21 = 2,283,000 \text{ in-lb.}$$

A comparison of the two approaches shows a negligible difference in the final results. The latter method has no particular advantage over the former other than that it is a good check. For this purpose it would have been quite sufficient to assume that d is at the centroid of the two rows of bars, and that the stress in the steel is the average stress in the two rows. The elaborate analysis in our checks was made only to illustrate the basic concept involved in the two methods.

Example 2–8.   Design

Given: Allowable f_s and f_c of 20,000 psi and 1350 psi, respectively; $n = 10$; $M_{DL + LL} = 400,000$ in-lb, the span is 14 ft, the thickness of the slab is about 4 in., and the beams are 4 ft center to center (c.c.).

Find: A suitable design for the T-beam.

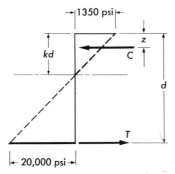

Figure 2–19

SOLUTION: As a guide, assume that $d = 1.2L$, or $1.2 \times 14 = 16.8$ in., say 17 in., and $b' = 9$ in. (d is to be in inches, not in units of the span L). For a balanced design (that is, $f_s = 20{,}000$ psi, $f_c = 1350$ psi), the neutral axis falls at a distance of $0.4d$ from the top, or $dk = 0.4d$. [See Table 3, Appendix B, or derive it, or use Eq. (2–1).] From Eq. (2–21), z can be estimated as follows:

$$z = \left(\frac{3kd - 2t}{2kd - t} \right) \frac{t}{3} = \frac{(3 \times 0.4 \times 17 - 2 \times 4)}{(2 \times 0.4 \times 17 - 4)} \frac{4}{3} = 1.95 \text{ in.}$$

and

$$jd = d - z = 15.05 \text{ in.}$$

Thus

$$A_s = \frac{M_s}{f_s jd} = \frac{400{,}000}{20{,}000 \times 15.05} = 1.328 \text{ in}^2.$$

Try three No. 6 rods, $A_s = 1.32$. From Table 4, Appendix B, the recommended minimum width of the beam (b') is 8 in. Thus, a choice of 9 in. is satisfactory.

Now let us check the stresses, remembering that kd is not necessarily the same as that assumed above. From Eq. (2–18)

$$kd = \frac{(bt^2/2) + nA_s d}{bt + nA_s} = \frac{(48 \times 4^2)/2 + 10 \times 1.32 \times 17}{48 \times 4 + 10 \times 1.32} = 2.96 \text{ in.,}$$

$$z = \left(\frac{3 \times 2.96 - 2 \times 4}{2 \times 2.96 - 4} \right) \frac{4}{3} = \left(\frac{0.88}{1.92} \right) 1.33 = 0.61 \text{ in.,}$$

$$jd = d - z = 17 - 0.61 = 16.39 \text{ in.}$$

Therefore we have an allowable steel moment of

$$M_s = A_s f_s jd = 1.32 \times 20{,}000 \times 16.39 = 432{,}696 \text{ in-lb,}$$

$$M_c = \frac{f_c bt}{2kd} (2kd - t)jd = \frac{1350 \times 48 \times 4}{2 \times 2.96} (2 \times 2.96 - 4)16.39,$$

$$M_c = 1{,}377{,}000 \text{ in-lb.}$$

Hence the design is satisfactory. Note that for this design and analysis the moment of inertia of the section was not needed.

2-8   T-SECTIONS IN SIMPLE BENDING; STRESS IN STEM INCLUDED

It is conceivable that there might be a case where the neutral axis is far enough below the bottom of the flange that the effect of the stem should be considered in the analysis. From Fig. 2-16, it is evident that for such a case C would be equal to the force given by the trapezoid, as expressed in Eq. (2-15), plus that from the stem. In other words,

$$C = \frac{f_c bt}{2kd}(2kd - t) + \frac{f_c}{2kd}(kd - t)^2 b',\qquad(2\text{-}22)$$

where b' is the width of the stem (see Fig. 2-14). Letting the tensile force equal the compressive force, $T = C$, we obtain

$$f_s A_s = \frac{f_c bt}{2kd}(2kd - t) + \frac{f_c}{2kd}(kd - t)^2 b'.\qquad(2\text{-}23)$$

By using the expression given by Eq. (2-17), we can eliminate f_s and f_c and get

$$n\left(\frac{d - kd}{kd}\right) = \frac{bt}{2kdA_s}\left[(2kd - t) + (kd - t)^2\frac{b'}{bt}\right],$$

Solving for kd we get

$$kd = \sqrt{\frac{2nA_s d + (b - b')t^2}{b'} + \left[\frac{nA_s + (b - b')t}{b'}\right]^2} \\ - \left(\frac{nA_s + (b - b')t}{b'}\right),$$

$$kd = \frac{1}{b'}\left\{\sqrt{[2nA_s d + (b - b')t^2]b' + [nA_s + (b - b')t]^2} - [nA_s + (b - b')]t\right\}.$$

$$(2\text{-}24)$$

Knowing $kd,$ we can express the distance from the top to C as

$$z = \frac{1}{3}\left[\frac{t^2(b - b')(3kd - 2t) + b'(kd)^3}{t(b - b')(2kd - t) + b'(kd)^2}\right].\qquad(2\text{-}25)$$

(The derivations of the equations for kd and z are left as an exercise for the student.)

Since the distance jd may be easily found, the moment resisted by the steel and concrete, respectively, can now be determined. The T-beams considered so far were subjected to simple bending, and thus the moment was assumed to be positive. It should be kept in mind, however, that for continuous T-beams over the supports, proper reinforcement must be introduced or added to take care of the negative moment. Remember that the concrete alone, regardless of the width or thickness of the flange, is not sufficient, or at least not considered to be sufficient, to take care of the tensile forces.

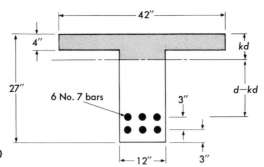

Figure 2-20

Example 2-9. Analysis

Given: $f_s = 18,000$ psi, $f_c = 1000$ psi, $n = 10$.

Find: The resisting bending moment of the T-beam (Fig. 2-20). Include the effect of the portion of the stem above the neutral axis.

SOLUTION:
$$\sum M_{NA} = 0,$$

$$(b \times t)\left(kd - \frac{t}{2}\right) + b'\frac{(kd - t)^2}{2} = nA_s(d_{ave} - kd),$$

$$(42 \times 4)(kd - \tfrac{4}{2}) + 12\frac{(kd - 4)^2}{2} = 10 \times 3.6(22.5 - kd),$$

$$168(kd - 2) + 6[(kd)^2 - 8kd + 16] = 36(22.5 - kd),$$

$$kd^2 + 26kd - 175 = 0, \quad kd = 5.55 \text{ in.}$$

This can be checked by using Eq. (2-24). Now we proceed to find I_c, M_s, M_c:

$$I_c = I_{NA} = \frac{42 \times 4^3}{12} + (42 \times 4)(5.55 - \tfrac{4}{2})^2 + \frac{12 \times 1.55^3}{12}$$

$$+ 12 \times 1.55\left(\frac{1.55}{2}\right)^2 + \frac{nA_s}{2}[(24 - 5.55)^2 + (21 - 5.55)^2] = 12,800 \text{ in}^4,$$

$$M_s = \frac{f_s I_c}{n(d - kd)} = \frac{18,000 \times 12,800}{10(24 - 5.55)} = 1,246,600 \text{ in-lb},$$

$$M_c = \frac{f_c I_c}{kd} = \frac{1000 \times 12,800}{5.55} = 2,302,300 \text{ in-lb}.$$

Compare this example with Example 2-7.

2-9   THE ULTIMATE-STRENGTH THEORY FOR BEAMS

The straight-line or elastic theory is not reliable beyond the elastic limit of the concrete or steel. The beam does not fail as stresses in the steel or concrete approach and pass their respective yield points. Frequently the collapse load is twice or more the load which causes yield stresses. It is therefore desirable to predict the ultimate strength of a flexure member.

The inelastic behavior of a concrete beam is difficult to predict with any accuracy—certainly with less accuracy than the elastic behavior. We attempted to illustrate in Fig. 2–2 a general stress distribution as the load is increased. The shape of the curve and the location of the neutral axis depend upon the magnitude of load, the time the load is sustained, the strength, creep, shrinkage, the material content of the concrete, and the type as well as the percentage of steel. A particular observation frequently made in tests is that as the load is increased, the neutral axis shifts upward for under-reinforced beams and downward (toward the reinforcement) for over-reinforced beams. To relate all these factors to the shape of a stress diagram or to the position of the neutral axis is impossible. The best we can do at this time is to empirically adjust and arrange the variables such that the results resemble those obtained in experiments.

2–10   ULTIMATE STRENGTH OF RECTANGULAR BEAMS WITH ONLY TENSILE REINFORCEMENT

For calculation of ultimate strength of flexure members, the ACI Code permits the assumption that the diagram of compressive stress distribution in concrete is a rectangle or trapezoid, or parabola, or any other shape which yields predictions of ultimate strength that are in reasonable agreement with the results of comprehensive tests (Article 1503f).

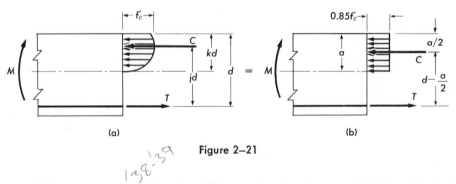

Figure 2–21

A little over two decades ago Whitney developed an empirical method of predicting the ultimate strength of a beam. He simplified the stress block by proposing an equivalent rectangular stress block of stress intensity equal to 0.85 f_c' and height a, as given in Fig. 2–21(b). If there are no axial loads, then it follows that C is equal to T, or

$$0.85f_c'ab = A_sf_y; \qquad a = \frac{A_sf_y}{0.85f_c'b},$$

where f_y equals the yield stress of steel.
If p is the ratio of the area of steel to that of concrete, then a becomes

$$a = \frac{pf_yd}{0.85f_c'}. \tag{2-26}$$

From Fig. 2–21(b), it is evident that the ultimate internal moment is equal to T times the moment arm and that it also equals C times the moment arm. Thus

$$M_s = Tjd = Cjd = A_s f_y(d - a/2), \qquad (2\text{–}27)$$

and

$$M_c = C(d - a/2) = 0.85 f_c' ab(d - a/2). \qquad (2\text{–}28)$$

From his studies, Whitney determined an empirical value of $a = 0.537d$ for beams of balanced design. Therefore, the ultimate moment for a rectangular *balanced-design* beam is

$$M_c = 0.333 f_c' bd^2. \qquad (2\text{–}28a)$$

The ACI specifications recommend that p should not exceed $0.75\,p_b$ and that

$$M_u = bd^2 f_c' q(1 - 0.59q)\phi = A_s f_y(d - a/2)\phi \qquad (2\text{–}28b)$$

where

$$q = \frac{pf_y}{f_c'}, \qquad p_b = \frac{0.85 k_1 f_c'}{f_y}\, \frac{87,000}{87,000 + f_y}, \qquad \text{and} \qquad k_1 = 0.85$$

for $f_c' \le 4000$ psi. The value for k_1 is to be reduced continuously at a rate of 0.05 for each 1000 psi of strength in excess of 4000 psi.

Note that the formula given is for a simple beam having tensile reinforcement only. The ultimate-load theory also applies to beams that have compressive reinforcement. This aspect is discussed in Section 2–11.

Example 2–10.   **Analysis**

Given: The slab considered in Example 2–2; assumptions $f_c' = 3500$ psi, $f_y = 40,000$ psi.

Find: The ultimate uniform live load that the slab can carry on a 10-ft simple span.

SOLUTION: Assume that we have a 12-in. strip, that is, $b = 12$ in. From Eqs. (2–27) and (2–28),

$$M_s = A_s f_y(d - a/2),$$
$$M_c = 0.85 f_c' ab(d - a/2).$$

From Eq. (2–26),

$$a = \frac{pf_y d}{0.85 f_c'} = \frac{(0.531/12 \times 6) \times 40,000 \times 6}{0.85 \times 3500} = 0.60 \text{ in.}$$

Therefore,

$$M_s = 0.531 \times 40,000 \left(6 - \frac{0.60}{2}\right) = 121,060 \text{ in-lb},$$

$$M_c = 0.85 \times 3500 \times 0.6 \times 12 \left(6 - \frac{0.60}{2}\right) = 122,090 \text{ in-lb}.$$

Hence the steel governs

$$M = \frac{wl^2}{8} = \frac{121{,}060}{12} \text{ ft-lb,}$$

$$w_{DL+LL} = \frac{121{,}060 \times 8}{12 \times 10^2} = 807,$$

$$w_{LL} = 807 - \frac{(6+2)}{12} \times 150 = 807 - 100 = 707 \text{ lb/lin. ft.}$$

This is $807\!/\!342 = 2.35$ times the load calculated in Example 2–2. The difference may be thought of as a safety factor. Note that Eq. (2–28a) cannot be used since the value of a on which it is based is not the same as the value calculated.

Example 2–11.   Design

Given: $M_u = 100{,}000$ ft-lb, $f_c' = 3500$ psi, $f_y = 40{,}000$ psi.

Find: Suitable dimensions and reinforcement of a rectangular beam which is to carry the ultimate moment given above.

SOLUTION: First let us assume that $q = 0.2$, $\phi = 0.9$ (ACI, Section 1504).   Then

$$M_u = bd^2 f_c' q(1 - 0.59q)\phi = bd^2 f_c'[0.2 - (1 - 0.118)]0.9 = 0.176bd^2 f_c' \times 0.9.$$

Thus

$$M_u = 1{,}200{,}000 \text{ in-lb} = 0.176bd^2 f_c' \times 0.9,$$

$$bd^2 = \frac{1{,}200{,}000}{0.176 \times 3500 \times 0.9} = 2160 \text{ in}^3,$$

If it is assumed that $b = 9$ in., then $d = 15.3$, say 15 in.   Hence

$$a = (0.2/0.85)d = 3.53 \text{ in.}$$

Let us recheck M_c by using Eq. (2–28):

$$M_c = 0.85 \times 3500 \times 3.53 \times 9(15 - 1.77),$$
$$M_c = 1{,}250{,}000 \text{ in-lb.}$$

From Eq. (2–27),

$$A_s = \frac{M_s}{f_y(d - a/2)} = \frac{1{,}250{,}000}{40{,}000(13.23)} = 2.26 \text{ in}^2.$$

Using two No. 10 bars, we find that $A_s = 2.54$ in², and the spacing is satisfactory.

In this particular case, the beam is on the verge of failure since no safety factor was considered. It is common practice to add a safety factor to a design by simply adding to the actual loads. For instance, if our design were to have a safety factor of two, then the beam can only carry $100{,}000\!/\!2$ ft-lb of moment. Should a 100,000 ft-lb moment be carried with a safety factor of two, then our design moment would be 200,000 ft-lb, and we would have to make a new design etc.

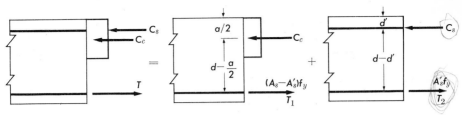

Figure 2–22

2–11   ULTIMATE STRENGTH OF RECTANGULAR BEAMS WITH COMPRESSION REINFORCEMENT

For beams of this type the total compressive force, C, is composed of the total concrete stress block, C_c, and the force in the compression steel, C_s. The total tensile force, T, must be of the same magnitude but its direction must be opposite to that of C. For convenience, let $T = T_1 + T_2$, where T_1 and T_2 have magnitudes equal to C_c and C_s, respectively. In terms of stresses, the above expression can be written as

$$A_s f_y = (A_s - A_s') f_y + A_s' f_y$$

(Fig. 2–22). The total internal moment is composed of the sum of the two couples:

$$M_u = [(A_s - A_s') f_y (d - a/2) + A_s' f_y (d - d')]\phi, \qquad (2\text{–}29)$$

where

$$a = (A - A_s') f_y / 0.85 f_c' b.$$

Equation (2–29) is the expression that the ACI Code recommends for rectangular beams with compression reinforcement. Note that it is only valid when the compression steel reaches the yield point, f_y, at ultimate strength. This condition is satisfied when

$$p - p' \ge 0.85 k_1 \frac{f_c' d'}{f_y d} \frac{87,000}{87,000 \oplus f_y}. \qquad (2\text{–}30)$$

should be negative
$P_r - 69$ eq. 16-4

Example 2–12.   *Analysis*

Given: $f_c' = 2500$ psi and $f_y = 50,000$ psi.

Find: The ultimate moment that the beam can carry.

SOLUTION: Equation (2–29) applies to this problem, provided the conditions of Eq. (2–30) are satisfied. From Eq. (2–30),

$$p = \frac{A_s}{bd} = \frac{2.4}{12 \times 16} = 0.0125,$$

$$p' = \frac{A_s'}{bd} = \frac{1.2}{12 \times 16} = 0.00625.$$

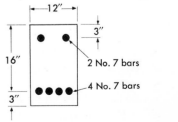

Figure 2–23

Thus

$$0.85k_1 \frac{f_c'd'}{f_yd} \frac{87,000}{87,000 + f_y} = 0.85 \times 0.85 \frac{2500 \times 3 \times 87,000}{50,000 \times 16 \times 137,000} = 0.006.$$

Therefore, since $p - p' = 0.00625 > 0.006$, Eq. (2–29) is applicable in this case, and we obtain

$$M_u = [(A_s - A_s')f_y(d - a/2) + A_s'f_y(d - d')]\phi,$$

$$\phi = 0.9 \text{ (Article 1504b, ACI Code)},$$

$$a = \frac{(A_s - A_s')f_y}{0.85f_c'b} = \frac{(2.4 - 1.2)50,000}{0.85 \times 2500 \times 12} = 2.4 \text{ in.,}$$

$$M_u = [(2.4 - 1.2)50,000(16 - 1.2) + 1.2 \times 50,000(16 - 3)]0.9,$$

$$M_u = 1,520,000 \text{ in-lb.}$$

We see that we have here the same beam as in Example 2–5. Comparing the moments based on the two different methods and assumed stresses, we find that

$$\frac{M_u}{M} = \frac{1,520,000}{666,000} = 2.27,$$

which might be considered as a safety factor.

2–12 ULTIMATE STRENGTH OF T-BEAMS

With only minor modification the techniques discussed in the previous two sections may be adapted to the solution of problems involving T-beams.

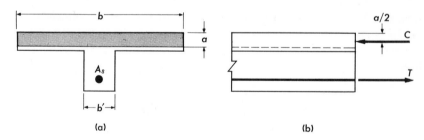

Fig. 2–24. The flange takes the entire compressive force.

(a) *Neutral axis at the bottom of or within the flange.* When the neutral axis falls within or at the bottom of the flange, the problem of analysis is similar to that of analyzing a rectangular beam having only tensile reinforcement. The total compressive force is developed by the flange, and the total tensile force by the steel. The width b of the stress block is that of the effective flange, as shown in Fig. 2–24(a). Then

$$M_u = bd^2f_c'q(1 - 0.59q)\phi = A_sf_y(d - a/2)\phi. \tag{2–28b}$$

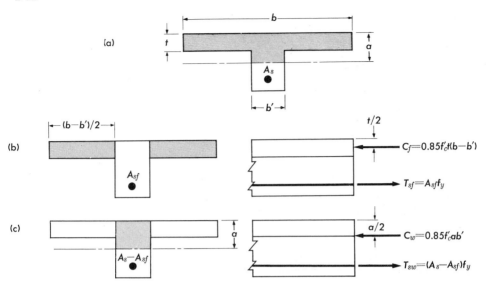

Figure 2–25

This result applied if $t \geq 1.18\ qd/k_1$. Another approach is to calculate a:

$$a = A_s f_y/0.85 f_c' b.$$

Therefore, if $1.18a \leq t$, Eq. (2–28b) applies.

(b) *Neutral axis within web.* When the neutral axis is below the bottom of the flange, we have to modify our approach as follows. We assume that the tensile reinforcement is divided into two portions: A_{sf}, the area of steel which is to develop compressive strength for the *overhanging* flange, and $(A_s - A_{sf})$, the area which is to take care of the force developed by the web portion. Figure 2–25 is a diagrammatic representation of this assumption. In the figure parts (b) and (c) are equivalent to (a). Therefore, the ultimate moment that the section can sustain is

$$M_u = [(A_s - A_{sf})f_y\,(d - a/2) + A_{sf}f_y(d - 0.5t)]\phi. \qquad (2\text{–}31)$$

In Eq. (2–31)

$$A_{sf} = \frac{0.85(b - b')t f_c'}{f_y}, \qquad a = \frac{(A_s - A_{sf})f_y}{0.85 f_c' b'}.$$

Example 2–13.   Analysis

Given: $f_c' = 2500$ psi, $f_y = 40{,}000$ psi.

Find: The ultimate strength the T-beam (Fig. 2–26) can carry.

SOLUTION: We first determine the location of the neutral axis:

$$\frac{1.18qd}{k_1} = \frac{1.18 p f_y d}{f_c' k_1} = \frac{1.18 A_s f_y}{b f_c' k_1} \cong 1.18a,$$

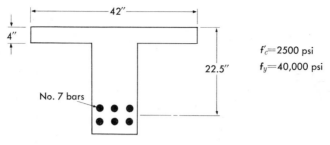

Figure 2-26

where k_1 is the factor defined in Article 1503(g) of the ACI Code.

$$1.18 \frac{qd}{k_1} = \frac{1.18 \times 3.6 \times 40,000}{42 \times 2500 \times 0.85} = 1.9 \text{ in.} < 4 \text{ in.}$$

Thus Eq. (2-28b) applies when we solve for a either from $a = A_s f_y / 0.85 f_c' b$ or from $qd/k_1 = a$. We obtain $a = 1.62$ in. Then

$$M_u = A_s f_y (d - a/2)\phi = 3.6 \times 40,000(22.5 - 1.62/2)0.9,$$
$$= 2,810,000 \text{ in-lb.}$$

Comparing this moment with the result obtained for the same beam by means of elastic-stress analysis (Example 2-7), we find that

$$\frac{M_u}{M_e} = \frac{3,125,000}{1,259,000} = 2.48.$$

2-13 REINFORCEMENT OF CONTINUOUS BEAMS

Up to this point the discussion was limited to simply supported beams. The basic idea of reinforcing concrete so that it will sustain bending moments (discussed in this chapter) and shears (Chapter 3) also applies to continuous beams, with special attention focused on the details of connections, splices, and the continuity of the steel. The ACI Code is a useful guide to such details.

If the moments and shears are known, the problem of reinforcing is considerably simplified since it is reduced to that encountered for simple beams. What is difficult is the process of determining these moments and shears for a continuous structure yet to be designed. However, for a start, let us assume that the cross section (or moment of inertia or section modulus, etc.) is given and that the moments, reactions, and shears may be computed by using methods such as the three-moment theorem, the area moment, or the moment distribution. Then the section may be "adjusted" and the procedure repeated until a satisfactory section is found.

A discussion of the methods of analyzing the moments and shears may be found in any text on structural analysis. Moreover, Appendix A of this text, which covers a series of general loading conditions and spans, may prove helpful in this respect.

PROBLEMS

BEAMS IN BENDING

Solve Problems 2–1 through 2–18 by the elastic theory. Problems 2–19 through 2–26 are to be solved by the ultimate-load theory.

Analysis of Beams—Elastic-Load Theory

2–1. The cross section in Fig. 2–27 is that of a beam simply supported over a 20-ft span. Besides its own weight, it carries a uniform live load of 1.1 k/ft and a concentrated load of 5 kip at the center. Given that $n = 10$, compute the total compressive force C and the total tensile force T. What are the maximum unit stresses in concrete, f_c, and steel, f_s?

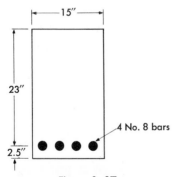

Figure 2–27

2–2. What is the maximum uniform live load that the beam described in Problem 2–1 can carry if the 5-kip load remains on the beam? The allowable stresses are $f_c = 1200$ psi and $f_s = 18,000$ psi; $n = 12$.

2–3. Compute the total load that may be concentrated at the third points of a beam over an 18-ft span, which has the cross section shown in Fig. 2–28, given that $n = 12$, and allowable stresses are $f_c = 1200$ psi and $f_s = 20,000$ psi.

2–4. A 12-ft cantilever beam has the cross section shown in Fig. 2–29. It carries a uniform live load of 0.4 k/ft

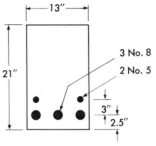

Figure 2–28

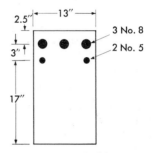

Figure 2–29

and a concentrated load at the free end of 2 k. Given that $n = 10$, determine f_s and f_c.

2–5. In Problem 2–4, given that the 2-k load remains as stated, what is the maximum live load the beam can carry if $f_c = 1350$ psi, $f_s = 20,000$ psi and $n = 10$? Note that the weight of the beam is considered to be dead weight.

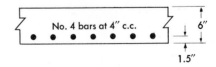

Figure 2–30

2–6. Calculate the maximum uniform LL (weight of the slab is considered DL) that the slab (Fig. 2–30) can carry for a 10-ft span, given that $f_c = 900$ psi, $f_s = 18,000$ psi, and $n = 12$.

2–7. Assuming $n = 10$, $f_c = 1350$ psi, and $f_s = 20,000$ psi, determine how long the cantilever beam of Problem 2–4 may be if it is to safely carry a 1-k/ft live load (LL) and a 1.5-k load concentrated at the free end.

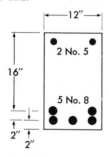

Figure 2–31

2–8. Determine the maximum moment that can be carried by the beam whose cross section is shown in Fig. 2–31. Assume that $n = 12$, $f_c = 1350$ psi, and $f_s = 18,000$ psi.

2–9. The cross section of a sign post subjected to a wind load in the y-direction is shown in Fig. 2–32. What is the maximum moment that the post can carry in that direction if $n = 10$, $f_s = 18,000$ psi, and $f_c = 900$ psi.

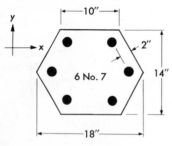

Figure 2–32

2–10. Compute the safe bending moment for the channel section shown in Fig. 2–33, given that $n = 12$, $f_c = 1200$ psi, and $f_s = 18,000$ psi.

2–11. Determine the maximum bending moment that can be carried by the

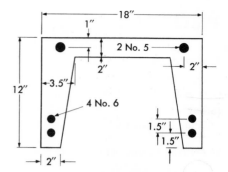

Figure 2–33

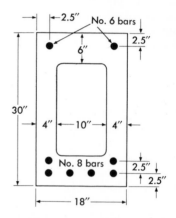

Figure 2–34

box section shown in Fig. 2–34, given that $f_c = 1350$ psi, $f_s = 20,000$ psi, and $n = 10$.

2–12. Compute the safe bending moment that can be carried by the beam shown in Fig. 2–35, given that $f_c = 1350$ psi, $f_s = 22,000$ psi, and $n = 10$.

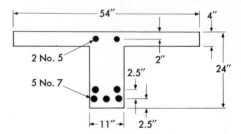

Figure 2–35

Design of Beams—Elastic Theory

2–13. A slab is supported by two walls 16 ft center to center (Fig. 2–36) and carries a uniform LL of 150 lb/ft² and a concentrated load of 1500 lb/ft of structure at the center of the span. For $f_s = 20,000$ psi, $f_c = 1200$ psi, and $n = 10$, determine the thickness of the slab, as well as the quantity and arrangement of the steel.

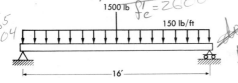

Figure 2–36

2–14. The slab and beams shown in Fig. 2–37 act as a unit to form T-beams. Assuming that the negative bending moment in the slab over the beam is 120,000 in-lb per 1-ft strip, $n = 10$, $f_s = 20,000$ psi, and $f_c = 1350$ psi, design the slab for this moment.

2–15. For Problem 2–6, adjust the steel area and spacing so that the slab can carry a uniform LL of 300 lb/ft.

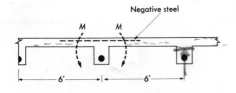

Fig. 2–37. End view of Fig. 2–38.

2–16. Design the T-beams shown in Fig. 2–37 to support a uniform LL of 300 lb/ft² and a concentrated total load of 16 k applied at the third points, as shown in Fig. 2–38. Let $n = 10$, $f_s = 20,000$ psi, and $f_c = 1350$ psi.

2–17. A rectangular beam which carries a bending moment of 1,250,000 in-lb is limited to a 20-in. overall depth. Assume that $n = 12$, $f_s = 20,000$ psi, and

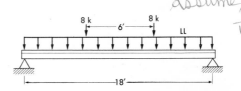

Fig. 2–38. Side view of Fig. 2–37.

$f_c = 1200$ psi. Find the width of the beam and the reinforcement required to carry this moment. (Use both tensile and compressive reinforcement.)

2–18. For a cross section of 24 in. × 16 in., determine the amount and location of the compressive and tensile reinforcement required, given that the beam is to support a uniform live load of 450 lb/ft on a 40-ft simple span. Let $f_c = 1000$ psi, $f_s = 18,000$ psi, and $n = 12$.

Analysis of Beams—Ultimate-Strength Theory

2–19. Compute the ultimate bending moment that the beam (cross section shown in Fig. 2–39) can carry. Let $f_c' = 3500$ psi and $f_y = 50,000$ psi.

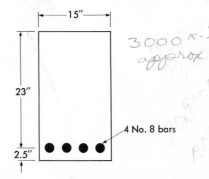

Figure 2–39

2–20. Compute the ultimate bending moment that can be carried by the beam whose cross section is shown in Fig. 2–40. Let $f_c' = 4000$ psi and $f_y = 50,000$ psi.

2–21. Calculate the ultimate uniform LL that can be carried by the one-way

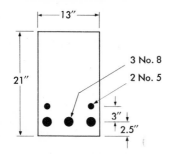

Figure 2–40

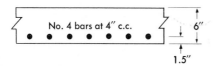

Figure 2–41

slab simply supported on a 10-ft span. The weight of the slab is considered to be DL. A typical section of the slab is shown in Fig. 2–41.

2–22. Calculate the ultimate moment that the T-beam (Fig. 2–42) can resist. Let $f_c' = 3000$ psi and $f_y = 50,000$ psi.

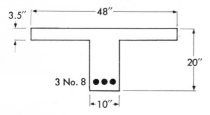

Figure 2–42

2–23. Determine the ultimate moment that the T-beam can carry (Fig. 2–43). Let $f_c' = 3500$ psi and $f_y = 60,000$ psi.

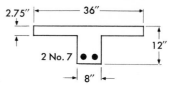

Figure 2–43

Design of Beams—Ultimate-Strength Theory

2–24. Design a rectangular beam to carry a working uniform live load of 2 kip/ft. The beam is simply supported over a span of 16 ft. Use the ultimate-strength theory and assume that $f_c' = 3000$ psi and $f_y = 60,000$ psi. To get the ultimate live load multiply the working load by 2.3.

2–25. A cantilever beam 10 ft long is to support a working uniform live load of 1.33 kip/ft and a concentrated load of 4.5 kip at the free end. To design the beam, use the ultimate-strength theory with a load factor of 2.5 and $f_c' = 4000$ psi, $f_y = 50,000$ psi.

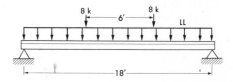

Figure 2–44

2–26. Design a T-beam supported and loaded as shown in Fig. 2–44 which is to carry a live load of 300 lb/ft² and a total concentrated load of 16,000 lb applied at the third points. Assume a safety factor of one.

REFERENCES

1. WILLIS A. SLATER and INGE LYSE, "Compressive Strength of Concrete in Flexure as Determined from Tests of Reinforced Beams," *ACI Journal,* June 1930.
2. KENNETH C. COX, "Tests of Reinforced Concrete Beams with Recommendations for Attaining Balanced Design," *ACI Journal,* Sept. 1941.
3. HENRY J. COWAN, "Direct Design of T-Beams," *ACI Journal,* March, 1951.
4. THOMAS E. STELSON and J. N. CERNICA, "Fatigue Properties of Concrete Beams," *ACI Journal,* Aug. 1958.
5. T. D. MYLREA, "Effect of Impact on Reinforced Concrete Beams," *ACI Journal,* June 1940.
6. DAVID WATSTEIN, "Bond Stress in Concrete Pull-Out Specimens," *ACI Journal,* Sept. 1941.
7. S. D. LASH and J. W. BRISON, "The Ultimate Strength of Reinforced Concrete Beams," *ACI Journal,* Feb. 1950.
8. C. P. SIESS, "Review of Research on Ultimate Strength of Reinforced Concrete Members," *ACI Journal,* June 1952.
9. EIVIND HOGNESTAD, N. W. HANSON and DOUGLAS MCHENRY, "Concrete Stress Distribution in Ultimate Strength Design," *ACI Journal,* Dec. 1955.
10. CHARLES S. WHITNEY and EDWARD COHEN, "Guide for Ultimate Strength Design of Reinforced Concrete," *ACI Journal,* Nov. 1956.
11. TUNG AU, "Ultimate Strength Design of Rectangular Concrete Members Subject to Unsymmetrical Bending," *ACI Journal,* Feb. 1958.

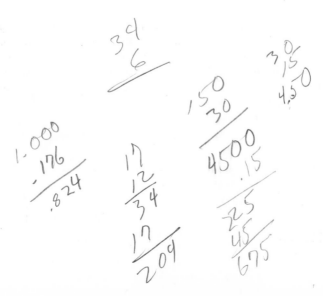

3 BOND, SHEAR, AND DIAGONAL TENSION IN BEAMS

Multiple-span girder bridge, Minneapolis, Minnesota. Four-span deck girder bridge carrying Glenwood Parkway over Wayzata Boulevard (U.S. Route 12).

3–1 INTRODUCTION

In the preceding chapters, we have established methods for determining the tensile and/or compressive stresses in the steel, and the compressive stresses in the concrete of a beam subjected to bending. Important as they might be, these stresses are not the only ones that have to be considered in the design of a beam. Bond, shear, and diagonal tension must also be investigated and appropriately taken into account.

The tensile forces T in Fig. 3–1b would not develop if there did not exist an adhesive or frictional force between the steel reinforcement and the concrete. (The steel would simply pull out.) The intensity of this force is called *bond stress*.

In Chapter 2, we established that C is equal to T (Fig. 3–1b). However, these two forces are equal only because the concrete between the C- and the T-levels is able to transmit shear. We may perform an analysis of this by imagining the beam cut between these two planes and taking the sum of the forces acting in the horizontal direction. The intensity of this horizontal force is known as

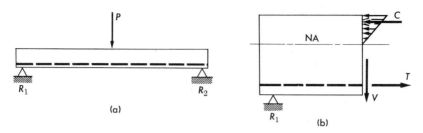

Figure 3-1

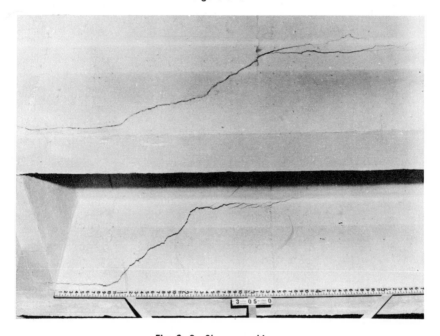

Fig. 3-2. Shear cracking.

shear stress. In the same manner, taking the sum of the forces acting in the vertical direction, we find the intensity of the vertical shear stresses acting on the face of the cut. As we shall see later, if the shearing stresses are high enough, they will cause cracks in the concrete along an inclined plane, as shown in Fig. 3-2. However, for such a crack to occur, the concrete must have been subjected to diagonal tension (see Section 3-6).

3-2 BOND BETWEEN CONCRETE AND LONGITUDINAL REINFORCEMENT

In plain bars, some bond between the concrete and the reinforcement may develop due to the frictional forces; in deformed bars, the bond is developed by both frictional and direct interlocking arising from the deformities of the bars. Deformed bars are essentially plain bars with shoulders or irregularities which project into the concrete to prevent slippage. The plain bar is seldom, if ever,

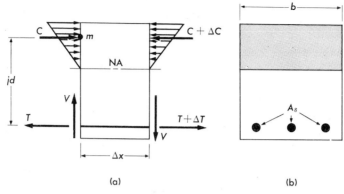

(a)   (b)

Figure 3–3

used anymore, and therefore in discussing reinforcing bars we shall always imply deformed bars, unless otherwise specified.

Let us now derive the bond stress for the beam illustrated in Fig. 3–1. An increment of length Δx along this beam is set in equilibrium (Fig. 3–3). It is readily evident that since the tension forces T and $(T + \Delta T)$ are not the same, the difference must be carried by the bond over the length Δx:

$$\Sigma F_x = 0; \quad (T + \Delta T) = T + \text{bond force along } \Delta x.$$

The bond force is equal to the bond stress times the surface area on which the bond acts. The area is the circumferences of the bars times the length Δx, or

$$\text{area of contact} = (\Sigma_0) \, \Delta x,$$

where Σ_0 is the sum of the perimeters or circumferences of all the bars. The bond force is therefore:

$$\text{bond force} = u(\Sigma_0) \, \Delta x,$$

where u is the bond stress. It follows that

$$\Delta T = u(\Sigma_0) \, \Delta x.$$

Also, summing the moments with respect to point m in Fig. 3–3 yields

$$\Delta T = \frac{V \, \Delta x}{jd}.$$

Combining the last two expressions, we obtain

$$u(\Sigma_0) \, \Delta x = \frac{V \, \Delta x}{jd}, \quad u = \frac{V}{(\Sigma_0)(jd)}. \tag{3–1}$$

Again, let us keep in mind that Σ_0 is the sum of the perimeters of all bars and that jd is the distance from the compression force C to the centroid of the areas of all bars. It is easy to see that if we have two or more rows of bars, Eq. (3–1)

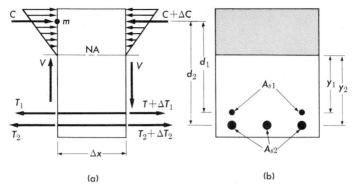

(a)   (b)

Figure 3–4

will cause a slight error in the bond stress u, depending on the distance between rows.

For a more general case, assume that there are two rows of bars with different cross-sectional areas, as shown in Fig. 3–4. As previously,

$$\sum M_m = 0; \qquad \Delta T_1 d_1 + \Delta T_2 d_2 = V \Delta x.$$

But the tensile force in one row is proportional to the area of the steel in that row and to its distance from the neutral axis. Thus

$$\frac{\Delta T_1}{\Delta T_2} = \frac{A_{s1}}{A_{s2}} \frac{y_1}{y_2}, \qquad \Delta T_2 = \left(\frac{A_{s2}}{A_{s1}} \frac{y_2}{y_1}\right) \Delta T_1.$$

Substituting this result in the preceding equation yields

$$\Delta T_1 d_1 + \Delta T_1 \frac{A_{s2}}{A_{s1}} \frac{y_2}{y_1} d_2 = V \Delta x,$$

$$\Delta T_1 \left(d_1 + \frac{A_{s2}}{A_{s1}} \frac{y_2}{y_1} d_2\right) = V \Delta x;$$

but

$$\Delta T_1 = u_1(\textstyle\sum_{01}) \Delta x.$$

Substituting the equivalent expression for ΔT_1 and solving for u_1, we obtain

$$u_1 = \frac{V A_{s1} y_1}{(\sum_{01})[A_{s1} y_1 d_1 + A_{s2} y_2 d_2]}. \qquad (3\text{–}2)$$

Similarly,

$$u_2 = \frac{V A_{s2} y_2}{(\sum_{02})[A_{s2} y_2 d_2 + A_{s1} y_1 d_1]}. \qquad (3\text{–}3)$$

If the bars are in the same row but have different areas, that is, $y_1 = y_2$,

$$d_1 = d_2 = jd, \qquad A_1 \neq A_2, \qquad A_{s1} + A_{s2} = A_s,$$

then the above expression reduces to

$$u_1 = \frac{VA_{s1}}{(\sum_{01})(A_{s2} + A_{s1})jd} = \frac{A_{s1}}{A_s}\frac{V}{(\sum_{01})jd},$$ (3–4)

and

$$u_2 = \frac{A_{s2}}{A_s}\frac{V}{(\sum_{02})jd}.$$ (3–5)

When the bars are in the same row and are of the same size, Eqs. (3–4) and (3–5) reduce to Eq. (3–1).

The bond stress in any row for any number of rows with different areas can be determined in a similar manner, although it is easy to see that the derivation becomes quite involved. Frequently, such an analysis is neither practical nor desirable, for when d_1 is approximately equal to d_2, Eq. (3–1) applies with reasonable accuracy. There are cases, however, where there are several rows of reinforcement and the difference between d_1 and d_2 is considerable (as for example for arches).

Example 3–1. *Analysis*

Given: The beam in Fig. 3–5 is simply supported on an 18-ft span. It supports a concentrated load of 14.5 k at each of the third points of the span.

Find: The maximum bond stress that develops.

SOLUTION: We first determine the weight of the beam:

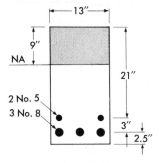

Figure 3–5

$$\frac{26.5 \text{ in.} \times 13 \text{ in.}}{144 \text{ in}^2/\text{ft}^2}\frac{150 \text{ lb}}{\text{ft}^3} 18 \text{ ft} = 6460 \text{ lb.}$$

Therefore one reaction is

$$14.5 \text{ k} + \frac{6.460 \text{ k}}{2} = 17.70 \text{ k} = V.$$

The area of two No. 5 bars is

$$0.62 \text{ in}^2, \quad \sum_0 = 3.92 \text{ in.}, \quad d_1 = 21 - \tfrac{9}{3} = 18 \text{ in.}, \quad y_1 = 12 \text{ in.}$$

The area of three No. 8 bars is

$$2.37 \text{ in}^2, \quad \sum_0 = 9.42 \text{ in.}, \quad d_2 = 24 - \tfrac{9}{3} = 21 \text{ in.}, \quad y_2 = 15 \text{ in.}$$

For two No. 5 bars,

$$u_1 = \frac{V}{\sum_{01}[d_1 + (A_2/A_1)(y_2/y_1)d_2]}$$ (3–2)

$$u_1 = \frac{17,700}{3.92[18 + (2.37/0.62)(15/12)21]} = 43.5 \text{ psi.}$$

For three No. 8 bars, we have from Eq. (3–3),

$$u_2 = \frac{17,700}{9.42[21 + (0.62/2.37)(12/15)18]} = 75.8 \text{ psi.}$$

As a comparison find the bond stress given by Eq. (3–1):

$$u = \frac{V}{(\sum_0)jd}.$$

The quantity j is calculated to be 0.872 and $d = 23.3$ in.;

$$\sum_0 = \sum_{01} + \sum_{02} = 3.92 + 9.42 = 13.34.$$

Therefore

$$u = \frac{17,700 \text{ lb}}{13.34 \times 0.872 \times 23.3} = 65.4 \text{ psi.}$$

Compare this stress with u_1 and u_2 above.

3–3 SPLICING AND HOOKING

The word "splicing" in concrete design refers to the overlapping of two reinforcing bars so that the tensile load will be transmitted from one to the other by bond. Using two or more pieces and splicing them together might not only be more economical and practical than using only one piece, but it might be a necessity. This is especially true when one pour is to be tied to another, as in the process of connecting a column or retaining wall to a base by dowels (Chapter 6). Welding two ends together is usually neither practical nor economical.

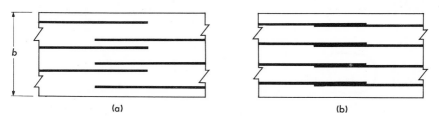

Fig. 3–6. Two beams showing two types of splices.

To determine the splicing length, let us assume that the bond stress is developed completely around the bar, such as might be the case for the beams illustrated in Fig. 3–6(a). This, of course, does not happen if the bars touch each other (Fig. 3–6b). Experiments, however, have shown little difference in strength, whether the splices were in contact or separated. For the sake of analysis, let us assume that the bar is completely encased and that it develops a uniform bond stress over its whole spliced length.

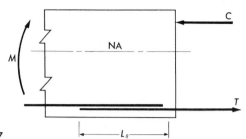

Figure 3–7

The tensile force in the steel (Fig. 3–7) must be developed by the bond strength over the splice length. Therefore

$$T = A_s f_s = u(\textstyle\sum_0)L_s, \qquad \text{or} \qquad \frac{\pi d^2 f_s}{4} = u(\textstyle\sum_0)L_s,$$

$$L_s = \frac{\pi d^2 f_s}{4}\frac{1}{u\sum_0} = \frac{\pi d^2 f_s}{4}\frac{1}{u\pi d},$$

$$L_s = \frac{d f_s}{4u}, \tag{3–6}$$

where u is assumed to be the *average* bond stress over the length L_s. Article 805(b) of the ACI Code specifies that the length of lap for deformed bars shall not be less than 24, 30, or 36 bar diameters, or 12 in., for specified yield points of 40,000, 50,000, and 60,000 psi, respectively.

Splicing is commonly found in a construction joint. For example, pouring a footer and a column is usually a two-step operation. The procedure is to pour the footer first, allowing the reinforcing bars (dowels), which join the column to the footer, to stick out of the footer. After the concrete in the footer solidifies, the steel of the column is added and the column poured. Such a joint is called a *construction joint*. It is obvious that this procedure is a form of splicing.

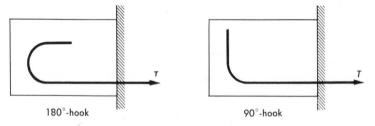

180°-hook   90°-hook

Figure 3–8

In some cases it may not be possible to extend a bar far enough to develop sufficient strength by bond alone. A suitable remedy for such a case is hooking the bar as shown in Fig. 3–8. The purpose of the hook is to increase the anchorage length of the reinforcing bar. In bending the bar, the tensile force tends to (a) pull on the bar along the path of the curvature, and (b) to shoulder, or interlock, the concrete. This interlocking action, however, is considered unreliable for design considerations. For small curvatures, the concrete inside the curvature may experience stresses above the allowable ones. Generally speaking, small curvatures are undesirable. [Article 801(b) of the ACI Code lists the minimum radii of bend].

The Code states that the term *standard hook* shall mean: (1) a semicircular turn plus an extension of at least 4 bar diameters but not less than $2\frac{1}{2}$ in. at the free end of the bar, or (2) a 90-degree turn plus an extension of at least 12 bar diameters at the free end of the bar, or (3) for stirrup and tie anchorage only, either a 90-degree or a 135-degree turn plus an extension of at least 6 bar diameters but not less than $2\frac{1}{2}$ in. at the free end of the bar.

Example 3–2. *Analysis*

Given: A beam whose cross section has the dimensions $b = 15$ in., $d = 23$ in. and is reinforced with four No. 8 bars (structural grade), all located at the same depth. Two of the bars are spliced with another pair of the same size at a point where the bending moment is 1,200,000 in-lb. Assume that $j = 0.89$.

Find: The length over which the rods must be lapped, given that the allowable bond stress is 180 psi.

SOLUTION: Assume that each of the four bars takes an equal share of the tensile force, i.e., one-quarter of the total. Then

$$Tjd = M = 1,200,000 \text{ in-lb},$$

$$T = \frac{1,200,000}{0.89 \times 23} = 58,600 \text{ lb},$$

$$\frac{\text{Force}}{\text{bar}} = \frac{58,600}{4} = 14,650 \text{ lb}.$$

This force must be developed by a bond equal to $2\pi r u L_s$, where the diameter of a No. 8 bar equals 1 in. Therefore

$$14,650 = 2 \times 3.14 \times \tfrac{1}{2} \times 180 L_s,$$

$$L_s = 26 \text{ in.}, \qquad L_{\min} = 24 \, d = 24 \text{ in.}$$

(Article 805(b), ACI Code.)

Remark: It is advisable to splice *only* at points of inflection (zero moment).

3–4 DISTRIBUTION OF BOND STRESSES

In the preceding chapter it was assumed that for a given beam the magnitude of stresses in the tensile reinforcement is a function of the external bending moment, as expressed by Eq. (2–8). This implies that for a beam with a variable moment along its span, the longitudinal reinforcement will be cut off appropriately to take care of the bending moment that exists at any one section.

Let us assume that the beam shown in Fig. 3–9 has a concentrated load in the center of its span. Following are the shear and moment diagrams, respectively,

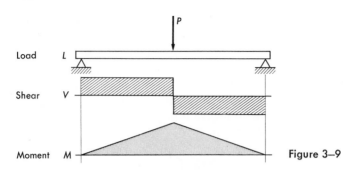

Figure 3-9

for this particular loading. Looking at the moment diagram, it is obvious that for a beam of constant cross section the tensile reinforcement necessary at the support of the beam is not the same as that required at the center of the beam. Hence it is desirable to reduce the reinforcement proportionately to the moment, and thereby keep the tensile stress approximately the same throughout the beam. A common and practical method of adjusting the tensile reinforcement is to divide the maximum ordinate of the moment diagram into the number of bars required to take care of the moment (tensile stresses) at that section. We then draw horizontal lines through these ordinates to meet the moment diagram. For each ordinate, on each side of the diagram, let us add a minimum length, L_s, to take care of anchorage. The length of any of these bars at any one ordinate is the length of the horizontal line at that ordinate. For example, assume that the load in Fig. 3-9 requires 5 bars at the center of the span where the bending moment is a maximum. We then take the bending moment from Fig. 3-9 and divide its ordinate into 5 equal increments, as shown in Fig. 3-10, and project the horizontals. Note that bar 1 extends over the length of the beam; bar 2, over the length within the moment diagram plus the anchorage length, etc., (see Art. 918, ACI Code).

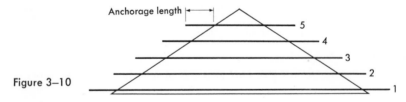

Figure 3-10

We should note that in such a case the neutral axis at the ends is different from that at the center of the span because the percentage of steel at the two cross sections varies as cutoffs occur. Therefore, the result obtained for the stress is in slight error if the neutral axis is assumed to be at the same depth throughout the span.

The shear in Fig. 3-9 is constant from one support to the center and from the center to the other support. For a constant shear force V and constant jd over any one length, the bond stress is constant over the length, provided that Σ_0 is a constant as expressed in Eq. (3-1). As mentioned previously, jd does change. However, the change is small, and for practical purposes, it may there-fore be assumed to be constant throughout the length. The quantity $\sum_0$, however, changes considerably with the change in the number of bars, and hence one must be careful in determining $\sum_0$. For simply supported beams, determining the bond stress near the support, where the shear V is a maximum and $\sum_0$ is a minimum, is sufficient for the whole beam if the bond stress found at this point is within the limit given by the specifications.

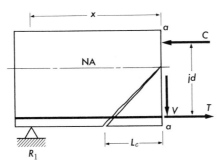

Figure 3–11

Now let us assume that there is a cracked section, as shown in Fig. 3–11. Before the crack occurred the tensile force, T, would have been about the same (neglecting tension in concrete) at section a–a as it is now. But note the dif-ference between the lengths along which this tensile force must be developed. The length L_c was lost during the cracking, therefore the portion that develops T must be under higher bond stress or the steel would slip out. Further, let us consider that in figuring the length necessary for anchorage, as in Fig. 3–11, we assume that the *average* bond stress governs. In practice, however, the stress near the crack may be appreciably greater than that near the left end. [Article 1301(c) of the ACI Code sets bond-stress limits that are appreciably lower than the ultimate strength of concrete in compression.]

3–5 SHEARING STRESSES

Transverse loads (Fig. 3–1a) cause a shear V and a bending moment M over the span of a reinforced concrete beam, and hence produce shear stresses and bending stresses. To determine the shear stresses over the cross section of the beam, let us assume that an increment of length Δx is cut along the length of the span and placed in equilibrium, as shown in Fig. 3–12. It is readily evident that due to the difference in the compressive and tensile forces on each side of the element, the element will tend to shear off and slide on a plane parallel to the longitudinal axis of the beam. This is shown schematically in Fig. 3–13. Taking the sum of the forces in the horizontal direction, we see that if we are to obtain equilibrium and thus prevent horizontal movement, the shear forces must balance the force ΔT. Denoting the intensity of the horizontal shear stress by v_c, we find

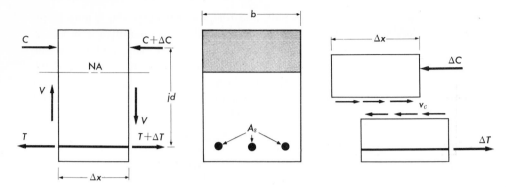

Figure 3–12   Figure 3–13

that the shear forces amount to v_c times the width of the beam, times the length of the element Δx, or

$$\sum F_x = 0; \qquad \Delta T = v_c b \, \Delta x.$$

Substituting $\Delta T = V\Delta x/jd$ (Art. 3–2), in the above expression, we get

$$(v_c b \, \Delta x) jd = V \, \Delta x,$$

$$v_c = \frac{V}{bjd}. \tag{3–7}$$

In 1950, a joint committee (Committee 326) composed of members of the American Concrete Institute and American Society of Civil Engineers was formed to develop methods for designing reinforced concrete members capable of resisting shear and diagonal tension. After extensive studies of available data, the committee recommended a shear stress of (see Article 1201, ACI Code)

$$v_c = \frac{V}{bd}, \tag{3–7a}$$

and reported that this formula represents the results of actual tests, although, admittedly, it is only an average of a stress distribution not fully understood. At this time, the author prefers to use the formula $v_c = V/bjd$ primarily because it may be expressed in more fundamental terms, as shown in its derivation.

To determine the transverse shear stress, we assume a cracked beam, as shown in Fig. 3–14. The section that resists the vertical shear is obviously that above the neutral axis, i.e., the area is equal to b times the distance kd. The vertical shear, or the transverse shear, is therefore equal to the vertical force divided by the area taking shear:

$$v_t = \frac{V}{kdb}. \tag{3–8}$$

From Eqs. 3–7 and 3–8, the relative magnitudes of the longitudinal shear stress

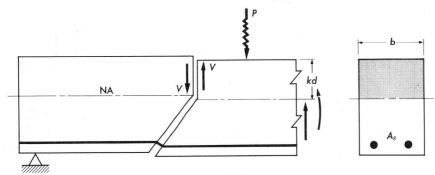

Figure 3–14

and transverse shear stress are given by

$$v_t = \left(\frac{V/kbd}{V/bjd}\right) v_c \qquad v_c = \frac{j}{k}\, v_c. \tag{3-9}$$

Example 3–3. *Analysis*

Given: A beam 15 in. wide and of 26-in. overall depth, reinforced with four No. 8 bars 23 in. from the top, carries a concentrated load of 5 k at the center of a 20-ft simple span and a live load of 1.2 k/ft.

Find: The longitudinal shear stress, v_c, and the transverse shear stress, v_t, given that $k = 0.36$, $j = 0.88$, and $f_c' = 4000$ psi.

SOLUTION: The total dead load (weight of concrete beam) is

$$\frac{26 \text{ in.} \times 15 \text{ in.}}{144 \text{ in}^2/\text{ft}^2} \times 150 \text{ lb/ft}^3 \times 20 \text{ ft} = 8.125\,k.$$

The total live load is $1.2 \times 20 = 24$ k; and one reaction is

$$V = \frac{8.125 + 5 + 24}{2} = 18.56\,k,$$

$$v_c = \frac{V}{bjd} = \frac{18560 \text{ lb}}{15 \times 0.88 \times 23} = 61.10 \text{ psi},$$

$$v_t = \frac{V}{bkd} = \frac{18560 \text{ lb}}{15 \times 0.36 \times 23} = 149.0 \text{ psi}.$$

From Article 1201 of the ACI Code, v_c allowable for $f_c' = 4000$ psi may be determined. No working limit is given for v_t, but it is generally accepted that the allowable longitudinal shear stress is several times larger than v_c (perhaps four to six times, depending on the particular design).

3–6 DIAGONAL TENSION

In the following we shall attempt to illustrate the effect of the shearing and bending stresses on the diagonal tension of a reinforced concrete beam. Assume that three very small elements are taken out of the portion of the beam shown

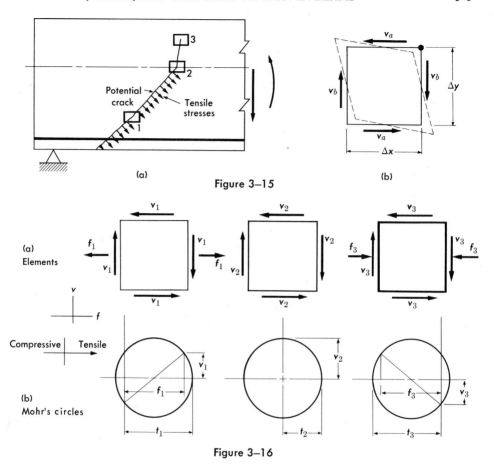

Figure 3–15

Figure 3–16

in Fig. 3–15(a) and set in equilibrium (Fig. 3–15b). First we must establish that the shear stresses are of the same magnitude on all four faces of the element. Assume that v_b and v_a in Fig. 3–16(b) represent these stresses:

$$\sum M_{\text{(upper right-hand corner)}} = 0,$$

$$(v_b \, \Delta y \times \text{thickness}) \, \Delta x = \underbrace{(v_a \, \Delta x \times \text{thickness})}_{\text{Force}} \cdot \underset{\downarrow}{\Delta y}._{\text{Moment arm}}$$

Hence

$$v_b = v_a.$$

Now take the elements 1, 2, and 3 shown in Fig. 3–15(a) and set them in equilibrium. Note that, in addition to the equal shear stress acting on the four faces, the element below the neutral axis experiences a tensile stress f_1 before cracking occurs. The element at the neutral axis has no bending (normal) stress. The one above the neutral axis experiences compressive stresses on two faces in addition to some shear stresses. These are in equilibrium, as shown in Fig. 3–16(a). For each element, a Mohr circle may be drawn to determine the principal stresses (Fig. 3–16b). From these circles, it is easy to see that

$$t_1 = \frac{f_1}{2} + \sqrt{(f_1^2/4 + v_1^2)}; \qquad t_2 = v_2; \qquad -t_3 = -[f_3/2 + \sqrt{f_3^2/4 + v_3^2}].$$
$$(3\text{–}10)$$

The expression for the angle that the plane makes with the vertical is

$$\tan 2\theta = \frac{v}{(f/2)} = \frac{2v}{f}.$$

Note that it is possible to obtain the diagonal tension stress even above the neutral axis.

3–7 WEB REINFORCEMENT: STIRRUPS AND BENT-UP BARS

The longitudinal reinforcement of a beam subjected to transverse loads does not provide an effective control of the shearing stresses in the concrete. If these stresses exceed the safe limit, one must provide additional reinforcement to compensate for the excess shear. This type of reinforcement is commonly referred to as *web reinforcement,* to distinguish it from flexure reinforcement.

The web reinforcement may be broken into two general groups, *stirrups* and *bent-up rods.* Both categories may be broken down further, depending on whether they are inclined or perpendicular to the longitudinal reinforcement, although bent-up rods are rarely perpendicular to the longitudinal axis of the beam. In the majority of cases they form an angle of 45° or less with the horizontal axis.

To analyze the action of stirrups, we use Fig. 3–17(b), which represents the portion of a beam near a support, where the shear force is the greatest. Assume

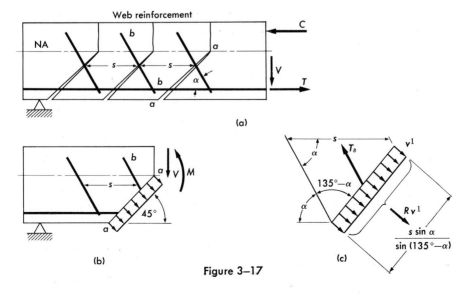

Figure 3–17

the web reinforcement to be either stirrups or bent-up bars making an angle α with the longitudinal reinforcement. Such a bar may be represented by b–b, which crosses a potential crack a–a. The force T_s in the bar b–b must withstand all the diagonal tensile force not resisted by the concrete alone. Since the unit shear at any one point in the beam is a measure of the diagonal tension (as shown in the previous article), the intensity of the tensile stress over a–a can be denoted by v^1. The difference between v^1 and v_c, the shear stress taken by the concrete, must be made up by the tensile force in the bar b–b. Let the intensity of this difference be represented by v^1, that is, $v^1 = v - v_c$.

If the horizontal distance or spacing between any two bars is represented by s (see Fig. 3–17a), then the force in the bar, T_s, is equal to the intensity of v^1 times the area for which the bar is assumed effective (Fig. 3–17b). Now let us magnify the portion of the beam over which T_s is effective (Fig. 3–17c). Note that the effective area is equal to the width of the beam web times the projected length of s. Therefore the resultant $R_v{}^1$ of the tensile forces is given by

$$R_v{}^1 = v^1 b \left(\frac{s \sin \alpha}{\sin (135° - \alpha)} \right) = \frac{v^1 bs \sin \alpha}{\sin (45° + \alpha)},$$

$$R_v{}^1 = \frac{v^1 bs \sin \alpha}{(1/\sqrt{2})(\cos \alpha + \sin \alpha)},$$

The summation of forces in the vertical direction gives

$$T_s \sin \alpha = R_v{}^1 \sin 45° = \frac{v^1 bs \sin \alpha}{\cos \alpha + \sin \alpha}.$$

In terms of bar stress, f_v, and cross-sectional area of bar, A_v, we have

$$T_s = A_v f_v.$$

Hence

$$A_v f_v \sin \alpha = \frac{v^1 bs \sin \alpha}{\cos \alpha + \sin \alpha},$$

or

$$A_v f_v = \frac{v^1 bs}{\cos \alpha + \sin \alpha}. \tag{3–11}$$

If V represents the shear force at a section near a–a, the relationship $v = V/bjd$ modifies Eq. (3–11) to

$$A_v f_v = \frac{v^1 bs}{\cos \alpha + \sin \alpha} = \frac{V^1 s}{jd(\cos \alpha + \sin \alpha)}, \tag{3–11a}$$

where V^1 is the total shear at the section minus that taken by the concrete. For $\alpha = 45°$, i.e., for stirrups perpendicular to the crack, we have

$$A_v f_v = \frac{v^1 bs}{\sqrt{2}} = \frac{V^1 s}{jd\sqrt{2}} \tag{3–12}$$

and for $\alpha = 90°$, i.e., for stirrups perpendicular to the longitudinal reinforcement, we obtain

$$A_v f_v = v^1 bs = \frac{V^1 s}{jd}.\tag{3-13}$$

The force that must be developed in the bar by the bond stress acting along the length of the bar can be found from Eq. (3–14), where u is the allowable bond stress:

$$L_s = \frac{A_v f_v}{(\Sigma_0)u}.\tag{3-14}$$

In vertical stirrups, the anchorage distance L_s can usually be obtained by either hooking the ends of the stirrup around the compressive reinforcement or by simply bending the stirrup. This is often necessitated by the lack of depth over which L_s can be developed.

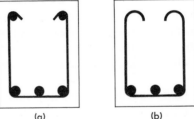

(a)   (b)   Figure 3–18

Figure 3–18(a) shows a stirrup bent around the tensile reinforcement for the purpose of developing better anchorage. The top portion of the stirrup may be welded or tied to the compression steel, whenever it is available, but the ends of the stirrups seldom overlap since this would hinder the placing of the longitudinal rods after the stirrups are in the forms. Figure 3–18(b) shows an alternative way of bending the stirrups, used in the absence of compressive reinforcement.

3–8 SPACING OF DIAGONAL TENSION REINFORCEMENT

From Eqs. (3–11) through (3–13) one can determine the theoretical spacing of the web reinforcement. The ACI Code and practical considerations, however, often alter the theoretical values obtained from these previous equations. Article 1206(a) of the ACI Code states, "that where web reinforcement is required it shall be so spaced that every 45° line, representing a potential crack, extending from the mid-depth, $d/2$, of the beam to the longitudinal tension bars, shall be crossed by *at least one* line of web reinforcement. When the shear stress exceeds $3\sqrt{f_c'}$ every 45° line shall be crossed by *at least two* lines of web reinforcement." To find the spacing of the web reinforcement solve Eq. (3–11) for s to obtain

$$s = \frac{A_v f_v(\cos \alpha + \sin \alpha)}{v^1 b}.\tag{3-15}$$

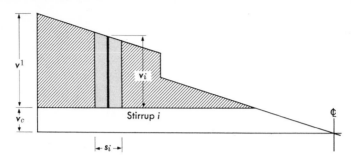

Figure 3–19

The stress v^1 of this equation is the average stress over the length s taken by any one stirrup. Customarily, the rods used for stirrups are of the same size. Therefore, if we wish to obtain a constant stress in all the stirrups, it follows from Eq. (3–15) that the spacing must vary inversely with respect to v^1 when $A_v f_v$ and b are constant. In Fig. 3–19 note that v^1 varies irregularly along the beam. For such a beam, the spacing for the stirrups would vary, decreasing per linear length from the left to the right, i.e., per foot of length there would be more stirrups at the left end than near the center of the span, within the limitations of the Code.

Equation (3–15) holds equally well for any varying v^1. However, for such a case, the formula may be not only troublesome but to some extent impractical since it may compound any error made during the laying-out of the stirrups in the field. Thus, it would be desirable to develop a formula for the location of the stirrups with reference to one point independent of any other stirrup. Such an equation can be obtained from Fig. 3–20. Rewriting Eq. (3–15), we have

$$sv^1 b = A_v f_v (\cos \alpha + \sin \alpha).$$

Assuming that all stirrups have the same size and the same slope with respect to the longitudinal reinforcement, we find that the term on the right-hand side of the above equation is constant. Thus the area under the v^1 diagram which is taken care of by one stirrup is $v^1 \cdot s$.

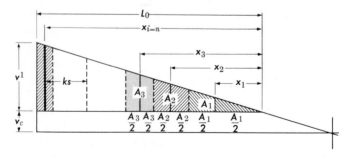

Fig. 3–20. v^1-diagram for one-half of a beam of constant cross section loaded with a uniform load. Each of the shaded trapezoids has the same area.

Now assume that each stirrup takes an equal portion of the v^1-diagram as shown in Figure 3–20. We would therefore need N stirrups, or

$$N = \frac{b \text{ (total area under } v^1\text{-diagram)}}{A_v f_v (\cos \alpha + \sin \alpha)}.$$

Referring to Figure 3–20, we determine the location of the stirrups as follows:

$$\text{Total area under the } v^1\text{-diagram} = \frac{v^1 L_0}{2},$$

$$A_1 = A_2 = \cdots = A_i = \cdots = A_N = \frac{v^1 L_0}{2N}.$$

By similar triangles,

$$\frac{A_1}{2} = \left[x_1 \left(\frac{v^1}{L_0} x_1 \right) \frac{1}{2} \right],$$

$$\frac{A_2}{2} = x_2 \frac{v^1}{L_0} x_2 \frac{1}{2} - 2x_1 \frac{v^1}{L_0} x_1 \frac{1}{2},$$

$$\frac{A_3}{2} = x_3 \frac{v^1}{L_0} x_3 \frac{1}{2} - 4x_1 \frac{v^1}{L_0} x_1 \frac{1}{2}.$$

From $A_1 = A_2 = A_3 = \cdots = A_i = \cdots = A_N$, it follows that, from

$$A_i = \frac{v^1 L_0}{2N}, \qquad i = 1, 2, 3, \ldots, N.$$

We get

$$A_1 = 2x_1 \frac{v^1}{L_0} x_1 \frac{1}{2} = \frac{v^1 L_0}{2N},$$

or

$$x_1 = \frac{L_0}{\sqrt{2N}} = L_0 \sqrt{\frac{1}{2N}},$$

and

$$A_2 = x_2^2 \frac{v^1}{L_0} - 2x_1^2 \frac{v^1}{L_0} = x_2^2 \frac{v^1}{L_0} - 2 \frac{L_0^2}{2N} \frac{v^1}{L_0} = \frac{v^1 L_0}{2N}.$$

Thus

$$x_2 = L_0 \sqrt{\frac{3}{2N}},$$

$$A_3 = x_3^2 \frac{v^1}{L_0} - 4x_1^2 \frac{v^1}{L_0} = x_3^2 \frac{v^1}{L_0} - 4 \frac{L_0^2}{2N} \frac{v^1}{L_0} = \frac{v^1 L_0}{2N},$$

$$x_3 = L_0 \sqrt{\frac{5}{2N}},$$

Finally, by induction,

$$x_i = L_0 \sqrt{\frac{2i - 1}{2N}}; \qquad i = 1, 2, \ldots, N. \tag{3–16}$$

Note that in Eq. (3–16), i represents the bar number in a sequence which runs from 1 to N, that is, it represents the first, second, third . . . , Nth bar.

It is not practical to work with spacings measuring fractional units. For example, if one obtained a theoretical spacing of 6.7 in., the number would be rounded to either 7 in. or 6 in. It is usually advisable to adopt the smaller of the whole numbers to ensure safety. Furthermore, the size of the stirrups should be chosen such that the spacing is practical and in compliance with the Code limitations. For example it is not recommended to place vertical stirrups at a distance of less than 3 in.

Article 1202a of the Code stipulates that web reinforcement be provided beyond the point theoretically required, for a distance equal to the depth d of the member. This usually means at least 2 more stirrups than the equation indicates and sometimes 4 or 5 more.

The procedure for stirrup spacing consists of the following steps:

(a) Determine the portion of the beam which requires web reinforcement.
(b) Pick a suitable stirrup size.
(c) From the theoretical evaluation and the Code limitation, determine an appropriate spacing.

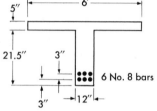

Example 3–4. Design

Given: The T-beam shown in Fig. 3–21 is simply supported on an 18-ft span. It carries a live load of 400 lb/ft² , and a concentrated load of 8 k applied at each of the third points of the span; $f_c' = 5000$ psi.

Figure 3–21

Find: A suitable design of U-shaped vertical stirrups if the allowable stresses are:

$$v_c = 75 \text{ psi,} \qquad f_s = 20{,}000 \text{ psi,} \qquad f_c = 1350 \text{ psi,} \qquad n = 10, \qquad u = 150 \text{ psi.}$$

SOLUTION:
Maximum shear $= \frac{1}{2}$ (total load),

total load $=$

$$\left[16 \text{ k} + (0.4 \text{ k/ft}^2 \times 6 \text{ ft}) \times 18 \text{ ft} + \left(\frac{6 \times 12 \times 5 + 21.5 \times 12}{144} \right) 150 \times 18 \text{ ft} \right]$$

$$= 16 \text{ k} + 43.2 \text{ k} + 10.6 \text{ k}$$

$$= 69.8 \text{ kip,}$$

where the fraction represents the weight of the beam per foot of length. Hence

$$V_{\max} = \frac{69.8}{2} = 34.9 \text{ kip,} \qquad v = \frac{V}{bjd}.$$

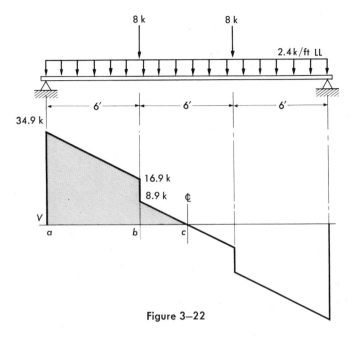

Figure 3–22

We use transformed section and calculate jd to be equal to 20.4 in. For analysis of T-beams, only $b'jd$ shall be assumed to resist shear. Hence

$$v = \frac{34.9}{12 \times 20.4} = 143 \text{ psi.}$$

From similar triangles, Fig. 3–23, we get

$$x = \frac{(143 - 75) \times 72}{143 - 69} = 66.2 \text{ in.}$$

Since $\alpha = 90°$ (i.e. vertical stirrups), we use Eq. (3–13) and obtain

$$A_v f_v = v^1 b s.$$

For vertical stirrups, Article 1206 of the ACI Code limits the maximum spacing to $d/2$, which in our case is 11 in.

Spacing. Approach 1: From Eq. (3–15) for $\alpha = 90°$, and assuming No. 3 bars, we find $A_s = 0.11$ in² times 2 since the bar is U-shaped $= 0.22$ in². Then, for $f_s = 20,000$ psi, the spacing becomes,

$$s = \frac{A_v f_v}{v^1 b} = \frac{4400}{12} \frac{1}{v^1},$$

or v_i^1 varies from $143 - 75 = 68$ psi at $x = 0$ to zero at $x = 66.2$ in. We have therefore

$$v^1 = 68 - \frac{68}{66.2} x = 68 \left(1 - \frac{x}{66.2} \right).$$

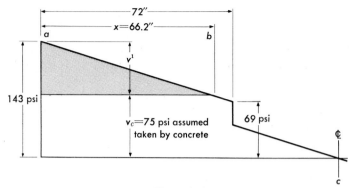

Figure 3–23

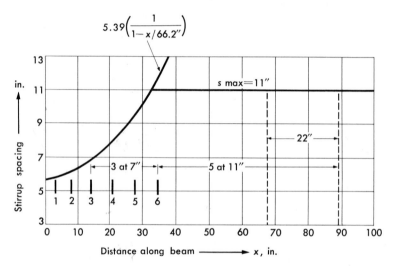

Figure 3–24

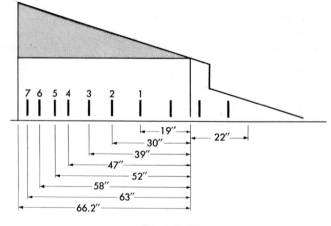

Figure 3–25

Thus

$$s = \left(\frac{4400}{12 \times 68}\right)\left(\frac{1}{1 - x/66.2}\right) = 5.39 \text{ in.} \left(\frac{1}{1 - x/66.2}\right).$$

Figure 3–23 serves as a guide for the appropriate spacing. For example, starting with one bar at a distance of 3 in. from the end of the support, one places the second bar at a distance of 5 in. from the first (conservative approximation), the third bar at a distance of about 6 in. from the second (the result being $3 + 5 + 6 = 14$ in. from the end point), the next three bars at a distance of 7 in., etc. Thus the number of bars is 11 for each end, or a total of 22 (symmetry of loading).

Approach 2 (theoretical): Approach 1, which provided equal spacing for some bars, resulted in a varied stirrup stress. Now let us determine the spacing, assuming a stress of 20,000 psi in each stirrup. We use N to denote the number of stirrups needed. Then

$$N = \frac{b' \text{ (area under } v^1\text{-diagram)}}{A_v f_v},$$

$$N = \frac{12(68 \times 66.2 \times \frac{1}{2})}{4400} = 6.14, \quad \text{say 7 stirrups.}$$

From Eq. (3–16) (also see Fig. 3–20):

$$x_i = L_0\sqrt{(2i - 1)/2N} = L_0\sqrt{(2i - 1)/(2 \times 7)}; \quad 1 = 1, 2, \ldots, N = 7,$$

$$x_1 = L_0 \frac{\sqrt{2i - 1}}{3.75}; \quad = (66.2)\frac{\sqrt{2i - 1}}{3.75} = 17.7\sqrt{2i - 1};$$

or in tabular form:

i	1	2	3	4	5	6	$N = 7$
x_i, in.	19	30	39	47	52	58	63

Note that the distance between any two adjacent stirrups cannot be greater than 11 in. Furthermore, Article 1202a of the specifications says that stirrups have to be extended $1d$ (approximately 22 in. in our case) beyond the point of $v^1 = 0$. One can do this by adding 19 in. + 22 in. and placing 4 stirrups over these 41 in. approximately 11 in. apart. Thus the total number of stirrups is 11 for each end. The arrangement is shown in Fig. 3–25.

Anchorage of stirrups: Assume that the anchorage for the stirrups is provided by the concrete above the mid-depth of the beam. Thus a stress of 20,000 psi in the stirrup requires a length of

$$L_s = \frac{f_s \text{ (diameter of stirrup)}}{4u},$$

$$L_s = \frac{20,000}{4 \times 150} \times \frac{3}{8} = 12.5 \text{ in.}$$

Hooks may be used to provide the anchorage.

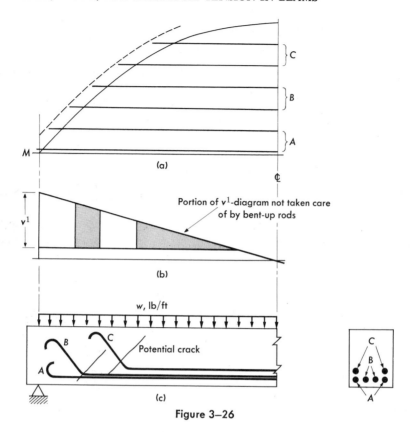

Figure 3–26

3–9 SPACING OF BENT-UP RODS

Figure 3–10 shows the permissible "cut-off" points of the bars which resist bending moment. One can utilize the remaining portion, i.e., that beyond the cutoff, to provide web reinforcement in a beam, by bending the bars upward and anchoring them. Note that the ACI Code specifies that for simply supported beams, no more than two-thirds of the reinforcement may be bent up. The other one-third must be carried through the whole length of the beam (Article 918, ACI Code).

The moment diagram can serve as a tool for determining the points at which bending-up is permissible. Assume that Fig. 3–25(a) represents the moment diagram of one-half of a simply supported beam loaded with a uniform load as shown in Fig. 3–25(c). For convenience, let us say that 6 bars are used to take care of the bending moment. If each bar is assumed to carry an equal share of load, the bars may be cut off as shown in Fig. 3–25(a) or they may be bent up to serve as web reinforcement.

It is advisable to keep symmetry whenever possible and therefore bend the bars accordingly. In our case, bending them in pairs preserves symmetry. For a series of parallel bars or group of bars bent up at different distances from the support, the required area shall be computed by (ACI Code, Article 1204c)

$$A_v = \frac{V^1 s}{f_v d(\sin \alpha + \cos \alpha)}.$$ (3–17)

When the web reinforcement consists of a single bent bar or of a single group of parallel bars all bent up at the same distance from the support, the required area is computed by (ACI Code, Article 1204b)

$$A_v = \frac{V^1}{f_v \sin \alpha},$$ (3–18)

where V^1 is not to exceed $1.5bdf_c'$. The distance separating bent-up bars must not exceed the spacing computed by Eq. (3–11) or that required by the Code. If the distance is exceeded, stirrups will be required to compensate for the lack of web reinforcement. Similarly, any part of the web which is not properly taken care of by the bent-up bars must be supported by stirrups, as explained in the previous section.

3–10   ULTIMATE SHEAR STRENGTH

The ACI Code (Article 1701) gives an expression for determining the nominal ultimate shear stress as a measure of diagonal tension in reinforced concrete members:

$$v_{uc} = \frac{V_u}{bd},$$ (3–19)

where V_u is measured at a distance l from the support (except for brackets or short cantilevers). This formula is largely based on test results which perhaps are not sufficient at this time for unquestioned validity. However, it fills a gap that has always led to difficulties in the analysis of the ultimate shear strength of beams. Whereas a formula for the ultimate flexure stresses was derived by Whitney many years ago, the ultimate-strength analysis of beams remained incomplete since the shear stresses were not fully investigated.

Note the marked similarity between Eqs. (3–19) and (3–7a). The shear force, V, is the only difference. This similarity is carried on to the design of stirrups or bent bars at ultimate strength. Articles 1703 and 1704 of the ACI Code give the expressions for these designs. Also, the Code places an upper limit on v_c, the shear stress carried by concrete. Since this information can be obtained directly from the Code, it is not repeated here.

3–11   ULTIMATE BOND STRENGTH

The ACI Code specifies that the ultimate flexural bond stress at any cross section shall be computed by

$$u_u = \frac{V_u}{(\Sigma_0)jd}.$$ (3–20)

Bent-up bars that are not more than $d/3$ from the level of the main longitudinal reinforcement may be included. Critical sections occur at the face of the support, at each point where tension bars terminate within a span, and at the point of inflection.

PROBLEMS

BOND, SHEAR, AND DIAGONAL TENSION

Analysis of Bond and Shear Stresses—Elastic Theory

3–1. Determine the "lapped" length of two No. 9 bars stressed to 20,000 psi, embedded in concrete of $f_c' = 3500$ psi.

3–2. In Problem 3–1, what stresses can safely be developed in the bars if the lapped length is 18 in.?

3–3. Two No. 8 bars are spliced by lapping them over a length of 20 in. Determine the maximum bond stress developed when $f_s = 18,000$ psi.

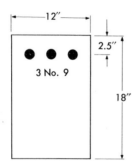

3 No. 9

Figure 3–27

3–4. A 12-ft long cantilever beam whose cross section is shown in Fig. 3–27 supports a concentrated load of 2 k at the free end and a uniform live load of 0.3 k/ft. Find the maximum bond stress developed. State your assumptions. How does the bond stress compare with that permitted by the Code?

3–5. For Problem 3–4, determine the anchorage distance required at the support if the bond stress is not to exceed that permitted by the ACI Code, $f_c' = 3500$ psi.

3–6. The section shown in Fig. 3–28 is subjected to a moment of 17,000 ft-lb. Assuming $f_c' = 3000$ psi, $k = 0.38$ design a hook to develop this moment.

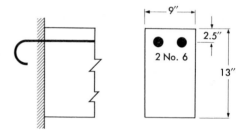

2 No. 6

Figure 3–28

3–7. A 10-in. cantilever beam is reinforced and has the cross section shown in Fig. 3–29. It carries a uniform live load of 0.4 k/ft and a concentrated load of 2.5 k at the free end. Assuming $n = 10$, $f_c' = 3000$ psi, determine the maximum bond stress by using Eqs. (3–1), (3–2), and (3–3).

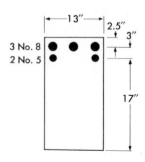

3 No. 8
2 No. 5

Figure 3–29

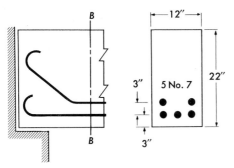

Figure 3–30

3–8. The shear force at *B–B* (Fig. 3–30) is 40 k. Assume that $f_c' = 3500$ psi. Determine the bond stress for each row of bars and for the average depth, *d,* of all the bars.

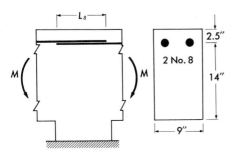

Figure 3–31

3–9. Figure 3–31 shows a continuous beam over a support. Using the stresses permissible according to the ACI Code, find the splicing length, L_s, that the bars must have if $M = 400,000$ in-lb. and $f_c' = 3000$ psi.

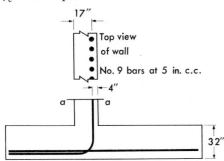

Figure 3–32

3–10. The retaining wall shown in Fig. 3–32 forms a unit with the base due to No. 9 dowels that are embedded in the base and spliced with the vertical reinforcement of the wall. The shear force/lin ft of wall is 15 k. Determine the bond and longitudinal shear stresses at section *a–a.*

3–11. In Problem 3–10, the bending moment per foot of wall at section *a–a* is 800,000 in-lb. Determine the length that the dowels must extend in the wall (splice length) above section *a–a* in order to develop the tensile stress required at section *a–a.* Assume that $j = 0.88$.

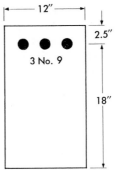

Figure 3–33

3–12. Determine the intensity of longitudinal and transverse shear stresses (v_L and v_T) and bond stress, *u,* for the beam shown in Fig. 3–33, given that $V_{max} = 23$ k, $k = 0.38$, and $j = 0.88$.

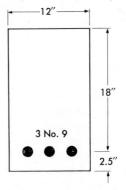

Figure 3–34

3–13. The cross section shown in Fig. 3–34 is that of a beam simply supported over a 14-ft span. It carries a uniform live load of 4 k/ft. Find the bond unit stress, and v_L and v_T near the supports. Assume that $k = 0.38$ and $j = 0.88$.

Design Analysis of Bond and Shear Stresses—Elastic Theory

3–14. For Problem 3–13, determine the size and number of stirrups needed, given that the concrete has $f_c' = 3000$ psi, and intermediate-grade steel is used as web reinforcement.

3–15. For the beam of Problem 3–13, determine a new effective depth, d, of the beam so that no web reinforcement will be required, keeping the same width and same steel. Take $f_c' = 3000$ psi and $n = 10$. How does this new depth dimension effect the flexure stresses?

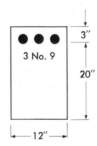

Figure 3–35

3–16. The cross section shown in Fig. 3–35 is that of a cantilever beam 6 ft long. Over this length it supports a uniform load (dead load included) of 5.0 k/ft. Assume that $f_c' = 3000$ psi, $f_v = 18,000$ psi, $j = 0.88$. Design U-shaped, vertical stirrups to take care of the excess shear stress.

3–17. For Problem 3–16, design and show the arrangement of No. 3, U-shaped stirrups inclined at an angle of 60° with the horizontal.

3–18. The beam shown in Fig. 3–36 supports a live load of 3.3 k/lin ft uniformly distributed over its 15-in. span.

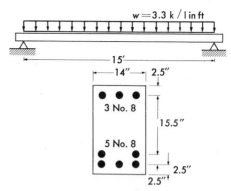

Figure 3–36

Assume that I_c and d are constant over the whole span. Determine the cut-off points of both the tensile and compressive reinforcement in compliance with the code. Find the average stress of the compressive steel. Assume that $f_c' = 4000$ psi concrete.

3–19. For the beam and load of Problem 3–18, design U-shaped vertical stirrups to take care of v'. Assume that $f_c' = 4000$ psi, $j = 0.88$, and $f_v = 18,000$ psi.

3–20. For the beam shown in Fig. 3–37 design the necessary U-shaped vertical stirrups. Assume that $j = 0.88$, $f_v = 18,000$ psi, and $f_c' = 3000$ psi.

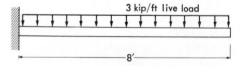

Figure 3–37

3–21. For Problem 3–20, determine the cut-off points of the steel. The section shown in Fig. 3–38 is at the support. For this analysis assume all the tension bars to be at the same depth. Consult the ACI Code on the permissible percentage of steel to be cut.

3–22. Derive an expression for the theoretical cut-off length of the ith bar of the n tension bars required to carry the bending moment caused by a con-

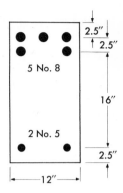

Figure 3–38

Analysis of Bond and Shear Stresses—Ultimate-Load Theory

3–24. Determine the ultimate shear, V_u, at section B–B, that the beam of Problem 3–8 can carry. Base your calculations on ultimate bond stresses and shear. Assume that the steel conforms with ASTM A 305 and that $f_c' = 3500$ psi. Consult the ACI Code for permissible ultimate bond and shear stresses.

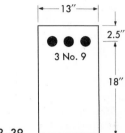

Figure 3–39

centrated load, P, applied at the center of span L. Assume that each bar takes an equal share of the moment and that they are all located at the same depth. Figure 3–10 might help.

3–23. Derive an expression for the theoretical cut-off length of the ith bar of the n tension bars required to carry the bending moment caused by a uniformly distributed load, w, over a span, L. Assume that each bar takes an equal share of the moment and that all bars are located at the same depth.

3–25. Using the ultimate bond and shear stresses of the ACI Code given in Chapters 17 and 18, respectively, determine the ultimate shear force, V_u, that the section shown in Fig. 3–39 can carry if $f_c' = 3500$ psi and the steel is of intermediate grade.

REFERENCES

1. CARL A. MENZEL, "Some Factors Influencing Results of Pull-Out Bond Tests," *ACI Journal,* June 1939.
2. BRUCE JOHNSTON and KENNETH C. COX, "The Bond Strength of Rusted Deformed Bars," *ACI Journal,* Sept. 1940.
3. RALPH W. KLUGE and EDWARD C. TUMA, "Lapped Bar Splices in Concrete Beams," *ACI Journal,* Sept. 1946.
4. ARTHUR P. CLARK, "Comparative Bond Efficiency of Deformed Concrete Reinforcing Bars," *ACI Journal,* Dec. 1946.
5. DAVID WATSTEIN, "Distribution of Bond Stress in Concrete Pull-Out Specimens," *ACI Journal,* May 1947.
6. T. D. MYLREA, "Bond and Anchorage," *ACI Journal,* Mar. 1948.
7. ARTHUR P. CLARK, "Bond of Concrete Reinforcing Bars," *ACI Journal,* Nov. 1949.
8. RAYMOND C. REESE, "New-Style Deformed Reinforcing Bars," *ACI Journal,* May 1950.
9. R. M. MAINS, "Measurement of the Distribution of Tensile and Bond Stresses Along Reinforcing Bars," *ACI Journal,* Nov. 1951.
10. K. G. MOODY and I. M. VIEST, "Shear Strength of Reinforced Concrete Beams, Part 4, Analytical Studies," *ACI Journal,* Mar. 1955.
11. COMMITTEE 208, "Proposed Test Procedure to Determine Relative Bond Value of Reinforcing Bars," *ACI Journal,* Aug. 1957.
12. E. M. RENSAA, "Shear, Diagonal Tension, and Anchorage in Beams," *ACI Journal,* Dec. 1958.

4 AXIALLY LOADED COLUMNS

Pier 5, South End of Glenwood Bridge, L.R. 376–12A, Allegheny County, Pennsylvania. (Note that the columns serve as supports for the "cap" formwork.)

4–1 INTRODUCTION

Main members that support a structure are usually *columns*. Sometimes walls are used as substitutes. A column is frequently defined as " . . . a structural member subjected to primarily axial load." Since the columns transmit the loads of a structure to the foundation, they are in many respects the most important part of the structure. A portion of a floor slab, a beam, or a girder may fail without serious damage to the whole structure, but the failure of a column may have severe consequences.

There are several "forms" of columns. An isolated, relatively short column with a ratio of length to least width equal to or less than 6 is called a *pier*. If the length is less than three times the least lateral dimension, the column is called a *pedestal*. Principal circular columns in buildings must have a minimum diameter of 12 in., and rectangular columns must have a thickness of at least

89

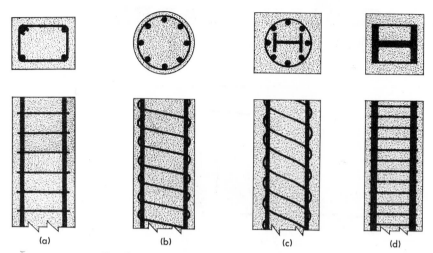

Fig. 4–1. Various types of reinforced columns.

8 in. and a gross area of not less than 96 in². A member which is not continuous from story to story may be smaller, but its thickness may not be less than 6 in. Such a column is more commonly referred to as a *post*. Since most of the columns are in vertical positions, inclined or horizontal compression members may be called *struts* to avoid confusion.

There are four basic types of reinforced concrete columns, namely:

(1) Columns reinforced with longitudinal steel and lateral ties (Fig. 4–1a).
(2) Columns reinforced with longitudinal steel and spirals (Fig. 4–1b).
(3) Composite columns, in which a structural steel or cast iron shape is encased in a concrete core (Fig. 4–1c).
(4) Combination columns, in which either a steel pipe is filled with concrete or a structural steel shape is encased in at least 2½ in. of concrete cover and wrapped with wire mesh (Fig. 4–1d).

4–2 BEHAVIOR OF REINFORCED COLUMNS UNDER LOAD

The longitudinal rods in a column carry part of the column load. They also contribute to the lateral stability of the column. This combination of steel and concrete forms a composite which is superior to either a plain steel section (in case of fire, for example) or to a plain concrete section (for "longer" columns, in particular).

When this composite is subjected to an axial load, there occur a longitudinal shortening and a lateral expansion in all directions perpendicular to the column's longitudinal axis. This phenomenon is readily explained in terms of Poisson's ratio (μ): $\mu =$ lateral strain/longitudinal strain. In a sense, the longitudinal rods tend to act as slender columns. They undergo a compression equal to that

$\mu = .15 - .20$,1^4 good avg.

Fig. 4–2. A spiral column with a square cross section.

of the concrete. But because they are slender, they tend to buckle in the direction of least resistance unless "held in place." The least resistance to buckling is provided by the reinforcement *cover*. The lateral deformation of the core causes an outward push and thus provides additional transverse (lateral) deflection of the rods. If large enough, this outward-buckling action of the steel will cause the shell or steel cover to spall off.

The buckling tendency may be counteracted by using ties either in the form of bands (Fig. 4–1a and d) or of spirals (Fig. 4–1b or 4–1c). Note that for this purpose the spiral is more effective than a rectangular band. While the rectangular band provides good lateral support for the rods at the corner of the rectangle, it does not add resistance to the bars located on the side of the rectangle. As the buckling of such a bar exerts an outward force on the tie, the tie simply bends, tending to acquire a round shape. Hence, whenever a rectangular form of lateral reinforcement is used, every longitudinal bar should have a corner of the rectangle.

The above discussion might help to clarify at least one of the advantages of spiral lateral reinforcement over ties. Economy resulting from labor and materials is frequently another advantage, experienced even for columns with a square cross section and a circular pattern of the longitudinal reinforcement, as shown in Fig. 4–2.

Under sustained load, creep of the concrete (Article 1–11) causes the load to shift from concrete to steel, thus increasing the share of load that the steel carries. This condition prevails unless the steel reaches the yield stress during the shift, in which case a reversal of load transfer may occur.

4–3   DESIGN CONSIDERATIONS OF REINFORCED CONCRETE COLUMNS

For many years the design of a reinforced concrete column was based on the elastic relationship between the stress in the steel and that in the concrete. A constant ratio *n* was used to relate these stresses. However, results of many comprehensive tests, especially those carried out at the University of Illinois and at Lehigh University (see references at end of chapter), were used to develop formulas that are based on the strength of the steel and the concrete and which contain a certain safety factor to account for the uncertain behavior of creep, shrinkage, and overall composite action. Tests and experience have proved that the ratio of the steel stress to the concrete stress is not a constant, but depends on the history of the load and the creep property of the concrete. The formula based on ultimate strength of the column can be used to compute unit stresses in the steel and concrete only when the load on the column *is* the ultimate load. At the working-load level, the relation between the stress in steel and the stress in concrete depends on the type of load, the duration of its application, and the properties of the concrete and the steel. Since a "spiral" column has a higher ultimate strength than a similar "tied" column, a higher factor of safety should be inherent in the formula for the design of tied columns. The quantity of lateral reinforcement for ties and spirals is based almost completely on experimental results, and no attempt is made to compute its stress.

Fig. 4–3.   Reinforcement for round columns before forms were placed around the reinforcement.

The ACI Code is a useful guide in designing columns. It provides formulas and lists considerations which designers have followed for many years with satisfactory results. Although all these requirements are contained in the ACI Code (Appendix D), they are scattered through various articles, and hence one or the other might easily be overlooked. For this reason we repeat some of them here:

1. *Spacing of bars*

    (a) In spirally reinforced and in tied columns, the clear distance between longitudinal bars shall be not less than 1½ times the bar diameter, 1½ times the maximum size of the coarse aggregate, nor 1½ in.

2. *Splices in reinforcement* (see Article 805 of the Code):

    (a) Where lapped splices are used, the minimum amount of lap shall be: With concrete having a strength of 3000 psi or more, the length of lap for deformed bars shall not be less than 20, 24, 30 bar diameters for specified yield points 50,000 and under, 60,000 and 75,000 psi respectively, nor less than 12 in. When the specified concrete strengths are less than 3000 psi, the amount of lap shall be one-third greater than the values given above. For plain bars, the minimum amount of lap shall be twice that specified for deformed bars.

    (b) Where longitudinal bars are offset at a splice, the slope of the inclined portion of the bar with the axis of the column shall not exceed 1 in 6, and the portions of the bar above and below the offset shall be parallel to the axis of the column. Adequate horizontal support at the offset bends shall be treated as a matter of design, and shall be provided by metal ties, spirals, or parts of the floor construction. Metal ties or spirals so designed shall be placed near (not more than eight bar diameters from) the point of bend. The horizontal thrust to be resisted shall be assumed as 1½ times the horizontal component of the nominal stress in the inclined portion of the bar. Offset bars shall be bent before they are placed in the forms. No field bending of bars partially embedded in concrete shall be permitted.

    (c) Where column faces are offset 3 in. or more, splices of vertical bars adjacent to the offset face shall be made by separate dowels overlapped as specified above.

    (d) In tied columns the amount of reinforcement spliced by lapping shall not exceed a steel ratio of 0.04 in any 3 ft. length of column.

3. *Lateral reinforcement* (see Article 806 of ACI Code):

    (a) Spiral column reinforcement shall consist of evenly spaced continuous spirals held firmly in place and true to line by vertical spacers, using at least two for spirals 20 in. or less in diameter, three for spirals 20 to 30 in. in diameter, and four for spirals more than 30 in. in diameter or composed of spiral rods ⅝ in. or larger in size. The spirals shall be of such size and so assembled as to permit handling and placing without being distorted from the designed dimensions. The material used in spirals shall have a minimum diameter of ¼ in. for rolled bars or No. 4 AS&W gage for drawn wire. Anchorage of spiral reinforcement shall be provided by 1½ extra turns of spiral rod or wire at each end of the spiral unit. Splices when necessary shall be made in spiral rod or wire by welding or by a lap of 1½ turns. The center-to-center spacing of the spirals shall not exceed one-sixth of the core diameter. The clear spacing between spirals shall not exceed 3 in. nor be less than 1⅜ in. or 1½ times the maximum size of coarse aggregate used. The reinforcing spiral shall extend from the floor level in any story or from the top of the footing to the level of the lowest horizontal reinforcement in the slab, drop panel or beam above. In a column with a capital, it shall extend to a plane at which the diameter or width of the capital is twice that of the column.

(b) Lateral ties for tied columns shall be at least ¼ in. in diameter and shall be spaced apart not over 16 bar diameters, 48 tie diameters, or the least dimension of the column. When there are more than four vertical bars, additional ties shall be provided. The ties shall be so arranged that every longitudinal bar is held firmly in its designed position and has lateral support provided by a bend or corner of a tie having an included angle of not more than 135 degrees. Where the bars are located around the periphery of a circle, a complete circular tie may be used.

4. *Concrete protection for reinforcement*

(a) Column spirals or ties shall be protected everywhere by a covering of concrete cast monolithically with the core, for which the thickness shall be not less than 1½ in. nor less than 1½ times the maximum size of the coarse aggregate.

5. *Minimum size of columns*

(a) Columns constituting the principal supports of a floor or roof shall have a diameter of at least 10 in., or in the case of rectangular columns, a thickness of at least 8 in., and a gross area not less than 96 in². Auxiliary supports placed at intermediate locations and not continuous from story to story may be smaller but not less than 6 in. thick.

6. *Limits for reinforcement of columns*

(a) The vertical reinforcement for columns shall be not less than 0.01 nor more than 0.08 times the gross cross-sectional area i.e., $0.01 \, A_g \leq p_g \leq 0.08 \, A_g$. The minimum size of bar shall be No. 5. The minimum number of bars shall be six for spiral columns and four for tied columns.

(b) The ratio of spiral reinforcement, p_s, shall be not less than the value given by

$$p_s = 0.45 \left(\frac{A_g}{A_c} - 1\right) \frac{f_c'}{f_y},$$

wherein f_y is the yield point of spiral reinforcement but not more than 60,000 psi.

7. *Length of columns*

  (a) For purposes of determining the limiting dimensions of columns, the unsupported length of reinforced concrete columns shall be taken as the clear distance between floor slabs, except that

      (i) In flat slab construction, it shall be the clear distance between the floor and the lower extremity of the capital, the drop panel or the slab, whichever is least.

      (ii) In beam and slab construction, it shall be the clear distance between the floor and the underside of the deeper beam framing into the column in each direction at the next higher floor level.

      (iii) In columns restrained laterally by struts, it shall be the clear distance between consecutive struts in each vertical plane provided that to be an adequate support, two such struts shall meet the column at approximately the same level, and the angle between vertical planes through the struts shall not vary more than 15 degrees from a right angle. Such struts shall be of adequate dimensions and anchorage to restrain the column against lateral deflection.

      (iv) In columns restrained laterally by struts or beams, with brackets used at the junction, it shall be the clear distance between the floor and the lower edge of the bracket, provided that the bracket width equals that of the beam or strut and is at least half that of the column.

  (b) For rectangular columns, that length shall be considered which produces the greatest ratio of length to radius of gyration of section.

  (c) The effective length, h', of columns in structures where lateral stability is provided by shear walls or rigid bracing, by fastening to an adjoining structure of sufficient lateral stability, or by any other means that affords adequate lateral support, shall be taken as the unbraced length, h.

  (d) For columns with special "restraints" see Articles 915(d) and 916(a) through 916(d) of the ACI Code.   *See*   −43

4-4 SPIRALLY REINFORCED COLUMNS

The ACI Code specifies that the maximum allowable axial load, P, on columns with closely spaced spirals enclosing a circular core reinforced with vertical bars shall be that given by

$f_s = .4 f_y$

$$P = A_g(0.250f_c' + f_s p_g),\tag{4-1}$$

where f_s is the nominal allowable stress in vertical column reinforcement, to be taken at 40% of the minimum specification value of the yield point but not to exceed 30,000 psi. As stated in Article 4–3, p_g falls in the range of

$$0.01A_g \le p_g \le 0.08A_g,$$

and

$$p_s = 0.45\left(\frac{A_g}{A_c} - 1\right)\frac{f_c'}{f_y},\tag{4-2}$$

(margin handwriting) for intermediate steel $f_s = 30,000$ $f_y = 50,000$ 20,000

Fig. 4–4. Spirally reinforced columns for a canopy.

where p_s is defined as the ratio of volume of spiral to the volume of core (see Example 4–2). Read carefully the specifications covering spirals summarized in Article 4–3 under "Lateral Reinforcement."

Example 4–1. *Analysis*

Given: The short-column cross sections shown in Fig. 4–5; $f_c' = 3000$ psi, $f_s = 20,000$ psi.

Find: The safe axial load P that the column can carry.

PROCEDURE: Equation (4–1) gives the expression for a safe column load:

$$P = A_g(0.250 f_c' + p_g f_s),$$

$$A_g = \frac{\pi(D)^2}{4} = 380 \text{ in}^2.$$

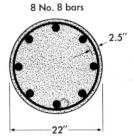

8 No. 8 bars

2.5″

22″

Figure 4–5

Note that in determining A_g, we did not subtract the area of the longitudinal reinforcement from the core.

$$p_g = \frac{A_s}{A_g} = \frac{6.32}{380} = 0.0166,$$

$$P = 380(0.250 \times 3000 + 0.0166 \times 20,000)$$

$$= 413 \text{ kip}.$$

Example 4–2. *Design*

Given: An axial load of 375 kip is to be carried by a spirally reinforced round column. Assume that $f_c' = 3000$ psi, $f_s = 20,000$ psi (intermediate grade steel).

Find: A suitable design.

PROCEDURE: We assume that $p_g = 0.02$ (larger p_g means a reduction in the column cross section). Then

$$P = A_g(0.250f_c' + p_g f_s),$$
$$375{,}000 = A_g(0.250 \times 3000 + 0.02 \times 20{,}000).$$

Solving, we find:

$$A_g = 325 \text{ in}^2 = \pi D^2/4;$$

hence

$$D = 20.33 \text{ in., } \text{ say } 20.5 \text{ in.,}$$
$$A_s = p_g A_g \doteq 4.1 \text{ in}^2. \qquad = 6.5$$

Thus we may use $D = 20.5$ in. and a core diameter of $20.5 - 3$-in. cover (assumed) $= 17.5$ in. For spiral columns, the Code (Article 913a) requires a minimum of six bars (minimum size No. 5). Hence we may use:

$$10 \text{ No. 6 bars} \quad (A_s = 4.40 \text{ in}^2),$$

or

$$7 \text{ No. 7 bars} \quad (A_s = 4.20 \text{ in}^2),$$

or

$$6 \text{ No. 8 bars} \quad (A_s = 4.74 \text{ in}^2).$$

Let us assume that No. 7 bars are used and let us check the spacing. For this purpose, we must take into account the possibility of splicing, in which case the clear distance between bars is $(\pi D_s - 14 \times \frac{7}{8})/7$. Assuming a No. 4 spiral, $D_s = 17.5 - 2 \times 0.5 - \frac{7}{8} = 15.6$ in. Therefore, the clear distance is $(\pi \times 15.6 - 12.25)/7 = 5.25$ in. The minimum permitted by the Code (Article 804d) is $1\frac{1}{2}$ times the bar diameter, or $1\frac{1}{2}$ times the maximum size of the coarse aggregate, or $1\frac{1}{2}$ in. In our case, 5.25 in. is above any of these minima, and hence is satisfactory.

To determine the spiral design, we use Eq. (4–2):

$$p_s = 0.45(A_g/A_c - 1)f_c'/f_y.$$

Note that

$$A_g/A_c = (\pi/4)(D)^2/(\pi/4)(D_c)^2 = (D/D_c)^2,$$
$$p_s = 0.45[(20.5/17.5)^2 - 1]\,3000/40{,}000 = 0.0125.$$

Also,

$$p_s = \frac{\text{Volume of spiral/round}}{\text{Volume of core/round}}. \qquad core = out\text{-}to\text{-}out\ spiral$$

Taking one round (one loop) and unwinding it might help visualize the operation involved in determining the volume of the spiral. Let:

$$d_i = \text{diameter of spiral bar,}$$
$$A_i = \text{area of spiral bar,}$$
$$p_i = \text{spacing of spiral windings} = \text{pitch of spiral,}$$
$$D_i = \text{diameter of winding} = \text{diameter of core} - d_i.$$

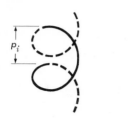
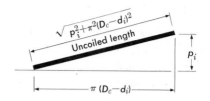

Figure 4–6

Note that p_i is small compared to $\pi(D_c - d_i)$ (Fig. 4–6). Neglecting p_i and d_i in the radical, we may approximate the length of the spiral by πD_c. Therefore

$$\text{Volume of spiral} \cong A_i \pi D_c,$$

where A_i is the cross-sectional area of the spiral bar and p_i is the pitch of the spiral. Then

$$\frac{\text{Volume of core}}{\text{turn}} = \frac{\pi D_c^2}{4} p_i;$$

hence

$$p_s = \frac{A_i \pi D_c}{\pi D_c^2 p_i / 4} = \frac{4 A_i}{p_i D_c}.$$

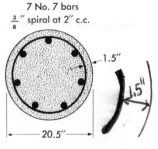

7 No. 7 bars
$\frac{3}{8}''$ spiral at 2" c.c.

Figure 4–7

It is customary to first make an assumption regarding the size of the spiral and then solve for the spacing. For example, arbitrarily selecting a ½-in. bar, then

$$A_i = 0.2 \text{ in}^2,$$

and

$$p_s = 0.0125 = \frac{4 \times 0.2}{\wedge p_i D_c} = \frac{4 \times 0.2}{p_i \times 17.5},$$

$$p_i = \frac{0.8}{0.2187} = 3.66 \text{ in.},$$

and therefore the clear distance between spirals is $3.66 - 0.5 = 3.16$ in.

Article 806(a) of the Code sets the following limits on spacing:

3.0 in. $\geq$ clear spacing $\geq$ 1.5 times maximum aggregate size   or $\geq 1\frac{3}{8}$ in.

Also, the center-to-center spacing must be $\leq \frac{1}{6}D_c = 2.91$ in. (for $D_c = 17.5$ in.). In this case the use of a ½-in. bar is somewhat uneconomical because of the spacing. Hence let us try a ⅜-in. bar, for which

$$p_i = \frac{4 \times 0.11}{0.2187} = 2.00 \text{ in.} < 2.91 \text{ in.} > 1\frac{3}{8} \text{ in., etc.,}$$

if a ⅜-in. bar at 2.0-in. spacing is used for the spiral. The Code requirement is satisfied. Thus the section designed is as shown in Fig. 4–7.

4–5   DESIGN OF TIED COLUMNS

As is the case for spiral columns, the ACI Code also provides an allowable load formula for the design of tied columns. According to the Code, the maximum allowable axial load on columns reinforced with longitudinal bars and separate lateral ties shall be 85% of that for spiral columns, that is,

$$P = 0.85A_g(0.250f_c' + f_s p_g) = A_g(0.2125f_c' + 0.85f_s p_g), \qquad (4\text{–}3)$$

or, using the expression $p_g = A_s/A_g$, Eq. (4–3) becomes

$$P = 0.2125f_c'A_g + 0.85A_s f_s. \qquad (4\text{–}3a)$$

The load, P, given by Eqs. (4–3) and (4–3a) has to be reduced if the unsupported length gives values of R less than unity, where R is a reduction factor for long columns, defined in Article 916 of the Code. This restriction is also explained in the discussion of long columns (Section 4–8).

Example 4–3.   Analysis

Given: The section of a short column as shown in Fig. 4–8. Assume that the ties suffice, $f_c' = 3000$ psi, and $f_s = 20,000$ psi.

Find: The allowable load the column can carry. Base your calculations on the ACI Code formula.

PROCEDURE:

$$A_s = 8 \times 0.60 = 4.8 \text{ in}^2,$$

$$p_g = \frac{4.8}{20 \times 20} = 0.012.$$

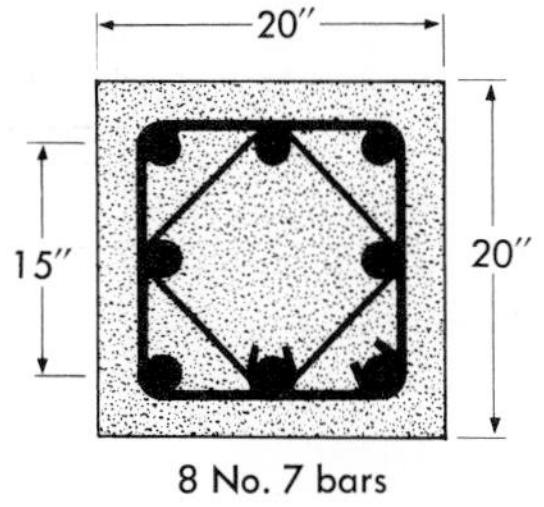

Using Eq. (4–3) we have

Figure 4–8

8 No. 7 bars

$$P = 0.85 \times 400(0.250 \times 3000 + 20,000 \times 0.012) = 337 \text{ kip.}$$

Example 4–4.   Design

Given: $f_c' = 3500$ psi, $f_s = 18,000$ psi, $P = 400$ kip.

Find: A suitable section of a short tied column to carry the load. Also design the ties.

PROCEDURE: Let us make the arbitrary assumption that $p_g = 0.020$. Then from Eq. (4–3),

$$A_g = \frac{P}{0.2125f_c' + 0.85f_s p_g},$$

$$A_g = \frac{400,000}{0.2125 \times 3500 + 0.85 \times 18,000 \times 0.020} = 381 \text{ in}^2,$$

or, for a square section, a side of 20 in. is seen to be satisfactory. Then

$$A_s = p_g A_g = 0.02 \times 20 \times 20 = 8 \text{ in}^2.$$

Figure 4–9

Thus we find that we may use eight No. 9 bars symmetrically placed as shown in Fig. 4–10. The ties must be at least ¼ in. in diameter, and the distance between them is not to exceed 16 bar diameters, 48 tie-bar diameters, or the least dimension of the column [Article 806(b) of the Code].

Let us assume that the ties have a rod diameter of ⅜ in. Then

$$16 \times \tfrac{9}{8} \text{ in.} = 18 \text{ in.,}$$

$$48 \times \tfrac{3}{8} \text{ in.} = 18 \text{ in.,}$$

and the dimension of one column is 20 in. Therefore the spacing of 18 in. controls; the cross-sectional design is shown in Fig. 4–10.

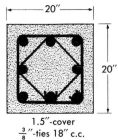

1.5″-cover
$\tfrac{3}{8}$″-ties 18″ c.c.

Figure 4–10

4–6 COMPOSITE COLUMNS

A *composite* column consists of a structural-steel or cast-iron column thoroughly enclosed in concrete which has both longitudinal and lateral reinforcement as shown in Fig. 4–1(c). The cross section of the concrete in a composite column is large enough so that the concrete plays an important part in resisting the axial load. In fact, the area of the steel should *not exceed* 20% of the gross area of the column. If it does, the column is called a *combination column* (see Article 4–7).

The axial-load capacity within the elastic limit of a composite column cannot be computed reliably as the sum of the loads taken by the various component parts of the composite—concrete, core, reinforcing bars—because not all of the materials in the composite reach their working stresses at the same time. The ACI Code provides an experimentally proved, empirical formula for determining the allowable load on a composite column with spiral reinforcements:

$$P = 0.225A_g f_c' + f_s A_{st} + f_r A_r, \qquad (4-5)$$

where f_r is the allowable unit stress in the metal core, which is not to exceed 18,000 psi for steel conforming to ASTM A36, 16,000 psi for steel conforming to ASTM A7, or 10,000 psi for a cast-iron core; A_r is the area of the steel core; A_g is the area of the concrete encasement; A_{st} is the area of the longitudinal reinforcing bars; and f_s is the allowable stress to which these bars may be subjected.

The requirements for the longitudinal and lateral reinforcement should meet those specified for spiral columns. Three-inch clearance shall be maintained between the tie or spiral and the metal core at all points unless a structural H-column is used, in which case the minimum clearance may be reduced to 2 in. If the metal core is hollow, it is to be filled with concrete.

Example 4–5. Analysis

Given: The composite column shown in Fig. 4–11 The core of the section is an H-section of 8 WF 31 steel. Let us assume that the steel meets ASTM A7 requirements, and that $f_c' = 3000$ psi, $f_s = 18,000$ psi, and that the column is short.

Find: Allowable axial load on the column.

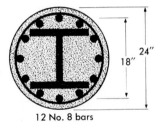

12 No. 8 bars

Figure 4–11

SOLUTION:

$$A_{st} = 12 \times 0.785 = 9.42 \text{ in}^2,$$
$$A_r = 9.12 \text{ in}^2, \qquad f_r = 16,000 \text{ psi},$$
$$A_g = \pi D^2/4 - A_s - A_{rt} = \pi(24)^2/4 - 18.54 = 433 \text{ in}^2;$$
$$P = 0.225 \times 433 \times 3000 + 18,000 \times 9.42 + 16,000 \times 9.12$$
$$= 292,000 + 169,000 + 146,000 = 607 \text{ kip}.$$

4–7   COMBINATION COLUMNS

A combination column consists of a structural steel column encased in concrete at least $2\frac{1}{2}$ in. thick, with the concrete covering all the metal, except the rivet heads. In this type of column, the steel takes up a large percentage of the effective gross area. The concrete receives much of its load by means of bond with the steel. The ACI Code specifies that the allowable load on a combination column is

$$P = A_r f_r'[1 + (A_g/100A_r)], \qquad (4-6)$$

where A_g is the total area of the concrete encasement of the combination column,

f_r' is the allowable unit stress on an uncased steel column, and A_r is the area of the steel core.

The ACI Code specifies that "the concrete used must develop a compressive strength, f_c', of at least 2000 psi at an age of 28 days. The concrete may be reinforced by welded wire fabric having wires of No. 10 AS&W gage, the wires encircling the column being spaced not more than 4 in. apart and those parallel to the column axis not more than 8 in. apart. This fabric shall extend around the entire column at a distance of 1 in. inside the outer concrete surface and shall be lap-spliced for a length of at least 40 wire diameters and wired at the splices. Special brackets shall be used to receive the entire floor load at each floor level. The steel column shall be designed to carry safely any construction or other loads to be placed upon it prior to its encasement in concrete."

4–8 LONG COLUMNS

The lateral stability of columns decreases as the ratio of unsupported height to lateral dimension increases. This slenderness ratio is most frequently expressed as h/r, where h represents the unsupported length of the column as defined by Article 915 of the ACI Code, and r represents the radius of gyration of the gross concrete area of the column. The radius of gyration may be approximated to be 0.3 times the overall depth in the direction of bending for a rectangular column and 0.25 times the diameter of circular columns. For other shapes, r may be computed for the gross concrete section.

Since the more slender columns tend to buckle sooner than the heavier ones, the allowable axial load of a "long" column is reduced. The criteria for differentiating between a long and a short column are defined by Article 916, ACI Code. The axial load is reduced by a factor R, which is less than unity for long columns. Note that R is a function of the end conditions (fixed, free end, pinned, etc.) Example 4–6 might help to illustrate the design "treatment" of long columns.

Example 4–6. Analysis

Given: The column section of Example 4–3. Assume that the unsupported length of the column is 18 ft, and that it is "hinged" at the top end; $f_c' = 3000$ psi, $f_s = 20,000$ psi.

Find: Allowable axial load on column.

PROCEDURE:

$$R = 1.07 - 0.008\,h/r \quad \text{(Article 916, ACI Code)},$$

$$h = 18 \text{ ft}; \quad r = 0.3(20/12) = \tfrac{1}{2} \text{ ft}.$$

Hence

$$R = 1.07 - 0.008 \times 18/\tfrac{1}{2} = 0.782,$$

and the allowable load is $P' = R \times P = 0.782\,P$, where $P = 337$ kip (from Example 4–3). Therefore $P' = 264$ kip.

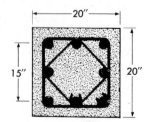

8 No. 7 bars

Figure 4–12

4–9   ULTIMATE STRENGTH OF AXIALLY LOADED COLUMNS

As mentioned in Article 4–2, a reinforced concrete column subjected to axial compression shortens in the axial and expands in the lateral direction. Lateral reinforcement is used to resist lateral expansion. Below the elastic limit of the column, the lateral reinforcement is not so efficient as the axial reinforcement. However, it does raise the ultimate strength of the column and delays its ultimate failure.

Since the turn of the century many column experiments or tests have been carried out, particularly at the University of Illinois and at Lehigh University. The majority of the tests have shown that up to about the yield point of the column, the relationship between the applied loads and the deformation of the columns is about the same for both spiral and tied columns. However, after the applied load passes the yield strength of the column, the tied column fails rather rapidly with spalling concrete and buckled longitudinal bars. The yielding load and the ultimate load for tied columns have about the same value.

For spiral columns, the shell spalls after the applied load passes the yield point. Effective lateral resistance significantly increases the strength of the core of the column and thus raises its ultimate load capacity. However, if excessive deformation takes place, the column becomes unfit for service. Thus the higher ultimate strengths give spiral columns only one advantage over tied columns: the safety factor is higher.   Figure 4–13 illustrates the relationship between applied load and deformation.

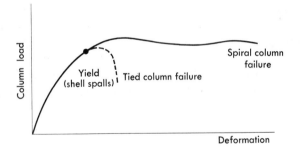

Figure 4–13

We know from observation that under sustained load, actual stresses in concrete and in longitudinal bars cannot be determined accurately, since the shrinkage and creep of concrete cause the stresses to shift and vary with time. The actual steel stress is higher than that computed by means of formulas based on the elastic properties (strains and E) of the steel and the concrete. Under the elastic-load theory, the ratio of steel stress to concrete stress can be established by equating the unit deformations of the steel and the concrete. Tests clearly show that this ratio changes when shrinkage and creep are taking place in the concrete, and that it varies with the extent of shrinkage and creep. The tests also show that the column reaches a yield point when the load is about 85% of the load the concrete can take if it had the strength determined by cylinder tests. Thus the load capacity of the column might be expressed as the sum of the loads the concrete and the steel can resist individually:

$$P_u = 0.85f_c'A_g + f_yA_s, \tag{4-7}$$

where

P_u = ultimate load of the concrete column, lb,

f_c' = ultimate cylinder strength of concrete, psi,

A_g = gross area of concrete, in^2,

f_y = yield strength of the steel, psi,

A_s = area of the reinforcing steel, in^2.

We can approximate the stresses that are caused by the live load in the concrete and in the reinforcing steel of a concrete column by assuming that the elastic deformations of the concrete and the steel are equal to each other. When a load is applied to the column, the concrete and the steel will deform equally, provided the stresses in both materials are below their elastic limits and creep is neglected. In other words, the deformation e_c of the concrete is equal to the deformation of the steel e_s. Thus, for short-time loads,

$$e_c = f_c/E_c = e_s = f_s/E_s,$$

or

$$f_s = f_c(E_s/E_c) = f_c n, \tag{4-8}$$

where

ϵ_s = the unit deformation of the steel, in/in,

ϵ_c = the unit deformation in the concrete, in/in,

E_s = modulus of elasticity of the steel, psi, and

E_c = modulus of elasticity of the concrete, psi.

The load in the steel is equal to f_sA_s, which is also equal to $f_c nA_s$ from the relationship $n = E_s/E_c = f_s\epsilon_c/f_c\epsilon_s$ when $\epsilon_c = \epsilon_s$. The transformed area of the column is equal to A_c plus the transformed area nA_s. Since the gross area of the concrete, A_g, is equal to the net concrete area, A_c, plus the holes filled by the steel, the final area is equal to A_g plus $(n-1)A_s$, which is called the effective transformed area. Then the total load a concrete column can take is expressed as

$$P = f_cA_c + f_sA_s = f_c(A_g - p_gA_g) + f_c np_gA_g$$
$$= f_cA_g[1 + (n-1)p_g] = f_c[A_g + (n-1)A_s], \tag{4-9}$$

where

P = total load in the concrete column, lb,

f_s = unit compressive stress in steel, psi,

f_c = unit compressive stress in concrete, psi,

A_s = area of reinforcing longitudinal steel, in^2,

A_g = gross area of the concrete, in^2,

A_c = net area of the concrete, in^2.

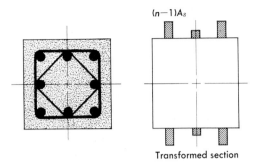

Transformed section   Figure 4–14

In Eq. (4–9), the concrete stress f_c is assumed to be uniformly distributed on the section in which the steel area A_s can be replaced by an effective transformed area $(n-1)A_s$. The transformed area for a rectangular column is shown in Fig. 4–14.

PROBLEMS

AXIALLY LOADED COLUMNS

Problems 4–1 through 4–30 refer to the columns illustrated in Figs. 4–15 through 4–19. Several "far-end" restrictions against movement, rotation, etc., and two different grades of steel are specified to provide the reader with the opportunity to apply various design principles and to familiarize himself with the relative strengths required by different conditions and materials. In all cases, follow the ACI Code requirements to determine the axial load the column can safely carry and assume that the ties or spirals meet the Code requirements.

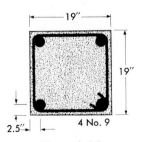

Figure 4–15

Analysis of Columns

4–1. The column in Fig. 4–15 is 10 ft long and is hinged at the far end. Determine the safe axial load, given that intermediate grade steel is used, and (a) $f_c' = 2500$ psi, (b) $f_c' = 3000$ psi, and (c) $f_c' = 3750$ psi.

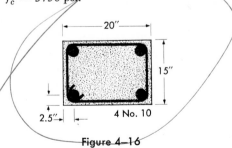

Figure 4–16

4–2. The column in Fig. 4–16 is 11 ft long and is hinged at the far end. Determine the safe axial load, given that intermediate grade steel is used, and (a) $f_c' = 2500$ psi, (b) $f_c' = 3000$ psi, and (c) $f_c' = 3750$ psi.

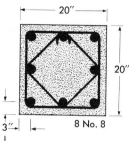

Figure 4–17

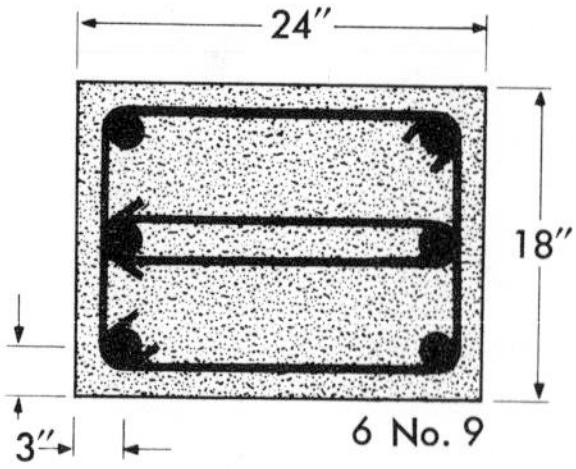

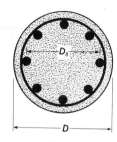

Figure 4–18

Figure 4–19

4–3. The column in Fig. 4–17 is 15 ft long and is hinged at the far end. Determine the safe axial load, given that intermediate grade steel is used, and (a) $f_c' = 2500$ psi, (b) $f_c' = 3000$ psi, and (c) $f_c' = 3750$ psi.

4–4. The column in Fig. 4–18 is 14 ft long and is hinged at the far end. Determine the safe axial load, given that intermediate grade steel is used, and (a) $f_c' = 2500$ psi, (b) $f_c' = 3000$ psi, and (c) $f_c' = 3750$ psi.

4–5. The column in Fig. 4–19 is 12 ft long and is hinged at the far end. The longitudinal steel consists of 8 No. 9 bars, $D_s = 18$ in., $D = 23$ in. Determine the safe axial load, given that intermediate grade steel is used, and (a) $f_c' = 2500$ psi, (b) $f_c' = 3000$ psi, and (c) $f_c' = 3750$ psi.

4–6. The column in Fig. 4–15 is 10 ft long and is hinged at the far end. Determine the safe axial load, given that rail steel is used, and (a) $f_c' = 2500$ psi, (b) $f_c' = 3000$ psi, and (c) $f_c' = 3750$ psi.

4–7. The column in Fig. 4–16 is 11 ft long and is hinged at the far end. Determine the safe axial load, given that rail steel is used, and (a) $f_c' = 2500$ psi, (b) $f_c' = 3000$ psi, and (c) $f_c' = 3750$ psi.

4–8. The column in Fig. 4–17 is 15 ft long and is hinged at the far end. Determine the safe axial load, given that rail steel is used, and (a) $f_c' = 2500$ psi, (b) $f_c' = 3000$ psi, and (c) $f_c' = 3750$ psi.

4–9. The column in Fig. 4–18 is 14 ft long and is hinged at the far end. Determine the safe axial load, given that rail steel is used, and (a) $f_c' = 2500$ psi, (b) $f_c' = 3000$ psi, and (c) $f_c' = 3750$ psi.

4–10. The column in Fig. 4–19 is 12 ft long and is hinged at the far end. The longitudinal steel consists of 8 No. 9 bars, $D_s = 18$ in., $D = 23$ in. Determine the safe axial load, given that rail steel is used, and (a) $f_c' = 2500$ psi, (b) $f_c' = 3000$ psi, and (c) $f_c' = 3750$ psi.

4–11. The column in Fig. 4–15 is 10 ft long and is fixed against lateral displacement and end rotation at the far end. Determine the safe axial load, given that intermediate grade steel is used, and (a) $f_c' = 2500$ psi, (b) $f_c' = 3000$ psi, and (c) $f_c' = 3750$ psi.

4–12. The column in Fig. 4–16 is 11 ft long and is fixed against lateral displacement and end rotation at the far end. Determine the safe axial load, given that intermediate grade steel is used, and (a) $f_c' = 2500$ psi, (b) $f_c' = 3000$ psi, and (c) $f_c' = 3750$ psi.

4–13. The column in Fig. 4–17 is 15 ft long and is fixed against lateral displacement and end rotation at the far end. Determine the safe axial load, given that intermediate grade steel is used, and (a) $f_c' = 2500$ psi, (b) $f_c' = 3000$ psi, and (c) $f_c' = 3750$ psi.

4–14. The column in Fig. 4–18 is 14 ft long and is fixed against lateral displacement and end rotation at the far end. Determine the safe axial load, given that intermediate grade steel is used, and (a) $f_c' = 2500$ psi, (b) $f_c' = 3000$ psi, and (c) $f_c' = 3750$ psi.

4–15. The column in Fig. 4–19 is 12 ft long and is fixed against lateral displacement and end rotation at the far end. The longitudinal steel consists of 8 No. 9 bars, $D_s = 18$ in., $D = 23$ in. Determine the safe axial load, given that intermediate grade steel is used, and (a) $f_c' = 2500$ psi, (b) $f_c' = 3000$ psi, and (c) $f_c' = 3750$ psi.

4–16. The column in Fig. 4–15 is 10 ft long and is fixed against lateral displacement and end rotation at the far end. Determine the safe axial load, given that rail steel is used, and (a) $f_c' = 2500$ psi, (b) $f_c' = 3000$ psi, and (c) $f_c' = 3750$ psi.

4–17. The column in Fig. 4–16 is 11 ft long and is fixed against lateral displacement and end rotation at the far end. Determine the safe axial load, given that rail steel is used, and (a) $f_c' = 2500$ psi, (b) $f_c' = 3000$ psi, (c) $f_c' = 3750$ psi.

4–18. The column in Fig. 4–17 is 15 ft long and is fixed against lateral displacement and end rotation at the far end. Determine the safe axial load, given that rail steel is used, and (a) $f_c' = 2500$ psi, (b) $f_c' = 3000$ psi, (c) $f_c' = 3750$ psi.

4–19. The column in Fig. 4–18 is 14 ft long and is fixed against lateral displacement and end rotation at the far end. Determine the safe axial load, given that rail steel is used, and (a) $f_c' = 2500$ psi, (b) $f_c' = 3000$ psi, (c) $f_c' = 3750$ psi.

4–20. The column in Fig. 4–19 is 12 ft long and is fixed against lateral displacement and end rotation at the far end. The longitudinal steel consists of 8 No. 9 bars, $D_s = 18$ in., $D = 23$ in. Determine the safe axial load, given that rail steel is used, and (a) $f_c' = 2500$ psi, (b) $f_c' = 3000$ psi, and (c) $f_c' = 3750$ psi.

4–21. The column of Fig. 4–15 is 10 ft long and the far end is free to move laterally. Determine the safe axial load, given that intermediate grade steel is used, and (a) $f_c' = 2500$ psi, (b) $f_c' = 3000$ psi, and (c) $f_c' = 3750$ psi.

4–22. The column in Fig. 4–16 is 11 ft long and the far end is free to move laterally. Determine the safe axial load, given that intermediate grade steel is used, and (a) $f_c' = 2500$ psi, (b) $f_c' = 3000$ psi, and (c) $f_c' = 3750$ psi.

4–23. The column in Fig. 4–17 is 15 ft long and the far end is free to move laterally. Determine the safe axial load, given that intermediate grade steel is used, and (a) $f_c' = 2500$ psi, (b) $f_c' = 3000$ psi, and (c) $f_c' = 3750$ psi.

4–24. The column in Fig. 4–18 is 14 ft long and the far end is free to move laterally. Determine the safe axial load, given that intermediate grade steel is used, and (a) $f_c' = 2500$ psi, (b) $f_c' = 3000$ psi, and (c) $f_c' = 3750$ psi.

4–25. The column in Fig. 4–19 is 12 ft long and the far end is free to move laterally. The longitudinal steel consists of 8 No. 9 bars, $D_s = 18$ in., $D = 23$ in. Determine the safe axial load, given that intermediate grade steel is used, and (a) $f_c' = 2500$ psi, (b) $f_c' = 3000$ psi, and (c) $f_c' = 3750$ psi.

4–26. The column in Fig. 4–15 is 10 ft long and the far end is free to move laterally. Determine the safe axial load, given that rail steel is used, and (a) $f_c' = 2500$ psi, (b) $f_c' = 3000$ psi, and (c) $f_c' = 3750$ psi.

4–27. The column in Fig. 4–16 is 11 ft long and the far end is free to move laterally. Determine the safe axial load, given that rail steel is used, and (a) $f_c' = 2500$ psi, (b) $f_c' = 3000$ psi, (c) $f_c' = 3750$ psi.

4–28. The column in Fig. 4–17 is 15 ft long and the far end is free to move laterally. Determine the safe axial load, given that rail steel is used, and (a) $f_c' = 2500$ psi, (b) $f_c' = 3000$ psi, and (c) $f_c' = 3750$ psi.

4–29. The column in Fig. 4–18 is 14 ft long and the far end is free to move laterally. Determine the safe axial load, given that rail steel is used, and (a) $f_c' = 2500$ psi, (b) $f_c' = 3000$ psi, and (c) $f_c' = 3750$ psi.

4–30. The column in Fig. 4–19 is 12 ft long and the far end is free to move laterally. The longitudinal steel is 8 No. 9 bars, $D_s = 18$ in., $D = 23$ in. Determine the safe axial load, given that rail steel is used, and (a) $f_c' = 2500$ psi, (b) $f_c' = 3000$ psi, and (c) $f_c' = 3750$ psi.

Design of Columns

In Problems 4–31 through 4–38, base your design on the ACI Code requirements.

4–31. Design square tied columns to support an axial load of 350 kip. Be sure to specify the size and spacing of ties and show a sketch of the cross section.

    (a) $f_c' = 2500$ psi,   intermediate grade steel, $p_g = 0.02$, $h = 12$ ft;
    (b) $f_c' = 3000$ psi,   intermediate grade steel, $p_g = 0.02$, $h = 12$ ft;
    (c) $f_c' = 3750$ psi,   intermediate grade steel, $p_g = 0.02$, $h = 12$ ft;
    (d) $f_c' = 2500$ psi,   rail steel, $p_g = 0.02$, $h = 12$ ft;
    (e) $f_c' = 3000$ psi,   rail steel, $p_g = 0.02$, $h = 12$ ft;
    (f) $f_c' = 3750$ psi,   rail steel, $p_g = 0.02$, $h = 12$ ft.

4–32. Design square tied columns to support an axial load of 350 kip. Be sure to specify the size and spacing of ties and show a sketch of the cross section.

    (a) $f_c' = 2500$ psi,   intermediate grade steel, $p_g = 0.03$, $h = 12$ ft;
    (b) $f_c' = 3000$ psi,   intermediate grade steel, $p_g = 0.03$, $h = 12$ ft;
    (c) $f_c' = 3750$ psi,   intermediate grade steel, $p_g = 0.03$, $h = 12$ ft;
    (d) $f_c' = 2500$ psi,   rail steel, $p_g = 0.03$, $h = 12$ ft;
    (e) $f_c' = 3000$ psi,   rail steel, $p_g = 0.03$, $h = 12$ ft;
    (f) $f_c' = 3750$ psi,   rail steel, $p_g = 0.03$, $h = 12$ ft.

4–33. Design square tied columns to support an axial load of 350 kip. Be sure to specify the size and spacing of ties and show a sketch of the cross section.

    (a) $f_c' = 2500$ psi,   intermediate grade steel, $p_g = 0.02$, $h = 15$ ft;
    (b) $f_c' = 3000$ psi,   intermediate grade steel, $p_g = 0.02$, $h = 15$ ft;
    (c) $f_c' = 3750$ psi,   intermediate grade steel, $p_g = 0.02$, $h = 15$ ft;
    (d) $f_c' = 2500$ psi,   rail steel, $p_g = 0.02$, $h = 15$ ft;
    (e) $f_c' = 3000$ psi,   rail steel, $p_g = 0.02$, $h = 15$ ft;
    (f) $f_c' = 3750$ psi,   rail steel, $p_g = 0.02$, $h = 15$ ft.

4–34. Design square tied columns to support an axial load of 350 kip. Be sure to specify the size and spacing of ties and show a sketch of the cross section.

    (a) $f_c' = 2500$ psi,   intermediate grade steel, $p_g = 0.03$, $h = 15$ ft;
    (b) $f_c' = 3000$ psi,   intermediate grade steel, $p_g = 0.03$, $h = 15$ ft;
    (c) $f_c' = 3750$ psi,   intermediate grade steel, $p_g = 0.03$, $h = 15$ ft;
    (d) $f_c' = 2500$ psi,   rail steel, $p_g = 0.03$, $h = 15$ ft;
    (e) $f_c' = 3000$ psi,   rail steel, $p_g = 0.03$, $h = 15$ ft;
    (f) $f_c' = 3750$ psi,   rail steel, $p_g = 0.03$, $h = 15$ ft.

4–35. Design spiral columns to support an axial load of 350 kip. Be sure to specify the size and pitch of the spiral and show a sketch of the cross section.

    (a) $f_c' = 2500$ psi,   intermediate grade steel, $p_g = 0.02$, $h = 12$ ft;
    (b) $f_c' = 3000$ psi,   intermediate grade steel, $p_g = 0.02$, $h = 12$ ft;

(c) $f_c' = 3750$ psi, intermediate grade steel, $p_g = 0.02$, $h = 12$ ft;
(d) $f_c' = 2500$ psi, rail steel, $p_g = 0.02$, $h = 12$ ft;
(e) $f_c' = 3000$ psi, rail steel, $p_g = 0.02$, $h = 12$ ft;
(f) $f_c' = 3750$ psi, rail steel, $p_g = 0.02$, $h = 12$ ft.

4–36. Design spiral columns to support an axial load of 350 kip. Be sure to specify the size and pitch of the spiral and show a sketch of the cross section.

(a) $f_c' = 2500$ psi, intermediate grade steel, $p_g = 0.03$, $h = 12$ ft;
(b) $f_c' = 3000$ psi, intermediate grade steel, $p_g = 0.03$, $h = 12$ ft;
(c) $f_c' = 3750$ psi, intermediate grade steel, $p_g = 0.03$, $h = 12$ ft;
(d) $f_c' = 2500$ psi, rail steel, $p_g = 0.03$, $h = 12$ ft;
(e) $f_c' = 3000$ psi, rail steel, $p_g = 0.03$, $h = 12$ ft;
(f) $f_c' = 3750$ psi, rail steel, $p_g = 0.03$, $h = 12$ ft.

4–37. Design spiral columns to support an axial load of 350 kip. Be sure to specify the size and pitch of the spiral and show a sketch of the cross section.

(a) $f_c' = 2500$ psi, intermediate grade steel, $p_g = 0.02$, $h = 15$ ft;
(b) $f_c' = 3000$ psi, intermediate grade steel, $p_g = 0.02$, $h = 15$ ft;
(c) $f_c' = 3750$ psi, intermediate grade steel, $p_g = 0.02$, $h = 15$ ft;
(d) $f_c' = 2500$ psi, rail steel, $p_g = 0.02$, $h = 15$ ft;
(e) $f_c' = 3000$ psi, rail steel, $p_g = 0.02$, $h = 15$ ft;
(f) $f_c' = 3750$ psi, rail steel, $p_g = 0.02$, $h = 15$ ft.

4–38. Design spiral columns to support an axial load of 450 kip. Be sure to specify the size and pitch of the spiral and show a sketch of the cross section.

(a) $f_c' = 2500$ psi, intermediate grade steel, $p_g = 0.03$, $h = 12$ ft;
(b) $f_c' = 3000$ psi, intermediate grade steel, $p_g = 0.03$, $h = 12$ ft;
(c) $f_c' = 3750$ psi, intermediate grade steel, $p_g = 0.03$, $h = 12$ ft;
(d) $f_c' = 2500$ psi, rail steel, $p_g = 0.03$, $h = 12$ ft;
(e) $f_c' = 3000$ psi, rail steel, $p_g = 0.03$, $h = 12$ ft;
(f) $f_c' = 3750$ psi, rail steel, $p_g = 0.03$, $h = 12$ ft.

REFERENCES

1. COMMITTEE 105, "Reinforced Concrete Column Investigation," *ACI Journal,* Feb. 1931.
2. W. A. SLATER and INGE LYSE, "First Progress Report on Column Tests at Lehigh University," *ACI Journal,* Feb. 1931.
3. F. E. RICHART and G. C. STAEHLE, "Progress Report on Column Tests at the University of Illinois," *ACI Journal,* Feb. 1931.
4. F. E. RICHART and G. C. STAEHLE, "Second Progress Report on Column Tests at the University of Illinois," *ACI Journal,* Mar. 1931.
5. W. A. SLATER and INGE LYSE, "Second Progress Report on Column Tests Made at Lehigh University," *ACI Journal,* Mar. 1931.
6. COMMITTEE 105, "Reinforced Concrete Column Investigation," *ACI Journal,* Nov. 1931.
7. F. E. RICHART and G. C. STAEHLE, "Third Progress Report on Column Tests Made at the University of Illinois," *ACI Journal,* Nov. 1931.
8. F. E. RICHART and G. C. STAEHLE, "Fourth Progress Report on the Column Tests Made at the University of Illinois," *ACI Journal,* Jan. 1932.
9. INGE LYSE and C. L. KREIDLER, "Fourth Progress Report on Column Tests at Lehigh University," *ACI Journal,* Jan. 1932.
10. COMMITTEE 105, "Reinforced Concrete Column Investigation," *ACI Journal,* Feb. 1933.
11. INGE LYSE, "Fifth Report on Column Tests at Lehigh University," *ACI Journal,* June 1933.
12. THOR GERMUNDSSON, "Columns with High Yield Point Reinforcement Designed under the ACI Code," *ACI Journal,* Apr. 1941.
13. L. J. MENSCH, "Composite Columns," *ACI Journal,* Nov. 1930.
14. S. J. CHAMBERLAIN, "Spacing of Reinforcement in Beams," *ACI Journal,* July 1956.

5 ECCENTRICALLY LOADED COLUMNS

Los Angeles Freeway Interchange, Los Angeles, California.

5–1 INTRODUCTION

Columns of buildings might well serve as illustrations of eccentric loading. The vertical load may be applied eccentrically through an eccentric connection such as shown in Fig. 5–1(a); a rigid-frame connection may induce a moment in a column (Fig. 5–1b); or a horizontal load may bend the column (Fig. 5–1c). In almost all instances, column loads exhibit a certain degree of eccentricity with respect to the centerline of the column.

When the eccentricity is quite small, the bending stresses caused by the load are small compared to the compression stresses, and the column may be designed as an axially loaded column (see discussion presented in Chapter 4). But most of the time the eccentricity is great enough that a new design approach has to be followed.

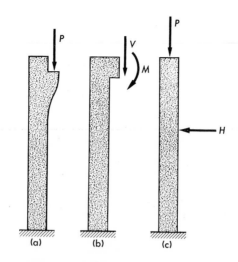

Fig. 5–1. Columns subjected to compression and bending.

5–2 BENDING AND DIRECT STRESSES; COMPRESSION OVER THE WHOLE SECTION—SMALL ECCENTRICITIES

Figure 5–2(a) shows a column subjected to a direct axial load P and a bending moment M. This combination is equivalent to an eccentric load acting as illustrated in Fig. 5–2(b). From the figure, the stresses at the two faces may be shown to be

$$f_{c\ \substack{max \\ min}} = P/A_t \pm Pec/I = P(1/A_t \pm ec/I), \tag{5-1}$$

where

$$A_t = \text{transformed area} = A_g[1 + (n-1)p_g], \qquad p_g = A_s/A_g,$$
$$I = I_{\text{conc}} + (n-1)I_s.$$

It is customary to use the overall dimensions to compute A_g and A_t for such columns. As the eccentricity increases, $f_{c\ min}$ (Eq. 5–1) approaches zero and becomes negative (tension) if e is increased further. From Eq. (5–1), the eccentricity for $f_{c\ min} = 0$ is

$$0 = P/A_t(1 - ecA_t/I).$$

Therefore

$$1 - ecA_t/I = 0$$

or

$$e = I/cA_t. \tag{5-2}$$

Note that e is independent of the magnitude of P. For a load P eccentric in one direction only, applied to a rectangular unreinforced section, as shown in Fig.

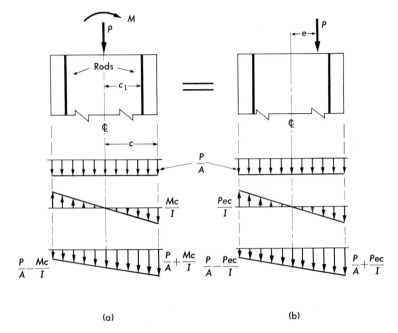

Fig. 5-2. Bending and direct concrete stresses in columns.

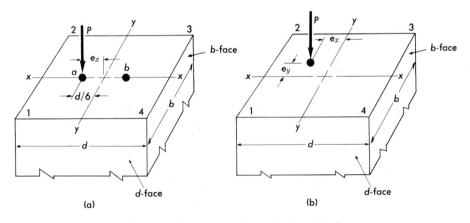

Fig. 5-3. Eccentrically located column loads.

5-3(a), e required to produce $f_c = 0$ is

$$e_x = \frac{bd^3/12}{(d/2)bd} = \frac{d}{6}.$$

In other words, P can be applied anywhere for a distance of $d/6$ on each side of the y-axis, and no tension is possible on the b-face of the column. Or, one may say that the load P does not create tension on the b-faces so long as it is located within the middle third of the dimension d. The distances $d/6$ on each side of the $(y–y)$-axis [points a and b in Fig. 5–3(a)] are usually referred to as *kern points* or *kern limits*—points of application of P for zero stress on a face. The presence of reinforcement increases the distance to slightly over $d/6$ (see Example 5–1).

When the load is eccentric with both the $(y–y)$-and $(x–x)$-axes of the plain section shown in Fig. 5–3(b), the stresses produced may be calculated by superimposing the stress effects of the individual loads, that is:

$$f_{c\,{\max \atop \min}} = \frac{P}{A} \pm \frac{Pe_xd/2}{I_{yy}} \pm \frac{Pe_yb/2}{I_{xx}}$$

$$= \frac{P}{A}\left(1 \pm \frac{Ae_xd}{2I_{yy}} \pm \frac{Ae_yb}{2I_{xx}}\right). \qquad (5–3)$$

As we can see in Fig. 5–3(b), the maximum stress occurs at point 2 and the minimum at point 4. Equation (5–3) may be also used to determine the stresses at points 1 and 3 by appropriately adjusting the plus and minus signs.

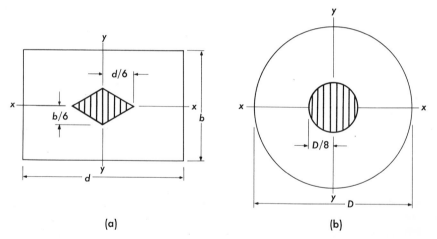

Fig. 5–4. Kern regions for columns.

Again, if $f_c = 0$, then from Eq. (5–3),

$$1 = \frac{Ae_xd}{2I_{yy}} + \frac{Ae_yb}{2I_{xx}} = \frac{6}{d}e_x + \frac{6}{b}e_y.$$

From this result we obtain four kern points, two on each axis at a distance of $\frac{1}{6}$ of the parallel dimension. Since the expression is linear, these four points may be connected by straight lines to give a region within which the load may be applied anywhere without creating tension stresses on any one of the four column faces. This area, known as the *kern region,* is shown shaded in Fig. 5–4(a) for a rectangular section and in Fig. 5–4(b) for a circular section. (Again, the kern points for a reinforced column are slightly greater than $d/6$ and $b/6$.)

The Code states that the strength of the column is controlled by compression if the axial load P (sometimes represented by N) has an eccentricity, e, in each principal direction no greater than that given by Eq. (5–4a), (5–4b), or (5–4c) below, and that tension is the controlling factor if e exceeds these values. Thus we have for symmetrical spiral columns:

$$e_b = 0.43p_g m D_s + 0.14t; \tag{5-4a}$$

for symmetrical tied columns:

$$e_b = (0.67p_g m + 0.17)d; \tag{5-4b}$$

and for unsymmetrical tied columns:

$$e_b = \frac{p'm(d - d') + 0.1d}{(p' - p)m + 0.6}. \tag{5-4c}$$

Columns controlled by compression shall be proportioned according to Eq. (5–5) except that the allowable load shall not exceed the load permitted when the column supports axial load only. Thus, from the Code we have

$$\frac{f_a}{F_a} + \frac{f_{bx}}{F_b} + \frac{f_{by}}{F_b} \le 1, \tag{5-5}$$

where

$$f_a = \frac{P}{A_g},$$

$$F_a = 0.34(1 + p_g m)f_c',$$

$$f_{bx} = \frac{Pe_y y}{I_{xx}},$$

$$f_{by} = \frac{Pe_x x}{I_{yy}},$$

$$F_b = 0.45f_c'.$$

Example 5–1. *Analysis (eccentricity in one direction)*

Given: Square cross section as shown in Fig. 5–5. The column supports a load of 150 k which has an eccentricity of 2.5 in. in one direction. Assume $f_y = 50{,}000$ psi, $f_c' = 2500$ psi, and $n = 12$.

Find: (a) Steel and concrete stresses. (b) Determine how closely the column meets the specification that $f_a/F_a + f_b/F_b \le 1$.

SOLUTION:

$I = bd^3/12 + (n - 1)A_s y^2$

  $= 18 \times (18)^3/12 + 11(6 \times 0.6)(12.6/2)^2,$

$I = 8748 + 1571 = 10{,}320$ in^4,

$p_g = 8 \times 0.6/(18)^2 = 0.0148,$

$m = f_y/0.85f_c' = 50{,}000/0.85 \times 2500 = 23.5,$

$A_t = A_g[1 + (n - 1)p_g]$

  $= (18)^2[1 + 11(8 \times 0.6)/(18)^2] = 376$ in^2.

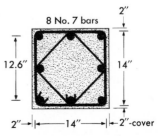

Figure 5–5

If no tension is to exist on any of the two faces, then the permissible eccentricity is

$$e = I/cA_t = 10{,}320/(9)(376) = 3.06 \text{ in.}$$

Hence an eccentricity of 2.5 in. is acceptable.
   Based on Eq. (5–4b),

$$e_b = (0.67 p_g m + 0.17)d = (0.67 \times 0.0148 \times 23.5 + 0.17)15.3$$
$$= (0.252 + 0.17)(15.3) = 6.45 \text{ in.} > 2.5 \text{ in. actual.}$$

Therefore, compression controls. The kern point for a plain cross section would be at $1\frac{5}{8} = 3$ in. Note that the permissible $e = 3.06$ in. is slightly greater than the limit $b/6 = 1\frac{5}{8} = 3$ in. given for plain sections.
   We next obtain the stresses:

$$f_a = P/A_g = 150{,}000/(18)^2 = 463 \text{ psi,}$$
$$F_a = 0.34(1 + p_g m)fc' = 0.34(1 + 0.0148 \times 23.5)2500$$
$$= 0.34 \times 1.35 \times 2500 = 1150 \text{ psi,}$$
$$f_b = \frac{Pey}{I} = \frac{150{,}000 \times 2.5 \times 9}{10{,}320} = 327 \text{ psi,}$$
$$F_b = 0.45 f_c' = 1125 \text{ psi.}$$

Therefore

$$\frac{f_a}{F_a} + \frac{f_b}{F_b} = \frac{463}{1150} + \frac{327}{1125} = 0.410 + 0.290 = 0.710 < 1.$$

Next we proceed to calculate stresses:

$$f_{c\,\min}^{\max} = P(1/A_t \pm ec/I),$$
$$f_{c\,\min}^{\max} = 150{,}000[1/376 \pm 2.5 \times 9/10{,}320]$$
$$= 150{,}000[2.66 \times 10^{-3} \pm 2.18 \times 10^{-3}],$$
$$f_{c\,\max} = 150{,}000 \times 4.84 \times 10^{-3} = 726 \text{ psi;}$$
$$f_{c\,\min} = 150{,}000 \times 0.48 \times 10^{-3} = 72 \text{ psi;}$$
$$f_{s\,\min}^{\max} = 2nf_c \text{ at } 12.6 \text{ in.}/2 \text{ from neutral axis} \qquad \text{(see ACI Code, Article 1407b),}$$
$$= 24\{P(1/A_t \pm ey/I)\} = 24[150{,}000(1/376 \pm 2.5 \times 6.3/10{,}320)],$$
$$f_{s\,\max} = 24[150{,}000(2.66 \times 10^{-3} + 1.526 \times 10^{-3})] = 15{,}100 \text{ psi,}$$
$$f_{s\,\min} = 24[150{,}000(2.66 \times 10^{-3} - 1.526 \times 10^{-3})] = 4100 \text{ psi.}$$

These stresses could have also been determined by direct proportion (Fig. 5–6), that is,

$$f_{s\,\max} = 24[72 + (15.3/18) \times 654] = 15{,}100 \text{ psi,}$$
$$f_{s\,\min} = 24[72 + (2.7/18) \times 654] = 4100 \text{ psi,}$$
$$f_{s\,\text{allowable}} = 0.34 \times 50{,}000 = 17{,}000 \text{ psi} \qquad \text{(see ACI Code, Article 1003b).}$$

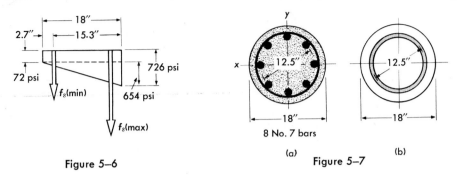

Figure 5–6   Figure 5–7

Example 5–2. Analysis (eccentricity in one direction)

Given: Round column section as shown in Fig. 5–7(a). The column supports a load of 150 k eccentric 2.0 in. along the x-axis. Assume that $f_y = 40,000$ psi, $f_c' = 3000$ psi, $n = 9$.

Find: (a) The concrete and steel stresses. (b) How closely the column meets the specifications, 1407b, ACI Code.

PROCEDURE: It is customary to investigate the moment of inertia of such a section by converting the bars into a ring whose area is equal to the area of all the vertical bars, as shown in Fig. 5–7(b). Then the moment of inertia of the section with respect to any axis passing through the center of the section is the same. We have

$$I_{xx} = I_{yy} = \frac{\pi D^4}{64} + (n - 1)\frac{A_s D_s^2}{8} \quad \text{(close approximation)},$$

$$I_{xx} = \frac{\pi(18)^4}{64} + \frac{8(8 \times 0.6)(12.5)^2}{8} = 5920 \text{ in}^4,$$

$$p_g = \frac{A_s}{A_g} = \frac{(8 \times 0.6)}{(\pi/4)(18)^2} = \frac{4.8}{254} = 0.0189,$$

$$A_t = A_g[1 + (n - 1)p_g] = \frac{\pi}{4}(18)^2[1 + 8 \times 0.0189] = 293 \text{ in}^2,$$

$$m = \frac{f_y}{0.85 f_c'} = \frac{40000}{0.85 \times 3000} = 15.7.$$

If no tension exists on any part of the column, then the permissible eccentricity is

$$e = I/cA_t = 5920/9 \times 293 = 2.25 \text{ in.} > 2.0 \text{ in.}$$

Hence the given eccentricity is acceptable. From Eq. (5–4a), we obtain

$$e_b = 0.43 p_g m D_s + 0.14t$$
$$= 0.43 \times 0.0189 \times 15.7 \times 12.5 + 0.14 \times 18$$
$$= 4.12 \text{ in.} > 2.0 \text{ in.}$$

Therefore, compression controls. We next check compliance with the Code:

$$f_a = P/A_g = 150,000/(\pi/4)(18)^2 = 590 \text{ psi},$$
$$F_a = 0.34(1 + 0.0189 \times 15.7)3000 = 1320 \text{ psi},$$
$$f_b = Pey/I = (150,000 \times 2)(9)/5920 = 457 \text{ psi},$$
$$F_b = 0.45f_c' = 1350 \text{ psi},$$
$$f_a/F_a + f_b/F_b = 590/1320 + 457/1350 = 0.447 + 0.339 = 0.786 < 1.$$

Hence our result is within the Code's limit.

We now determine the stresses by direct proportion (Fig. 5–8):

$$f_{c\;\substack{\max \\ \min}} = P(1/A_t \pm ec/I) = 150,000(1/293 \pm 2 \times 9/5920),$$
$$f_{c\;\max} = 150,000(3.41 + 3.05) \times 10^{-3} = 970 \text{ psi},$$
$$f_{c\;\min} = 150,000(3.41 - 3.05) \times 10^{-3} = 57 \text{ psi};$$
$$f_{s\;\min} = 2n[57 + (15.25/18) \times 913] = 15,000 \text{ psi},$$
$$f_{s\;\min} = 2n[57 + (2.75/18) \times 913] = 3550 \text{ psi}.$$

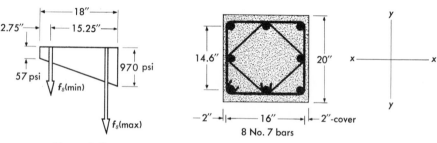

Figure 5–8   Figure 5–9

Example 5–3. *Analysis (eccentricity in two directions)*

Given: Square cross section as shown in Fig. 5–9. The column supports a load of 150 k and moments of $M_y = M_x = 500,000$ in.-lb. Assume that $f_c' = 3000$ psi, $f_y = 50,000$ psi, and $n = 9$.

Find: (a) How closely the column meets Code requirements, and (b) the concrete and steel stresses.

SOLUTION:

$$I_{xx} = I_{yy} = bd^3/12 + (n - 1)A_s y^2$$
$$= 20 \times 20^3/12 + 8(6 \times 0.6)(14.6/2)^2 = 14,860 \text{ in}^4,$$
$$p_g = A_s/A_g = 8 \times 0.6/(20)^2 = 0.012,$$
$$m = f_y/0.85f_c' = 50,000/0.85 \times 3000 = 19.6,$$
$$A_{\text{tot}} = A_g[1 + (n - 1)p_g]$$
$$= 400[1 + 0.096] = 438 \text{ in}^2.$$

The permissible eccentricity is

$$e = I/cA_t = 14{,}860/10 \times 438 = 3.4 \text{ in.} \qquad \text{(based on } d/6, e = 3.33 \text{ in.).}$$

The actual eccentricity is, from $e = M/P$,

$$\frac{500{,}000}{150{,}000} = e_y = e_x = 3.33 \text{ in.}$$

From Eq. (5–4b), we have, for $d \approx 17.25$ in. (Fig. 5–9),

$$e_b = (0.67 \times 0.012 \times 19.6 + 0.17)17.25 = 5.7 \text{ in.}$$

Therefore, compression controls. We now calculate

$$f_a = P/A_g = 150{,}000/400 = 375 \text{ psi,}$$
$$F_a = 0.34(1 + 0.012 \times 19.6)3000 = 1260 \text{ psi,}$$
$$f_b = Pey/I = (150{,}000 \times 3.33 \times 10)/14{,}860 = 336 \text{ psi,}$$
$$F_b = 0.45 f_c' = 0.45 \times 3000 = 1350 \text{ psi,}$$
$$f_a/F_a + f_{bx}/F_{bx} + f_{by}/F_{by} = 375/1260 + 336/1350 + 336/1350 = 0.796 < 1,$$

which is acceptable. Basing our calculations on Fig. 5–10, we obtain

$$f_{c\,\substack{\max \\ \min}} = 150{,}000(1/438 \pm 3.33 \times 10/14{,}860)$$
$$= [150{,}000(2.28 \pm 2.24) \times 10^{-3}],$$
$$f_{c\,\max} = 150{,}000 \times 4.52 \times 10^{-3} = 678 \text{ psi;}$$
$$f_{c\,\min} = 150{,}000 \times 0.04 \times 10^{-3} = 6 \text{ psi;}$$
$$f_{s\,\max} = 2n[(17.25/20) \times 678] \approx 10{,}520 \text{ psi;}$$
$$f_{s\,\min} = 2n[(2.75/20) \times 678] \approx 1678 \text{ psi.}$$

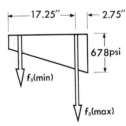

Figure 5–10

Example 5–4. Design

Given: A column has to support an eccentric load of 200 kip and a moment of 600,000 in.-lb. Assume that $f_c' = 3000$ psi, $f_y = 50{,}000$ psi, $n = 10$, $p_g = 0.02$, and $f_s = 16{,}000$ psi.

Find: A suitable design for a short, square, tied column.

SOLUTION: The dead weight of the column will be assumed to be negligible compared to the applied load. To help the designer select a section, the 1956 ACI Code provides a formula which converts the eccentric load into an equivalent axial load. This then permits a selection of A_g, etc. Thus

$$P = N_e(1 + Be/t),$$

where $P =$ equivalent axial load, lb,

         $N_e =$ eccentrically applied load, lb,

         $e =$ eccentricity, in.,

         $t =$ column depth, in.,

         $B =$ a factor (dimensionless). (The Code suggested a B of 3 to $3\frac{1}{2}$ for rectangular columns and of 5 to 6 for circular spiral columns.)

We first compute e:

$$e = M/N = 600,000/200,000 = 3.0 \text{ in.}$$

It is obvious that t has to be estimated at this time. We may do this by assuming that e is inside the kern region. Let us say that e is on the boundary, that is, $e = t/6$; then $t = 6e = 18$ in., and we find that

$$P = 200,000(1 + 3 \times \tfrac{3}{18}) = 300,000 \text{ lb.}$$

From Eq. (4–1),

$$P = 300,000 = 0.85A_g(0.250f_c' + f_s p_g),$$
$$t^2 = A_g = 300,000/0.85(0.250 \times 3000 + 16,000 \times 0.02) = 330,$$
$$t = \sqrt{330} = 18.3 \text{ in.} \qquad \text{(say 19 in.).}$$

For $p_g = 0.02$,

$$A_s = 0.02 \times 19 \times 19 = 7.22 \text{ in}^2, \qquad \text{approximately.}$$

It is desirable to make the section symmetrical, and hence the number of vertical bars will be multiples of 4. For eight No. 8 bars, $A_s = 6.32$ in^2, and for eight No. 9 bars, $A_s = 8$ in^2. As a check let us investigate the section shown in Fig. 5–11. We obtain

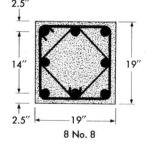

8 No. 8

Figure 5–11

$I_{xx} = 19 \times (19)^3/12 + 9(6 \times 0.79)7^2,$

$I_{xx} = 10,860 + 2090 = 12,950 \text{ in}^4,$

$p_g = A_s/A_g = 6.32/361 = 0.0175,$

$A_t = A_g[1 + (n - 1)p_g] = 361 \times 1.157 = 418 \text{ in}^2,$

$f_a = P/A_g = 200,000/361 = 555 \text{ psi},$

$F_a = 0.34(1 + 0.0175 \times 50,000/0.85 \times 3000)3000 = 1420 \text{ psi},$

$f_b = Pey/I = (200,000 \times 3)9.5/12,950 = 440 \text{ psi},$

$F_b = 0.45f_c' = 0.45 \times 3000 = 1350 \text{ psi},$

$f_a/F_a + f_b/F_b = 555/1420 + 440/1350 = 0.391 + 0.326 = 0.717 < 1.$

The result is seen to be within the Code's limit. The design should call for a 19 × 19 in. section as shown in the figure, although a smaller section might be satisfactory. (The checking of stresses in the steel will be left as an exercise for the student.) Thus the designer may use eight No. 8 bars and No. 3 ties placed at a distance of 16 in. center-to-center (see Article 806b, ACI Code).

5-3   BENDING AND DIRECT STRESSES; TENSION OVER PORTION OF RECTANGULAR COLUMN SECTION—LARGE ECCENTRICITIES

In the preceding article it was shown that a load eccentric up to approximately $D/6$ (see Fig. 5–12) on either side of the column centerline ($D/8$ for round columns) results in zero stress on "one" face of the column (D denotes here the overall dimension of the section). An eccentricity greater than these limits could produce some tension. Article 1407a of the ACI Code provides a limit for e expressed by Eq. (5–4a), (5–4b), or (5–4c), whichever applies. If the actual eccentricity exceeds that calculated by means of the governing equation of the group, the column is controlled by tension. In such cases, we assume that the modular ratio for the compressive reinforcement is $2n$; however, the calculated stress in the compressive reinforcement shall not be greater than the allowable stress given in Article 1003b of the ACI Code, and the maximum combined compressive stress in the concrete shall not exceed $0.45 f_c'$. In these instances, we must also examine the tensile steel.

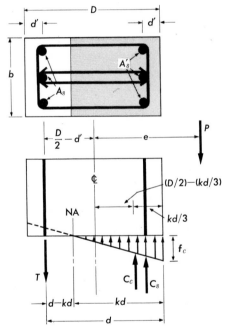

Figure 5–12

Let us assume that the section shown in Fig. 5–12 is stressed so that one face is placed in tension and cracked. Then taking the sum of the forces acting in the y-direction and noting that $d = D - d'$, we have

$$P + T - C_c - C_s' = 0, \tag{5–6}$$

where

$$C_c = f_c b k d / 2, \qquad C_s' = A_s' f_s' = A_s'(n - 1)f_c[(kd - d')/kd],$$

which is the compression force in excess of that taken by the concrete, and

$$T = A_s f_s = A_s n f_c [(d - kd)/kd].$$

To solve for kd, we take moments about P:

$$T[e + (D/2 - d')] - C_c[e - (D/2 - kd/3)] - C_s[e - (D/2 - d')] = 0.$$

On substitution of the values of T, C_s, and C_c, the above expression becomes

$$(f_c/kd)nA_s(d - kd)[e + (D/2 - d')] - (f_c/kd)b(kd)^2/2[e - (D/2 - kd/3)]$$
$$- (f_c/kd)(2n - 1)A_s'(kd - d')[e - (D/2 - d')] = 0,$$
$$nA_s(d - kd)[e + (D/2 - d')] - b(kd)^2/2[e - (D/2 - kd/3)]$$
$$- (2n - 1)A_s'(kd - d')[e - (D/2 - d')] = 0. \qquad (5\text{–}7)$$

Similarly Eq. (5–6) becomes

$$P = f_c/kd[-nA_s(d - kd) + (b/2)(kd)^2 + (2n - 1)A_s'(kd - d')]. \qquad (5\text{–}8)$$

Equation (5–7) is useful for the designer who wishes to *analyze* columns of known sections for a given e. In such procedures, all quantities except kd are known. A trial solution of Eq. (5–7) for kd is perhaps as good as any. With kd known, Eq. (5–8) gives the stress f_c (and by proportions, f_s) for a given load P.

If longitudinal reinforcement existed along faces 1–2 and 3–4 of Fig. 5–3, then Eq. (5–7) would have additional terms. However, in most instances, these would have an almost negligible effect on kd.

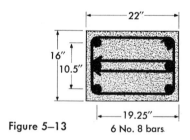

Figure 5–13

6 No. 8 bars.

Example 5–5. *Analysis (and design)*

Given: A load P exhibits an eccentricity of 16 in. along the x-axis. $f_c' = 3000$ psi, $f_s = 60,000$ psi, and $n = 10$ (Fig. 5–13).

Find: A safe load P.

SOLUTION: From Eq. (5–7), we have

$$nA_s(d - kd)[e + (D/2) - d'] - (b/2)(kd)^2[e - (D/2) + kd/3]$$
$$- (n - 1)A_s'(kd - d')[e - (D/2) + d'] = 0.$$

If we substitute the values given, that is,

$$d = 19.25 \text{ in.}, \quad e = 16 \text{ in.}, \quad D/2 = 11 \text{ in.}, \quad d' = 2.75 \text{ in.}, \quad n = 10,$$
$$A_s = A_s' = 2.37 \text{ in}^2, \quad b/2 = 8 \text{ in.},$$

we obtain

$$23.7(19.25 - kd)(24.25) - 8(kd)^2[5 + (kd/3)] - 19 \times 2.37(kd - 2.75)7.75 = 0.$$

Simplifying yields

$$1427.9 - 74.18kd - 5.16(kd)^2 - 0.344(kd)^3 - 42.66kd + 119.2 = 0,$$

or

$$-0.344(kd)^3 - 5.16(kd)^2 - 116.8kd + 1545 = 0.$$

TRIAL SOLUTION

kd		
10	$-344 - 516 - 1168 + 1545 = -483 \neq 0,$	unsatisfactory,
9	$-251 - 418 - 1051 + 1545 = -175 \neq 0,$	unsatisfactory,
8.5	$-215 - 373 - 991 + 1545 = -34 \neq 0,$	unsatisfactory,
8.3	$-200 - 360 - 971 + 1545 = +10$	close.

We therefore take $kd = 8.35$.

By proportions, the relation between f_c and f_s, and f_c and f_s' are found to be

$$f_s/f_s = n(d - kd)/kd$$

and

$$f_s'/f_c = 2n(kd - d')/kd \quad \text{(ACI Code)}.$$

We now check the stresses before finding P. Let us assume that f_c governs, i.e. that f_s and f_s' are equal to or less than 20,000 psi when f_c is 1350 psi. Then

$$f_s = [10(19.25 - 8.35)/8.35]1350 = 17,100 \text{ psi} < 20,000 \quad \text{(satisfactory)},$$
$$f_s' = [20(8.35 - 2.75)/8.35]1350 = 10,500 \text{ psi} < 20,000 \quad \text{(satisfactory)}.$$

From Eq. (5–8),

$$P = f_c/kd[-nA_s(d - kd) + (b/2)(kd)^2 + (2n - 1)A_s'(kd - d')],$$
$$P = 1350/8.35[-10 \times 2.37(19.25 - 8.35) + \tfrac{16}{2}(8.35)^2 + 19 \times 2.37(8.35 - 2.75)],$$
$$P = 161.5(-259 + 557 + 239) = 86,600 \text{ lb}.$$

5–4   BENDING AND DIRECT STRESSES

A circular column section subjected to loads of large eccentricities (Fig. 5–14) may be analyzed by means of the principles stated for rectangular columns in the previous article.

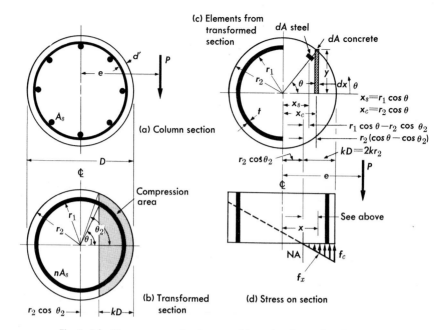

Fig 5–14. Stress on round columns subjected to heavy bending.

Let

C_c = resultant compressive force in concrete,

C_s = resultant force in steel,*

M_c = moment resisted by concrete, and

M_s = moment resisted by steel.

Equilibrium is assumed, i.e.,

$$P = C_c + C_s, \tag{5–9}$$

$$Pe = M_c + M_s, \tag{5–10}$$

or

$$e = \frac{M_c + M_s}{P}. \tag{5–10}'$$

For the elements of area dA (both steel and concrete) shown in Fig. 5–14(c), the intensities of stress f_x in terms of f_c can be determined by the principle of similar triangles. We find for concrete:

$$\frac{f_{xc}}{f_c} = \frac{r_2 \cos \theta - r_2 \cos \theta_2}{kD} = \frac{r_2(\cos \theta - \cos \theta_2)}{2kr_2},$$

$$f_{xc} = \frac{f_c(\cos \theta - \cos \theta_2)}{2k}; \tag{5–11}$$

---

* Note that if $kD = \frac{1}{2}D$, then $C_s = 0$. If kD is less than $\frac{1}{2}D$, C_s = tensile force (net). If kD is greater than $\frac{1}{2}D$, C_s = compressive force.

and for steel:

$$\frac{f_{xs}}{f_c} = \frac{r_1 \cos \theta - r_2 \cos \theta_2}{kD} = \frac{(r_1 \cos \theta - r_2 \cos \theta_2)}{2kr_2},$$

$$f_{xs} = \frac{f_c(r_1 \cos \theta - r_2 \cos \theta_2)}{2kr_2}, \tag{5–12}$$

$$C_c = \int f_{xc} \, dA_c = (f_c/2k) \int_{-\theta_2}^{\theta_2} (\cos \theta - \cos \theta_2) y \, dx_c,$$

$$x_c = r_2 \cos \theta; \qquad dx_c = -r_2 \sin \theta \, d\theta; \qquad y_c = r_2 \sin \theta.$$

Taking only the numerical value of dx_c, i.e., disregarding the minus sign, we have

$$C_c = (f_c r_2{}^2/2k) \int_{-\theta_2}^{\theta_2} (\cos \theta - \cos \theta_2)(\sin \theta)^2 \, d\theta.$$

Evaluating the integral and simplifying gives

$$C_c = (f_c r_2{}^2/2k)[\cos \theta_2(\cos \theta_2 \sin \theta_2 - \theta_2) + \tfrac{2}{3} (\sin \theta_2)^3]. \tag{5–13a}$$

Similarly,

$$C_s = \int f_{xs} \, dA_s = \int_{-\pi}^{\pi} (f_c/2kr_2)(r_1 \cos \theta - r_2 \cos \theta_2) t r_1 \, d\theta,$$

but from the transformed section, we have

$$A_s = n(p_g \pi r_2{}^2) = 2\pi r_1 t, \qquad \text{or} \qquad t = np_g r_2{}^2/2r_1.$$

Integrating the above and eliminating t, we obtain

$$C_s = -(\pi r_2{}^2 p_g n f_c/2k) \cos \theta_2 = -(f_c r_2{}^2/2k)(\pi np_g \cos \theta_2). \tag{5–13b}$$

Then Eq. (5–9) becomes

$$P = (f_c r_2{}^2/2k)[\cos \theta_2(\cos \theta_2 \sin \theta_2 - \theta_2) + \tfrac{2}{3}(\sin \theta_2)^3 - \pi p_g n \cos \theta_2].$$

Omitting several steps, we find that M_c and M_s are

$$M_c = \int_{-\theta_2}^{\theta_2} f_{xc} x_c \, dA_c = \frac{f_c r_2{}^3}{k} \left[\frac{\theta_2}{8} - \frac{(\sin 4\theta_2)}{32} - \frac{(\cos \theta_2 \sin^3 \theta_2)}{3} \right], \tag{5–14}$$

and

$$M_s = \int_{-\pi}^{\pi} f_{xs} x_s \, dA_s = \frac{\pi f_c p_g n r_2 r_1{}^2}{4k} = \frac{f_c r_2{}^2}{2k} \frac{np_g \pi r_1{}^2}{2r_2}. \tag{5–15}$$

Equation (5–10) then becomes

$$e = \frac{(f_c r_2{}^2/2k)\{2r_2[(\theta_2/8) - (\sin 4\theta_2/32) + (\cos \theta_2 \sin^3 \theta_2/3)] + \pi np_g r_1{}^2/2r_2\}}{(f_c r_2{}^2/2k)[\cos \theta_2(\cos \theta_2 \sin \theta_2 - \theta_2) + \tfrac{2}{3}(\sin \theta_2)^3 - \pi np_g \cos \theta_2]}.$$

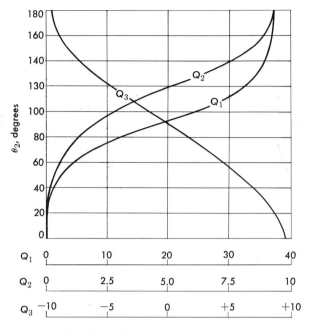

Fig. 5–15. Values for Q_1, Q_2, and Q_3.

Simplifying yields

$$e = \frac{\overbrace{(6r_2/96)[12\theta_2 - 3\sin 4\theta_2 - 32\cos\theta_2 \sin^3\theta_2 + 24\pi n p_g(r_1/r_2)^2]}^{Q_1}}{\underbrace{3\cos\theta_2(\cos\theta_2 \sin\theta_2 - \theta_2) + 2(\sin\theta_2)^3}_{Q_2} - \underbrace{3\pi\cos\theta_2\, np}_{Q_3\,=\,3\pi\cos\theta_2}}.$$

Letting Q_1, Q_2, and Q_3 represent the quantities shown above, and letting $D = 2r_2$, we obtain

$$e = \frac{(D/32)\{Q_1 + 96\pi np_g[(D - 2d')/D]^2\}}{(Q_2 - Q_3 np_g)}. \tag{5–16}$$

From Fig. 5–15, the values of Q_1, Q_2, and Q_3 may be easily obtained for any value of θ_2 from zero to 180°.

The values of Q' for the angles shown are as follows:

$\theta_2°$	0	15	30	45	60	75	90	105	120	135	150	165	180
Q_1	0	0.01	0.23	1.46	4.75	10.83	18.84	26.82	32.90	36.16	37.48	37.65	37.68
Q_2	0	0.005	0.017	0.102	0.37	1.00	2.00	3.43	5.08	6.75	8.18	9.07	9.42
Q_3	9.42	9.10	8.16	6.66	4.71	2.43	0	−2.43	−4.71	−6.66	−8.16	−9.10	−9.42

Example 5–6. *Analysis (and design)*

Given: A load, P, is 16 in. eccentric along the x-axis. Assume that $f_c = 1350$ psi, $f_s = 20,000$ psi, and $n = 10$.

Find: The allowable load P.

SOLUTION:

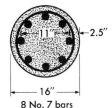

11" ← 2.5"

—— 16" ——

8 No. 7 bars

Figure 5–16

$$e = \frac{D}{32} \frac{[Q_1 + 96\pi np(D - 2d')/D]^2}{Q_2 - Q_3 np_g},$$

$$p_g = \frac{A_s}{A_g} = \frac{6.32}{\frac{1}{4}\pi(16)^2} = 0.0314;$$

$$np_g = 0.314; \qquad 96\pi np_g = 94.6.$$

Therefore

$$e = \frac{16}{32} \frac{Q_1 + 94.6(0.47265)}{Q_2 - Q_3 \times 0.314} = \frac{1}{2}\left[\frac{Q_1 + 44.71}{Q_2 - 0.314Q_3}\right],$$

and, for $e = 16$ in.,

$$2e = 32 = (Q_1 + 44.71)/(Q_2 - 0.314Q_3) = f(Q)$$

is to be solved.

The solution of the above equation requires the use of Fig. 5–15. Trial estimates of θ_2 give the following solutions:

θ_2	Q_1	Q_2	Q_3	$f(Q)$
120°	32.90	5.06	−4.71	11.88 $\neq$ 32 not satisfactory
75°	10.83	1.0	2.43	231. $\neq$ 32 not satisfactory
90°	18.84	2.0	0	31.77 $\neq$ 32, but it is a good approximation

We use the equation

$$M = Pe = M_c + M_s.$$

From Eqs. (5–14) and (5–15),

$$M_c + M_s = \frac{f_c r_2^3}{96k}\left[12\theta_2 - 3\sin 4\theta_2 - 32\cos\theta_2 \sin^3\theta_2 + 24\pi np_g\left(\frac{r_1}{r_2}\right)^2\right],$$

which reduces to

$$M_c + M_s = \frac{f_c(D/2)^3}{96k}\left[Q_1 + 96\pi np_g\left(\frac{D - 2d'}{D}\right)^2\right].$$

Substituting the values known, we obtain

$$Pe = P \times 16 = [f_c(8)^3/96 \times \tfrac{1}{2}](18.84 + 44.71),$$
$$P = f_c\tfrac{2}{3}(63.55) = 42.4f_c,$$
$$P = 42.4 \times 1350 = 57.25 \text{ k}.$$

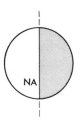

NA

Figure 5–17

We now check the stresses in the steel:

$$f_{s(tension)} = n \frac{(D/2 - d')}{(D/2)} f_c = 10 \times \frac{5.5}{8} \times 1350 = 9280 \text{ psi},$$

$$f_{s(compression)} < 20{,}000 \text{ psi}.$$

These results are satisfactory.

5–5 ULTIMATE STRENGTH OF COLUMNS; ACI CODE

Articles 1902 and 1903 of the ACI Code provide some formulas for determining the ultimate strength of eccentrically loaded columns. These fall into two categories: one group is used to calculate the ultimate load as controlled by tension failures; the other is used to determine the ultimate load as controlled by compression failures.

(a) *Rectangular sections.* To compute the ultimate strength of short members subjected to combined bending and axial load we use the equations of equilibrium. These may be expressed as given below, provided that (1) *a* is not more than *t* and (2) the reinforcement is limited to one or two faces each parallel to the axis of bending, and all the reinforcement in any one face is located at approximately the same distance from the axis of bending:

$$P_u = \phi[0.85f_c'ba + A_s'f_y - A_sf_s], \tag{5–17}$$
$$P_ue' = \phi[0.85f_c'bda(1 - a/2d) + A_s'f_y(d - d')], \tag{5–18}$$

where *a* is the depth of the equivalent stress block (see Section 1503g, ACI Code). For a given column, the ultimate load P_u can be found from Eq. (5–17). We use Eqs. (5–17) and (5–18) and find *a* by solving the two equations simultaneously (or by trial method). Note that *e'* is the distance from the load P_u to the centroid of tensile reinforcement. The other terms in the equations are known. Balanced conditions exist when for the ultimate strength of a member, the tension reinforcement reaches its yield stress just as the concrete in compression reaches its assumed ultimate strain of 0.003. To compute the balanced load, P_b, we use $a = a_b$ and $f_s = f_y$ in Eq. (5–17), and obtain

$$P_b = \phi[0.85f_c'ba_b + f_y(A_s' - A_s)]. \tag{5–19}$$

Likewise, the balanced moment, M_b, is computed as follows:

$$M_b = e_bP_b = 0.85\phi f_c'ba[(d - d'' - a_b/2) + A_s'f_y(d - d' - d'') + A_sf_yd'']. \tag{5–20}$$

When $P_u < P_b$ or $e_b < e = e' - D/2$, tension governs, and when $P_u > P_b$ or $e_b > e = e' - D/2$, compression governs. When tension governs, the ultimate strength shall not exceed that computed by

$$P_u = 0.85f_c'\phi bd\{p'm' - pm + (1 - e'/d)$$
$$+ \sqrt{(1 - e'/d)^2 + 2[(e'/d)(pm - p'm') + p'm'(1 - d'/d)]}\}; \quad (5\text{-}21)$$

when compression governs, the ultimate strength may be given by

$$P_u = \frac{P_0}{1 + [(P_0/P_b) - 1]e/e_b}, \quad (5\text{-}22)$$

where

$$P_0 = \phi[0.85f_c'(A_g - A_{st}) + A_{st}f_y],$$
$$e' = \text{eccentricity of } P_u \text{ from centroid of tensile steel,}$$
$$e = \text{eccentricity of } P_u \text{ from centroid of section,}$$
$$m = f_y/0.85f_c' \quad \text{and} \quad m' = m - 1.$$

For symmetrical reinforcement in single layers parallel to the axis of bending, the approximate value of P_u may be determined from

$$P_u - \phi\left[\frac{A_s'f_y}{e/(d - d') + 0.5} + \frac{btf_c'}{(3te/d^2) + 1.18}\right]. \quad (5\text{-}22)'$$

(b) *Circular section.* The ultimate strength of circular sections subjected to combined bending and axial load may be computed by the empirical formulas given below. When tension controls, we have

$$P_u = 0.85\phi f_c'D^2\{[\sqrt{[(0.85e/D) - (0.38)]^2 + p_tmD_s/2.5D_s} - [0.85e/D - (0.38)]\}; \quad (5\text{-}23)$$

and when compression controls,

$$P_u = \phi\left\{\frac{A_{st}f_y}{3e/D_s + 1} + \frac{A_gf_c'}{[9.6De/(0.8D + 0.67D_s)^2] + 1.18}\right\}, \quad (5\text{-}24)$$

where

$$D_s = \text{diameter of circle through centers of reinforcement in column of circular section;}$$
$$A_{st} = \text{total area of longitudinal reinforcement;}$$
$$p_t = A_{st}/A_g.$$

Example 5-7. *Analysis (ACI Code)*

Given: A short column whose cross section is shown in Fig. 5-18. Assume that $f_c' = 3750$ psi, and $f_y = 48,000$ psi (see Section 1505b of the ACI Code).

Find: P_u at eccentricity $e' = 10$ in. (measured from tensile reinforcement).

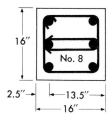

16″

No. 8

2.5″ —　—13.5″—

—16″—

Figure 5-18

SOLUTION: Either Eq. (5–21) or Eq. (5–22) gives the ultimate strength of our column. To decide which equation should be used, we must first determine what is the controlling factor: tension or compression. If $e_b < e = e' - D/2 + d'$, then tension controls and Eq. (5–21) is used. If

$$e_b \geq e = e' - D/2 + d',$$

then compression controls and Eq. (5–22) is used. Now

$$e_b = (0.67p_gm + 0.17)d,$$
$$p_g = A_s/A_g = 4.74/16 \times 16 = 0.0185,$$
$$m = f_y/0.85f_c' = 48,000/0.85 \times 3750 = 15.1,$$
$$e_b = (0.67 \times 0.0185 \times 15.1 + 0.17)13.5 = 4.83 \text{ in.},$$
$$e = e' - D/2 + d' = 10 \text{ in.} - 8 + 2.5 = 4.5 \text{ in.} < 4.83 \text{ in.}$$

Therefore compression controls.

Whether the equation for compression control or that for tension control should be used could have also been determined from the following rule: When $P_u < P_b$, then tension controls and Eq. (5–21) is used. When $P_u > P_b$, then compression controls and Eq. (5–22) applies. Equations (5–17) and (5–18) may be used to solve for a, and then P_u is determined from Eq. (5–17). Similarly, Eqs. (5–19) and (5–20) could be used to determine a_b (note that $e_b \neq e'$), and with a_b determined, P_b can be calculated.

Now to solve for the ultimate strength as given by Eq. (5–22) for sections controlled by compression, we proceed as follows:

$$P_u = \frac{P_0}{1 + [(P_0/P_b) - 1]e/e_b},$$
$$P_0 = \phi 0.85f_c'[(A_g - A_{st}) + A_{st}f_y],$$

where $\phi = 0.70$ (Article 1504b, Code).

$$P_0 = 0.70[0.85 \times 3750(256 - 4.74) + 4.74 \times 48,000] = 720,000 \text{ lb.}$$

To solve for P_b in Eq. (5–19), we first determine a_b by solving Eqs. (5–19) and (5–20) simultaneously:

$$[(0.85f_c'ba_b + f_y(A_s' - A_s)]e_b = 0.85f_c'ba_b[(d - d'' - a_b/2) \\ + A_s'f_y(d - d' - d'') + A_sf_yd''],$$
$$(0.85 \times 3750 \times 16 \times a_b)4.83 = 0.85 \times 3750 \times 16 \times a_b(13.5 - 5.5 - a_b/2) \\ + 2.37 \times 48,000(13.5 - 2.5 - 5.5) \\ + 2.37 \times 48,000 \times 5.5.$$

We find that $a_b = 10.87$ in., and therefore $P_b = 555,000$ lb, and

$$P_u = \frac{0.720 \times 10^6}{1 + [(1.027 \times 10^6/5.55 \times 10^5) - 1]\dfrac{4.5}{4.83}},$$
$$P_u = \frac{0.720 \times 10^6}{1 + 0.81} = 389,000 \text{ lb.}$$

Using the "approximate" formula, we obtain

$$P_u = \phi\left[\frac{A_s'f_y}{e/(d-d')+0.5} + \frac{bt f_c'}{(3te/d^2)+1.18}\right]$$

$$= \phi\left[\frac{2.37 \times 48{,}000}{4.5/11 + 0.5} + \frac{16 \times 16 \times 3750}{(3 \times 16 \times 4.5)/(16 \times 16) + 1.18}\right] = 419{,}000 \text{ lb.}$$

Example 5–8.   Analysis (ACI Code)

Given: The column section of Example 5–7 and $f_c' = 4000$ psi, $f_y = 45{,}000$ psi.

Find: P_u at eccentricity of 18 in. from the tensile reinforcement.

SOLUTION: In this case $e > e_b$ (see Example 5–7), and therefore tension controls. Using Eq. (5–21), we have

$$P_u = 0.85\phi f_c'bd\{p'm' - pm + (1 - e'/d)$$
$$+ \sqrt{(1 - e'/d)^2 + 2[(e'/d)(pm - p'm') + p'm'(1 - d'/d)]}\},$$

$$pm = (A_s/bd)(f_y/0.85f_c') = (2.37/16 \times 13.5)(45{,}000/0.85 \times 4000) = 0.145,$$

$$p'm' = (A_s'/bd)(f_y/0.85f_c' - 1) = 0.134,$$

$$e'/d = 1.333; \quad 0.85f_c'bd = 734{,}400; \quad d'/d = 0.185.$$

Hence

$$P_u = \phi734{,}400[0.011 - 0.33 + \sqrt{0.111 + 2(0.0146 + 0.109)}],$$

$$P_u = \phi734{,}400(0.011 + 0.33 + 0.60) = 188{,}000\phi \text{ lb } (\phi = 0.70, \text{ 1504b, Code}).$$

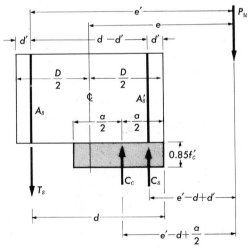

Figure 5–19

5–6   ULTIMATE STRENGTH OF COLUMNS; ALTERNATIVE APPROACH

The following is an attempt to clarify the formulas discussed in Section 5–5 by introducing equivalent but simpler expressions that are based on the static equilibrium for the assumed conditions. Figure 5–19 pictures an eccentric load acting on a rectangular section $D \times b$. The stress intensities for steel and concrete shall be assumed to be f_y and $0.85f_c$, respectively (Article 2–5). Then using the equation of static equilibrium, we obtain

$$C_s = A_s'f_y, \qquad C_c = 0.85f_c'ba, \qquad T_s = A_sf_y.$$

Failure may occur due to tension in the steel or compression in the concrete. For small eccentricities compression failures are more likely. Large eccentricities usually create tension failures for symmetrical sections. In equation form, with $\sum M_{Pu} = 0$, we have

$$C_s(e' - d + d') + C_c(e' - d + a/2) = Te'.$$

Assuming that a is constant for the given conditions, we see from the above expression that as e' increases, the left-hand side of the equation increases more rapidly than the right-hand side, making T the more critical factor. Conversely, small eccentricities decrease T and hence make a compressive failure likely.

(a) *Rectangular sections; tension failures due to large eccentricities.* Let us assume that we are given a rectangular section $D \times b$, and that $A_s = A_s'$. Then at the plastic condition, $A_sf_y = A_s'f_y$. Therefore $T_s = C_s$ and the two forces act in opposite directions, forming a couple: $T_s(d - d') = C_s(d - d')$. Summing the moments about C_c (Fig. 5–19), we have

$$A_sf_y(d - d') = P_u(e' - d + a/2),$$

or

$$P_u = A_sf_y(d - d')/(e' - d + a/2), \qquad (5\text{–}25)$$

where a is not a constant. But from $\sum F_y = 0$, we have $P_u = C_s$, and thus

$$P_u = 0.85f_c'ba. \qquad (5\text{–}26)$$

Solving Eqs. (5–25) and (5–26) simultaneously yields P_u.

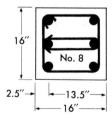

16″

No. 8

2.5″→ | ←13.5″→
←———16″———→

Figure 5–20

Example 5–9. *Analysis (alternative method of finding P_u)*

Given: The column section shown in Fig. 5–20; $f_y = 45{,}000$ psi, $f_c' = 4000$ psi.

Find: P_u at eccentricity of 18 in. from tensile reinforcement, using (a) Eqs. (5–25) and (5–26), (b) ACI Code equations (that is, Eq. 5–21).

SOLUTION: From Eqs. (5–25) and (5–26), we determine a:

$$P_u = \frac{A_s f_y (d - d')}{(e' - d + a/2)} = 0.85 f_c' ba,$$

$$\frac{2.37 \times 45,000 \times 11}{18 - 13.5 + a/2} = 0.85 \times 4000 \times 16a,$$

$$a^2 + 9a - 43 = 0, \qquad a = \frac{-9 + \sqrt{81 + 172}}{2} = 3.5 \text{ in.}$$

From Eq. (5–25) it follows that

$$P_u = \frac{2.37 \times 45,000 \times 11}{18 - 13.5 + 3.5/2} = 187,000 \text{ lb.}$$

From Example 5–8: $P_u = 188,000\phi$ lb (see above).

(b) *Rectangular section, compression failures due to small eccentricities.* For smaller eccentricities the probable cause of primary failure would be compression. The ultimate load a column can carry may be estimated by the ACI Code formulas 19–8 or 19–9, Article 1902c, or by using a somewhat simpler expression derived as follows. Summing the moments about the tensile steel (Fig. 5–19), we have

$$P_u e' = C_s (d - d') + C_c (d - a/2),$$
$$C_c (d - a/2) = 0.85 f_c' ab (d - a/2) \cong f_c' bd^2/3 \quad \text{(Chapter 2),}$$

and

$$C_s (d - d') = A_s' f_y (d - d').$$

Hence

$$P_u = \frac{A_s' f_y (d - d') + \frac{1}{3} f_c' bd^2}{e'}. \tag{5–27}$$

Example 5–10.   Analysis.

Given: A short column whose cross section is shown in Fig. 5–20; $f_c' = 3750$ psi, $f_y = 48,000$ psi, and the eccentricity of P_u (measured from tensile steel) is 10 in.

Find: P_u, using (a) Eq. (5–27), and (b) the applicable Code equations (i.e., Eq. (5–22).

SOLUTION: From Eq. (5–27),

$$P_u = \frac{A_s' f_y (d - d') + \frac{1}{3} f_c' bd^2}{e},$$

$$P_u = \frac{2.37 \times 48,000 \times 11 + \frac{1}{3} 3750 \times 16 \times (13.5)^2}{10},$$

$$P_u = \frac{1,250,000 + 3,660,000}{10} = 491 \text{ k.}$$

Using the ACI Code formula, we have from Example 5–7 that $P_u = 398$ k.

Example 5–11.   Design

Given: A short column is to carry an axial load of 200,000 lb and a moment of 1×10^6 in-lb. Assume a load factor of 2, $f_c' = 3000$ psi, and $f_y = 50,000$ psi.

Find: A suitable design for a square tied column, using the ultimate-strength formula. Assume that the steel arrangement is symmetric.

SOLUTION:

$$e = M/P = 1 \times 10^6/2 \times 10^5 = 5 \text{ in.}$$

Since e is small, compression is the controlling factor. Next let us assume that $p_g = $ total $A_s/bd = 0.02$, $A_s' = A_s/2 = 0.01 \, bd$, and that $d' = 2.5$ in. Then

$$b = d + 2.5 \text{ in.} \qquad \text{and} \qquad A_s' = 0.01(d + 2.5)d,$$
$$e' = e + b/2 - d' \qquad \text{(see Fig. 5–12).}$$

Using Eq. (5–26), we obtain

$$P_u = \frac{A_s' f_y(d - d') + \tfrac{1}{3} f_c' bd^2}{e'},$$

$$200,000 \times 2 = \frac{0.01(d + 2.5)d \times 50,000(d - 2.5) + \tfrac{1}{3} \times 3000(d + 2.5)d^2}{5 + (d + 2.5/2) - 2.5}.$$

Reducing and rearranging terms gives

$$1.5d^3 + 2.5d^2 - 203d - 1500 = 0.$$

We now solve for d by trial:

d	$f(d)$
14	260
13.8	27

and find that we should use 13.8 in. plus a cover of 2.5 in., that is, 16.3 in., say 16.5 in. Then

$$A_s' = A_s = 0.01(16.5)^2 = 2.72 \text{ in}^2,$$
$$\text{total } A_s = 5.54 \text{ in}^2.$$

Hence we may use eight No. 8 bars; $A_s = 6.32$. Number 3 ties may be placed at a center-to-center distance of 18 in.

PROBLEMS

ECCENTRICALLY LOADED COLUMNS

Solve Problems 1 through 16, using the elastic-analysis approach; for Problems 17 through 24, use the ultimate-strength theory. Assume that the columns are short.

Analysis of Columns—Elastic Theory

5–1. The column in Fig. 5–21 supports a load of 200 k eccentric 2.0 in. to the right of the column centerline. Determine the steel and concrete stresses, and check compliance with the ACI Code for: (a) $f_c' = 2500$ psi, $f_y = 50{,}000$ psi, $n = 12$; (b) $f_c' = 3000$ psi, $f_y = 50{,}000$ psi, $n = 9$; (c) $f_c' = 3750$ psi, $f_y = 50{,}000$ psi, $n = 9$.

$\left[f_c' = .786 \ KSC \right.$
$\left[\text{Actual} \right.$

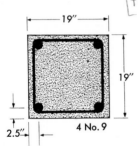

Figure 5–21

5–2. The column in Fig. 5–21 supports a load of 175 k eccentric 2.5 in. to the right of the centerline of the column. Determine the steel and concrete stresses, and check compliance with the code for: (a) $f_c' = 2500$ psi, $f_y = 50{,}000$ psi, $n = 12$; (b) $f_c' = 3000$ psi, $f_y = 50{,}000$ psi, $n = 9$; (c) $f_c' = 3750$ psi, $f_y = 50{,}000$ psi, $n = 9$.

5–3. The column in Fig. 5–21 supports a load of 150 k eccentric 3 in. to the right of the centerline of the column. Determine the steel and concrete stresses, and check compliance with the code. Assume $f_c' = 3750$ psi, $f_y = 50{,}00$ psi, and $n = 8$.

5–4. The column in Fig. 5–22 supports an eccentric load 6 in. to the right of the column centerline. Determine the maximum working load the code permits, given that (a) $f_c' = 3000$ psi, intermediate-grade steel, $n = 10$; (b) $f_c' = 3750$ psi, intermediate-grade steel, $n = 9$.

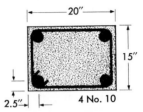

Figure 5–22

5–5. Follow the ACI Code specifications to determine the maximum working load, eccentric 8 in. to the right of the column centerline of Fig. 5–22 for: (a) $f_c' = 3000$ psi, hard-grade steel, $n = 10$; (b) $f_c' = 3750$ psi, hard-grade steel, $n = 10$.

5–6. The column shown in Fig. 5–22 supports a load eccentric 6 in. to the right along one axis, and 6 in. above the other axis. Follow the ACI Code to determine the working load that the column can support, given that (a) $f_c' = 3000$ psi, $f_y = 50{,}000$ psi, $n = 10$; (b) $f_c' = 3750$ psi, $f_y = 50{,}000$ psi, $n = 10$.

5–7. The column shown in Fig. 5–23 supports a load eccentric 3 in. to the

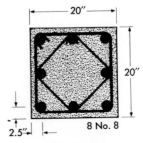

Figure 5–23

right along one axis and 5 in. above the other axis from the centerline of the column. Follow the ACI Code to determine the working load that the column can support, given that (a) $f_c' = 3000$ psi, structural-grade steel, $n = 10$; (b) $f_c' = 3750$ psi, structural-grade steel, $n = 10$.

5–8. Determine the maximum load that the column section of Fig. 5–23 can support given that the load is eccentric 5 in. along each axis: (a) $f_c' = 3000$ psi, $f_y = 50,000$ psi, $n = 10$; (b) $f_c' = 3750$ psi, $f_y = 50,000$ psi, $n = 10$.

5–9. The column section in Fig. 5–24 supports a load of 175 kip eccentric 2 in. from the centerline of the column. Given that $D = 22$ in. and $D_s = 18$ in., determine the maximum and minimum stresses in the steel and concrete and check compliance with the code. Use six No. 8 bars: (a) $f_c' = 2500$ psi, $f_y = 60,000$ psi, $n = 11$; (b) $f_c' = 3000$ psi, $f_y = 50,000$ psi, $n = 9$.

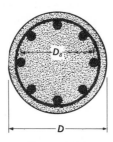

Figure 5–24

5–10. Determine the maximum moment that the column of Fig. 5–24 can carry in addition to an axial load of 150 kip, given that $D = 22$ in. and $D_s = 18$ in. Use six No. 8 bars: (a) $f_c' = 3000$ psi, $f_y = 50,000$ psi, $n = 10$; (b) $f_c' = 3750$ psi, $f_y = 50,000$ psi, $n = 8$.

5–11. Determine the maximum moment the column shown in Fig. 5–25 can carry in addition to an axial load of 200 kip, for $f_c' = 3000$ psi, $f_y = 50,000$ psi, given that (a) $D = 22$ in., $b = 18$ in., $d' = 2\frac{1}{2}$ in., A_s is six No. 8 bars; (b) $D = 22$ in., $b = 22$ in., $d' = 2\frac{1}{2}$ in., A_s is

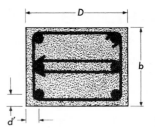

Figure 5–25

six No. 8 bars; (c) $D = 24$ in., $b = 22$ in., $d' = 2\frac{1}{2}$ in., A_s is six No. 10 bars.

Design of Columns—Elastic Theory

5–12. Design a spirally reinforced concrete column (round) to support a load of 150 kip and a bending moment of 350 kip-in., given that $f_c' = 3000$ psi, $f_y = 60,000$ psi. Assume that $D - D_s = 5$ in. (see Fig. 5–24) and $p = 0.02$.

5–13. A load of 200 kip is eccentric 4 in. along an axis of a column. Follow the ACI Code in designing a square tied column to take this load, given that $f_c' = 3750$ psi and $f_y = 50,000$ psi. Assume that $d' = 2\frac{1}{2}$ in. and $p = 0.0175$.

5–14. Design a square column with round spiral to support a load of 200 kip and a bending moment of 100 k-ft. Assume that $f_c' = 3000$ psi, $f_y = 40,000$ psi, $p = 0.02$ and proceed in accordance with the ACI Code.

5–15. Design a round spiral column to support a load of 175 kip and a bending moment of 200 k-ft for $f_c' = 3750$ psi, using about 2% of hard-grade steel.

5–16. Design a square tied column to support a load of 100 kip eccentric 3 in. along one axis and another load of 75 kip eccentric 6 in. along the other axis; comply with the ACI Code and assume that $f_c' = 60,000$ psi, $p = 0.0175$.

Analysis of Columns—Ultimate-Strength Theory

5–17. Determine the permissible load eccentric 6 in. to the centerline of the column shown in Fig. 5–21. Use the ultimate load theory (average load factor of 2.0), and assume that $f_c' = 3000$ psi and $f_y = 40,000$ psi.

5–18. Determine the permissible load eccentric 4 in. from the centerline along each of the axes of the column shown in Fig. 5–21. Use the ultimate-load theory with a load factor of 2.0 and assume that $f_c' = 3000$ psi, $f_y = 40,000$ psi.

5–19. Determine the permissible load eccentric 8 in. from the centerline along the x-axis of the column shown in Fig. 5–22. Use the ultimate-load theory for an average load factor of 2.2. Given: $f_c' = 3750$ psi, $f_y = 50,000$ psi.

5–20. Determine the maximum bending moment the column shown in Fig. 5–23 can carry in addition to an axial load of 175 kip. Use the ultimate-strength theory, and assume that $f_c' = 3750$ psi, $f_y = 50,000$ psi, and the load factor is 2.1.

5–21. Determine the permissible load eccentric 4 in. from the centerline of the column shown in Fig. 5–24, using the ultimate load theory with a load factor of 2.0. Given: $D = 22$ in., $D_s = 18$ in., $f_c' = 3000$ psi, and $f_y = 40,000$ psi.

Design of Columns—Ultimate-Strength Theory

5–22. Using the ultimate-load theory, design a square tied column to support a service load of 150 kip and a service moment of 200 k-ft in one direction. The load factor is 2.2, $f_c' = 3000$ psi, $f_y = 40,000$ psi, and $p = 0.02$.

5–23. Using the ultimate-load theory, design a square tied column to support a service load of 200 kip and a service moment of 200 k-ft in both the y–y and x–x planes. The load factor is 2.0. Assume that $f_c' = 3750$ psi, $f_y = 50,000$ psi, and $p = 0.025$.

5–24. Using the ultimate-load theory, design a round spiral column to support a service load of 200 kip eccentric 8 in. from the centerline of the column. The load factor is 2.0. Assume that $f_c' = 3000$ psi, $f_y = 40,000$ psi, and $p = 0.02$.

REFERENCES

1. J. R. SHANK, "Bond, Shear and Diagonal Tension in Reinforced Concrete," *ACI Journal,* Nov. 1931.
2. CHARLES S. WHITNEY, "Design of Reinforced Concrete Members Under Flexure or Combined Flexure and Direct Compression," *ACI Journal,* Mar.–Apr. 1937.
3. F. E. RICHART and T. A. OLSON, "The Resistance of Reinforced Concrete Columns to Eccentric Loads," *ACI Journal,* Mar.–Apr. 1938.
4. PAUL ANDERSON, "Design Diagrams for Square Concrete Columns Eccentrically Loaded in Two Directions," *ACI Journal,* Nov. 1941.
5. EIVIND HOGNESTAD, "Inelastic Behavior in Tests of Eccentrically Loaded Short Reinforced Concrete Columns," *ACI Journal,* Oct. 1952.
6. LU-SHIEN HU, "Eccentric Bending in Two Directions of Rectangular Concrete Columns," *ACI Journal,* May 1955.
7. TUNG AU, "Ultimate Strength Design Charts for Columns Controlled by Tension," *ACI Journal,* Dec. 1957.
8. FREDRICK P. WIESINGER, "Design of Symmetrical Columns with Small Eccentricities in One or Two Directions," *ACI Journal,* Aug. 1958.
9. P. M. FERGUSON, *Reinforced Concrete Fundamentals,* John Wiley, New York, 1958.
10. DEAN PEABODY, JR., *Reinforced Concrete Structures* (2nd Edition), John Wiley, New York, 1957.

6 RETAINING WALLS

Whitewater Bridge. Continuous girder bridge, Riverdale, California.

6–1 INTRODUCTION

A retaining wall may be defined as a structure whose primary purpose is to prevent lateral movement of earth or some other material. For some special cases, for example, basement walls of a home or certain bridge abutments, a retaining wall may also have the function of supporting a vertical load. The following discussion, however, shall assume that there are no vertical loads.

Figure 6–1 shows several common types of retaining wall. The type chosen for any one job depends on the soil conditions, construction conditions, economy, and function. Generally speaking, however, gravity walls are most frequently used for heights less than 15 ft, cantilever walls for walls up to 25 ft, and counterforts for greater heights.

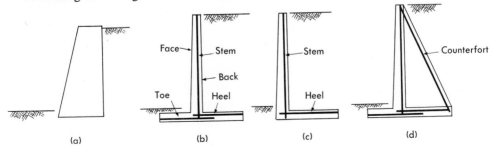

Fig. 6–1. Types of retaining walls.

A *gravity* retaining wall, shown in Fig. 6–1(a), is usually built of plain concrete, although stone is often used as a substitute. This type of wall depends only on its own weight for stability, and hence its height is subject to definite limits.

A *semigravity* wall is in essence a gravity wall which has been given a wider base (a toe, or heel, or both) to increase the stability. Some reinforcement is necessary for this type of wall.

A *T-shaped* wall (Fig. 6–1b) is perhaps the most common cantilever wall. For this type of wall, the weight of the earth in the back of the stem contributes to the stability.

An *L-shaped* wall (Fig. 6–1c) is frequently used when property-line restrictions forbid the use of a T-shaped wall. On the other hand, when it is not practical to excavate for a heel, a reverse *L-shape* may serve the need.

A *counterfort* wall (Fig. 6–1d) consists of three main components: base, stem, and intermittent vertical ribs, called counterforts, which tie the base and the stem together. The ribs, which act as tension ties, transform the *stem* and *heel* into continuous slabs supported on three sides—at two adjacent counterforts and at the base of the stem.

A *buttressed* wall is obtained by placing the ribs on the front face of the stem where they act in compression instead of tension (tension is the factor in a counterfort wall). The *toe* and *stem* become continuous slabs for this wall.

Fig. 6–2. Retaining walls, Westbound Parkway, West of 10th Street (Pittsburgh, Pa.), Allegheny County LR–764, Fort Pitt Bridge Works.

6-2 LATERAL EARTH PRESSURE

There are two kinds of lateral soil pressure. When the earth backfill, by virtue of its tendency to slide, exerts a thrust against a wall, the resulting pressure is known as *active* pressure. If the wall were to move against the soil in an attempt to push it back, the soil would passively resist such a movement. The pressure developed by this resistance is known as *passive* pressure. Note that the soil is the actuating element in the development of active pressure, and that the wall is the decisive factor in the development of passive pressure. Here we shall be concerned primarily with the active pressure, hereafter referred to as *earth pressure.*

The earth pressure exerted against a wall is a function of the type of soil, the degree of saturation, the compaction of the backfill, and perhaps the *surcharge,* a term explained in the next article.

Various theories have been developed for determining the magnitudes of these pressures (for details, see texts on soil mechanics). In this text, we shall use Coulomb's theory, which is based on the assumption that a wedge of dry, sandy backfill tends to fail by sliding on a steeply inclined plane (a *failure* plane) as the wall moves away by tilting or sliding.

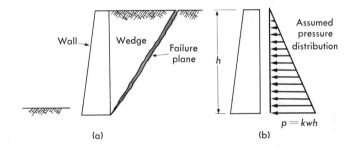

Fig. 6-3. The sliding of the wedge causes a pressure against the wall.

The pressure, p, which the wedge exerts on the wall is assumed to be proportional to the unit weight of soil and to the depth of fill. Thus we have

$$p = kwh \qquad (6-1)$$

per linear foot of wall. The pressure distribution is shown in Fig. 6-3(b), and we see that the total force P per linear foot of wall is equal to the area under the pressure diagram:

$$P = kwh(\tfrac{1}{2}h) = kwh^2/2, \qquad (6-2)$$

where

P = force per linear foot of wall, lb,
w = unit weight of soil, lb/ft^3,
h = height of vertical section, ft;

TABLE 6–1

Soil type	Unit weight, lb/ft^3	Safe bearing pressure, k/ft^2	Commonly used range of angles of repose, degrees	Coefficient of friction of concrete on foundation soil
Coarse sand or gravel	110–120	9–12	34–38	0.5–0.7
Fine sand or gravel	120–130	6–7	32–34	0.4–0.6
Clay with silty sand and gravel	105–120	4–5	31–34	0.3–0.5
Hard clay	100–120	4–6	34–36	0.3–0.5
Soft clay or silt	90–110	1–3	25–30	0.2–0.3

and, for walls of vertical back face,

$$k = \frac{\cos \phi}{\left(1 + \sqrt{1 - \cos 2\phi - \sin 2\phi \tan \alpha}\right)^2}, \quad (6\text{–}3)$$

where ϕ = angle of repose of the backfill,
α = angle the surface of backfill makes with the horizontal (Fig. 6–4).

k may also be obtained from a special case of Coulomb's formula:

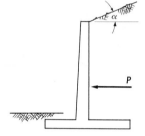

Figure 6–4

$$k = \frac{\cos^2 \phi}{\left(1 + \sqrt{\sin \phi(\sin \phi - \cos \phi \tan \alpha)}\right)^2}. \quad (6\text{–}3a)$$

Table 6–1 lists unit weights, bearing pressures, angles of repose, and coefficients of friction for various soil types.

6–3 SURCHARGE

Trains, cranes, vehicles, and storage of material on top of the earth behind a retaining wall create an additional load that must be resisted by the wall. Such a load is commonly referred to as *surcharge*. For design and analysis, one usually evaluates the surcharge by assuming it to be uniform along the length of the wall and then converting its effect into an equivalent height of earth backfill. This added height may be calculated by dividing the surcharge pressure, in pounds per square foot, by the unit weight of the soil, i.e.

$$h' = S/w, \quad (6\text{–}4)$$

where S is the surcharge load, in pounds per lineal foot. How one finds the equivalent effect of this added height on the pressure exerted on the retaining wall is explained in the example of Article 6–4 and in Fig. 6–5, which illustrates

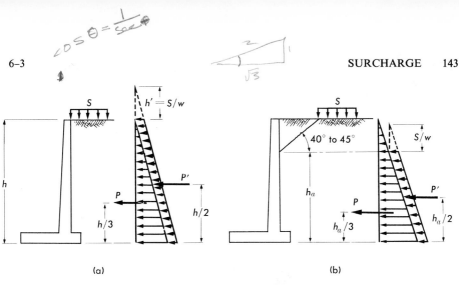

Fig. 6–5. Distribution of pressure including surcharge effects.

the combined effect of the earth pressure and the surcharge on a retaining wall and the distribution of this effect. Note that the distribution of the horizontal pressure caused by the surcharge is uniform. (An analogous situation exists when a pressure is applied to the surface of a liquid.) Therefore the resultant force caused by the surcharge pressure shall be assumed to be horizontal. Its magnitude is determined by calculating the area under the shaded portion. Its location is at the centroid of the shaded portion, as shown in Fig. 6–5(a) or (b).

In Fig. 6–5(b) the surcharge is located at some distance in back of the wall, and thus its effect on the overall pressure is slightly changed. The assumption is made that the surcharge does not affect the portion above the intersection of the back face of the wall with a line drawn at an angle of 40 to 45 degrees to the horizontal from the face of the surcharge.

Fig. 6–6. Retaining wall, Beaver County, Pa., LR 641–22A. Surcharge effects produced by moving trains are a significant source of lateral force.

One rarely finds a uniformly distributed surcharge as called for by our assumption. Most surcharge loads occur in concentrated or semidistributed forms. When and how to convert such surcharges into equivalent uniform surcharges is a matter of engineering judgment. Texts on soil mechanics give a more elaborate treatment of cases which require the use of concentrated surcharges in design. However, here too, engineering judgment is needed since no surcharge is completely "concentrated," nor is its effect the same on all types of soil and conditions. This should not suggest that the methods presented are not reliable but rather that they are approximate since for many factors we do not have accurate data and hence must work with assumptions.

6–4 DESIGN OF A CANTILEVER RETAINING WALL

Assume that we have to solve the following problem:

Design a cantilever retaining wall to resist a backfill 18 ft high; that is, the height of the stem is 18 ft. Assume that the toe is covered with 2 ft of earth. The following specifications are given:

Soil: Coarse sand and gravel.
Loads: 400 lb/ft² surcharge, horizontal backfill.
Stresses: $f_c' = 3000$ psi, $f_s = 20,000$ psi.
Code: ACI Building Code.
Design: The stem, heel, and toe are to be designed individually, with a final sketch showing the dimensions and steel arrangements. Each shall be treated as a cantilever slab. The calculations and assumptions will be complemented by the following brief explanation:

(a) *Stem:* Covering of the toe is frequently desirable to enhance stability against sliding. Also, the bearing soil is less affected by frost action. Esthetic or functional values might be further reasons for toe cover.

The active-pressure effect of the frontfill is considered zero. The total soil-pressure load per foot of wall, *p*, is assumed to act horizontally, rather than at an

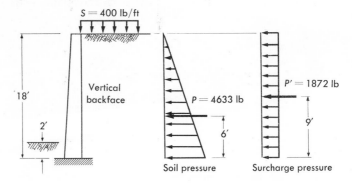

Fig. 6–7. Soil pressures on stem.

angle α, because of the surcharge effect. Assuming that the weight of the soil is equal to 110 lb/ft³ and $\theta = 36°$, we obtain from Eq. (6–3) and Table 6–1

$$k = \frac{\cos 36°}{(1 + \sqrt{1 - \cos 72° - \sin 72° \cdot \tan 0°})^2} = 0.260.$$

From Eq. (6–2),

$$P = kwh^2/2 = 0.13 \times 110 \times (18)^2 = 4633 \text{ lb/ft of wall.}$$

From Eq. (6–1), the surcharge is

$$p = kwh = 0.26 \times 110 \times 400/110 = 104 \text{ lb/ft}^2;$$

hence

$$P' = 104 \times 18 \text{ ft} = 1872 \text{ lb/ft of wall.}$$

The maximum moment in the stem, M_{stem}, occurs at the base and is equal to

$$M_{\text{stem}} = 4633 \times 6 + 1872 \times 9 = 44{,}650 \text{ ft-lb} = 535{,}800 \text{ in-lb.}$$

Assuming a balanced design, we obtain a K (see Article 2–4, Eq. 2–9) from Table 3, Appendix B, of

$$K = 235.4 \quad \text{for} \quad f_c = 0.45 \times 3000 = 1350 \text{ psi} \quad \text{and} \quad f_s = 20{,}000 \text{ psi.}$$

Hence

$$d^2 = \frac{M}{Kb} = \frac{535{,}800}{235.4(12\text{-in. length})} = 189.67 \text{ in}^2$$

$$d = 13.8 \text{ in.,} \quad \text{say 14 in.}$$

For shear

$$d = \frac{V}{bjv} = \frac{6505}{12 \times 0.88 \times 90} = 6.8 \text{ in.}$$

Therefore $d = 14$ in. governs (v was assumed to be 90 psi, a value sufficiently reasonable for a check on d). To this result add 3 in. for cover. Then

$$v = \frac{V}{bjd} = \frac{(P + P')}{bjd} = \frac{6505}{12 \times 0.88 \times 14} = 44 \text{ psi.}$$

From the Code, $v = V/bd = 38.8$ psi $< 1.1 \sqrt{f_c'}$, which is satisfactory. Now

$$A_s = \frac{M}{f_s jd} = \frac{535{,}800}{20{,}000 \times 0.88 \times 14} = 2.17 \text{ in}^2.$$

Use No. 8 bars at a distance of $(0.79/2.18) \times 12 = 4.37$ in., say $4\frac{1}{4}$ in. center-to-center. Thus

$$u = \frac{V}{(\Sigma_0)jd} = \frac{6505}{3.14 \times 12/4.25 \times 0.88 \times 14} = 59.5 \text{ psi} < \frac{4.8\sqrt{f_c'}}{D},$$

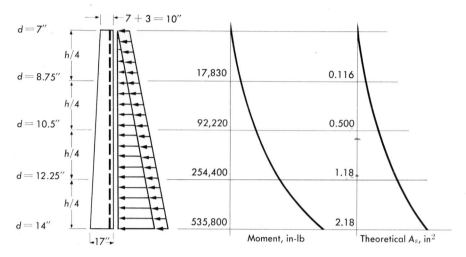

Figure 6–8

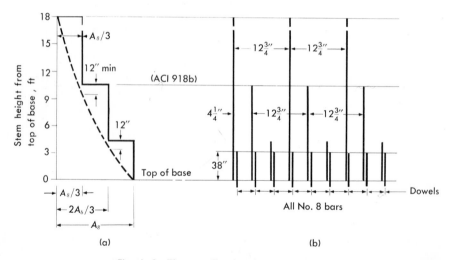

Fig. 6–9. The cut-off points for stem steel.

which satisfies the specifications (Article 1301, ACI Code). Since the bending moment varies from the top to the bottom of the stem, the longitudinal steel reinforcement should be "adjusted."

A variable effective depth, d, along the height of the stem, cut-off points (Article 3–4, Chapter 3), ACI Code (Article 918, for example), and good engineering judgment are some of the factors to be considered in this adjustment. The following procedure attempts to illustrate this point.

Effective depth. The depth, d, at the bottom of the stem was governed by the moment. This is not true for the top depth where the moment is zero. Common sense, experience, and good judgment are the guides for selecting a practical

Fig. 6–10. Workmen placing the reinforcing steel for a retaining wall. Note the various lengths of reinforcing.

depth. In our case, we shall assume that d at the top is 7 in. (plus a 3-in. steel cover). A general rule of thumb may be that $d_{\text{top}} = \frac{1}{2}d_{\text{bottom}}$.

Cut-off points. Not all bars need be extended the full height of the stem. Figure 6–8 shows the load on the stem, the bending moment at various heights, and values of A_s required for these heights. For vertical bars, the splicing length of dowels (see Article 805c, ACI Code) is $L = 30$ bar diameters, 12-in. minimum for steel of

$$f_y = 50,000 \text{ psi,}$$

or

$$L_s = f_s d/4u = 20,000 \times \tfrac{1}{4} \times 210 = 23.8, \quad \text{say 24 in.}$$

(it is assumed that $u = 210$ psi; see Article 1301b). Similarly the dowels should extend into the stem for a distance of at least 30 in., say 38 in., and should be adequately anchored in the base (Article 918b, ACI Code) to resist the bending at the base of the stem. Note that some of the toe steel may be extended up into the stem to serve as dowels, an arrangement which also satisfies the anchorage-length requirement for the toe steel.

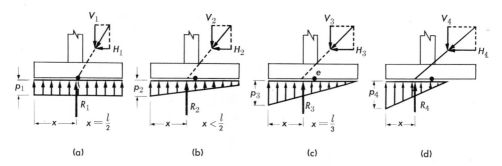

Fig. 6–11. Pressure distributions corresponding to changes in the resultant load.

Figure 6–9 shows the cut-off points of the steel stem, i.e. $\frac{1}{3}$ of the total area of tensile reinforcement has to extend up to 18 ft (ACI Code, 918f), $\frac{1}{3} A_s$ is cut off at less than 9 ft (Fig. 6–9a), and the other $\frac{1}{3} A_s$ at less than 5 ft. The arrangement may be similar to that shown in Fig. 6–9(b).

Base of the retaining wall. It is desirable to construct a base to provide compression under the entire base. From the point of view of tilting, differential settlement, and bearing capacity, the most desirable pressure distribution would be a rectangular one, as shown in Fig. 6–11(a). (From the standpoint of economy or design, the rectangular distribution may be unsatisfactory.) The rectangular shape may be attained by simply adjusting the length of the base (including toe and heel ratio) so as to make the resultant pressure coincide with the resultant load at the center of the base. Since this usually means an extra long toe, the most common shapes of pressure distributions are trapezoidal or triangular.

To calculate the size of the base of a retaining wall, we can proceed by either making an assumption regarding the base length, and then checking the stability,

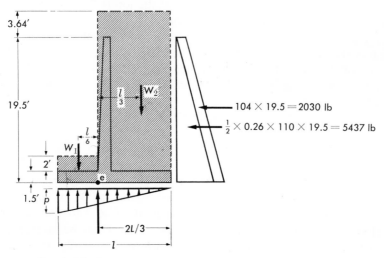

Fig. 6–12. Approximate forces for determining the base length l.

pressure, etc., or by calculating the length as follows. We begin by assuming that the soil pressure is distributed as shown in Fig. 6–11(c), that the length of the toe is $\frac{1}{3}l$, and that the material represented by the shaded area in Fig. 6–12 has a unit weight of 110 lb/ft³, including the concrete. This is a reasonable assumption for approximating the size of the base. Later the actual weight will be used. Thus, $W_1 = 3.5 \times l/3 \times 110$ acting at a distance of $l/6$ from e, $W_2 = (19.5 + 3.64)(2l/3) \times 110$ acting at a distance of $l/3$ from e, and

$$\sum M_e = 0;$$

$$\left(3.5 \times \frac{110}{3}\right) l \times \frac{l}{6} + 2030 \frac{19.5}{2}$$

$$+ 5437 \frac{19.5}{3}$$

$$= \left(2 \times 110 \times \frac{23.14}{3}\right) l \times \frac{l}{3},$$

$$21.4l^2 + 19{,}800 + 35{,}340 = 565.6l^2,$$

$$l^2 = 55{,}140/544.20 = 101.3,$$

$$l = 10.07 \text{ ft}, \quad \text{say 10 ft.}$$

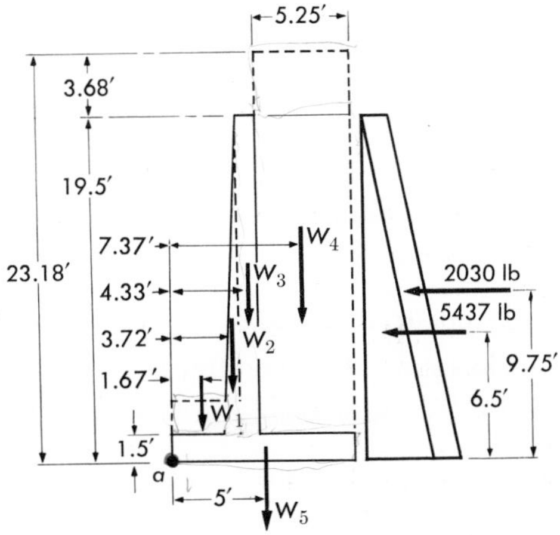

We make a preliminary check of the soil pressure:

Figure 6–13

$$R = W_1 + W_2 = p \times \tfrac{10}{2};$$

therefore

$$(3.5 \times \tfrac{10}{3} \times 110) + 23.14(\tfrac{2}{3} \times 10) \times 110 = 5p,$$

$$p = \frac{1283 + 16968}{5} = 3650 \text{ lb/ft}^2.$$

Hence we see that with respect to pressure the base length is satisfactory.

Stability. For a more exact approach, the stability analysis must take into account the actual volumes and weights for concrete and soil, and it must cover overturning, sliding, and maximum bearing pressures. For our calculations, we use a base thickness of 1.5 ft (see Fig. 6–13) and the base length computed above.

Weights, lb			Moment arm, ft	Righting moment (RM), ft-lb
$W_1 = 2 \times 3.33 \times 110$	$=$	732	1.67	1,222
$W_2 = \frac{1}{2} \times 18 \times \frac{7}{12} \times 150$	$=$	787	3.72	2,930
$W_3 = 18 \times \frac{10}{12} \times 150$	$=$	2,250	4.33	9,750
$W_4 = 21.68 \times 5.25 \times 110$	$=$	12,520	7.37	92,200
$W_5 = 10 \times 1.5 \times 150$	$=$	2,250	5.00	11,250
		18,539		117,352

Next we analyze the overturning effect:

Overturning force, lb	Moment arm, ft	Overturning moment (OM), ft-lb
$P' = 2030$	9.75	19,800
$P = 5437$	6.5	35,340
$\overline{7467}$		$\overline{55,140}$

Let us denote by x the distance of the resultant force from point a:

$$x = \frac{RM - OM}{\Sigma W} = \frac{117,352 - 55,140}{18,539} = 3.35 \text{ ft.}$$

The factor of safety (SF) against overturning is $117,352/55,140 = 2.12$.

Sliding. Let us assume that the coefficient of friction of soil on concrete is 0.50 (see Table 6–1). Then we have

Horizontal forces	$= P + P' = 5437 + 2030 = 7467 \text{ lb,}$
Resisting horizontal forces	$= P_r = \mu(\Sigma N) = 0.5 \times 18,539 = 9270 \text{ lb,}$
Safety factor against sliding	$= SF = 9270/7467 = 1.24,$

which is unsatisfactory. A shear key will have to be designed to increase the safety factor against sliding.

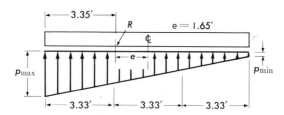

Fig. 6–14. Soil pressure on base.

Base pressure. Denoting the base pressure by p_s and assuming a straight-line pressure distribution, as shown in Fig. 6–14, we find that the formula

$$p_s = \frac{P}{A} + \frac{Mc}{I}$$

applies. In our case,

$$p_s = \Sigma W/A + \frac{We(L/2)}{I}; \qquad I = \frac{1 \times (10)^3}{12} = 83.33 \text{ ft}^4,$$

$$p_{max} = \frac{18,539}{1 \times 10} + \frac{18,539 \times 1.65 \times 5}{83.33} = 3694 \text{ lb/ft}^2,$$

$$p_{min} = \frac{18,539}{1 \times 10} - \frac{18,539 \times 1.65 \times 5}{83.33} = 14 \text{ lb/ft}^2.$$

Design of heel. We begin by calculating the moment M at the back face:

$$M = -\frac{(12{,}520 + 1183)5.25}{2} + \frac{14 \times 5.25 \times 5.25}{2} + \frac{(1957 - 14)}{2}\frac{(5.25)^2}{3}$$

$$\text{(upward reaction included)},$$

$$M = -35{,}950 + 193 + 8930 = -26{,}827 \text{ ft-lb};$$

$$V = W_4 + W_c - \text{upward pressure},$$

$$V = 13{,}703 - \frac{(1957 + 14)}{2} \times 5.25 = 8528 \text{ lb}.$$

Note that the plane of shear is not taken at a distance d from the face, since the plane of shear will look somewhat like that shown in Fig. 6–15.

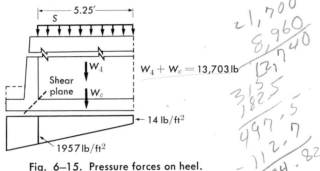

Fig. 6–15. Pressure forces on heel.

It is possible that the overturning tendency might cancel the foundation pressure (upward soil pressure) on the heel. Some specifications require that this pressure be assumed zero in the design (see ASSHO specifications), while others stipulate that the allowable unit stress shall not be exceeded by more than 50% when the uplift reaction is assumed zero (see the Joint Committee specifications and the AREA specifications). The latter is considered as the more realistic of the two extremes and will be used here. However, in computing d, A_s, u, etc., instead of using a unit stress 50% in excess of the allowable stress, we shall multiply the moment and shear for the case of zero foundation pressure by $\frac{2}{3}$. We calculate the moment at the back face, assuming that the upward force is 0:

$$M = -35{,}950 \text{ ft-lb}; \qquad \tfrac{2}{3}M = -23{,}970 \text{ ft-lb} \quad \text{approximately}.$$

The shear force V (upward force $= 0$) is

$$V = 13{,}703 \text{ lb}; \qquad \tfrac{2}{3}V = 9135 \text{ lb.},$$

$$d_m = \sqrt{M/Kb} = \sqrt{(23{,}970 \times 12)/(235.4 \times 12)} = 10.2 \text{ in.},$$

$$d_v = V/vb = 9135/60 \times 12 = 13.85 \text{ in.}$$

(where $v = 1.1\sqrt{3000} = 60$ psi, ACI, 1201c). Therefore

$$A_s = \frac{M}{f_s jd} = \frac{23{,}970 \times 12}{20{,}000 \times 0.875 \times 13.85} = 1.19 \text{ in}^2/\text{ft}.$$

Assuming that No. 8 bars (same as for stem and toe) are used, we find that we need the following number of bars per foot:

$$1.19 \text{ in}^2/0.79 \text{ in}^2 = 1.51 \text{ bar/ft},$$

or we may say that the spacing may be 8 in. center-to-center.

Bond check

$$u = \frac{V}{(\Sigma_0)jd} = \frac{9135}{6.28 \times 0.875 \times 13.85} = 120 \text{ psi}.$$

Hence the bond satisfies the requirement stated in Article 1301c of the ACI Code.

Article 808a requires a minimum coverage of 2 in. Therefore the minimum thickness is

$$13.85 + 2 \text{ in.} + \tfrac{1}{2} \text{ bar diameter} = 16.35 \text{ in}.$$

Since the concrete will be poured on earth, it is practical to increase the overall thickness of the heel by about one inch to compensate for unevenness in excavation. Hence we have an overall thickness of, say 18 in.

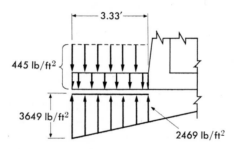

Fig. 6–16. Pressure forces on toe.

Design of toe. We base our calculation on Fig. 6–16. For the moment at the face of the stem, we obtain

$$M_{\text{toe at face of stem}} = \frac{(2468 - 445)(3.33)^2}{2} + (3694 - 2468)\frac{3.33}{2}\left(\frac{2}{3} \times 3.33\right),$$

$$M_{\text{toe}} = 11{,}250 + 4540 = 15{,}790 \text{ ft-lb} = 189{,}500 \text{ in-lb},$$

$$d = \frac{M}{Kb} = \frac{189{,}500}{235.4 \times 12} = 6.72 \text{ in}.$$

A d for the toe, near the stem, approximately the same as for the heel might be desirable in construction—when placing reinforcement, for forming, pouring operations, etc. Thus we shall assume, for calculating the shear stresses near the stem, a d of say, 13.5 in.

To check diagonal tension, assume that $d/2 = 6.75$ in. $= 0.56$ ft. The critical plane for diagonal shear will be at $(3.33 - 0.56) = 2.77$ ft (see Article 1207b of ACI Code). At this section the soil pressure is

$$2468 + (3694 - 2468)(0.56/3.333) = 2675 \text{ lb/ft}^2.$$

The shear force is

$$V = (2675 - 445)2.77 + \tfrac{1}{2}(3694 - 2675)2.77,$$
$$V = 6180 + 1412 = 7592 \text{ lb},$$
$$v = V/bd,$$

where $v = 110$ ($v = 2\sqrt{f_c'}$ according to the ACI Code, Article 1207c). Hence, for shear

$$d = 7592/12 \times 110 = 5.75 \text{ in}.$$

The minimum thickness for the toe is 13.5 in. + 3-in. cover + bar diameter/2. Given that No. 8 bars are used, we obtain a minimum toe thickness of 17.0 in. For expediency of construction, let us assume that the thickness of the toe near the stem is 18 in., as is that of the heel, and tapers to about 8 in. at the tip. Some of the cost incurred by the provision of extra thickness is compensated for by a reduction in the quantity of steel needed, which is now possible due to the increase in the effective depth.

$$A_s = \frac{M}{f_s d} = \frac{189,500}{20,000 \times 13.5} = 0.68 \text{ in}^2/\text{ft}.$$

For No. 8 bars, we find that the spacing is $0.79(12/0.68) = 14$ in. (minimum).

Shear keys. We have to consider the *stem key* and the *base key*.

1. *Stem key.* Since in pouring a retaining wall, one first pours the base and then the stem, it is evident that there will be a lack of homogeneity, and thus of shear strength, at the junction of the base and the stem. To remedy this situation a shear key (stem key) is commonly provided. In our case the horizontal forces are 6505 lb (Fig. 6–17).

Assuming a case of pure shear and a permissible shear stress of 110 psi, we find that the dimension $a = 6505 \text{ lb}/(12 \text{ in.}) (110 \text{ psi}) = 5$ in. The bearing stress is conservatively assumed to be $0.10 f_c' = 300$ psi. This is appreciably less than $0.25 f_c'$ (ACI Code, Article 1003), but may be considered appropriate for the joint under consideration. Then

$$b = 6505/12 \times 300 = 1.81 \text{ in.}, \quad \text{say } 1\tfrac{3}{4} \text{ in. minimum}.$$

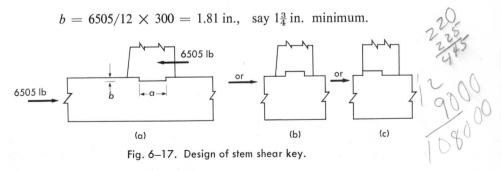

Fig. 6–17. Design of stem shear key.

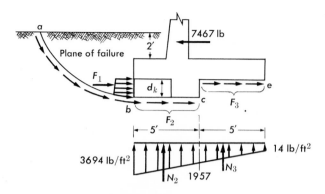

Figure 6–18

Base key. The stability analysis showed that the wall is not sufficiently safe with respect to sliding. Although the toe fill and the earth shoulder in front of the toe definitely increase the stability against sliding, their contribution can not always be relied upon to develop the expected passive resistance. Creep and frost action in the fill are two of the phenomena that lead to this unreliability. In Fig. 6–18, the region *abcde* is the failure plane.

From Fig. 6–18, we have

$$F_2 = (\mu_{\text{soil on soil}})N_2; \qquad F_3 = (\mu_{\text{concrete on soil}})N_3.$$

But assuming that the coefficient μ of soil equals the coefficient μ of concrete on soil, and that both are 0.5 (conservative), we find that $F_2 + F_3 = 9270$ lb (see previous calculations for sliding). If desired we may include a safety factor of 1.75 to safeguard against sliding.

The additional force to be taken by the shear key is $F_1 = 7467 \times 1.75 - 9270 = 3800$ lb. By adjusting k to read k_p, we obtain $k_p \cong 1/k_a = 1/0.26 = 3.846$. Equation 6–1 may be used to give the expression for passive resistance, p_p:

$$p_p = k_p wh = (3.846 \times 110)h = 423h.$$

From Fig. 6–19, we obtain $F_1 = (423/2)(h_2^2 - h_1^2)$ (for h, see Fig. 6–19);

$3800 = 211.5(h_2^2 - 10)$,   approximately,

$3800 = 211.5h_2^2 - 2115$,

$h_2^2 = \dfrac{(3800 + 2115)}{211.5}$, $h_2 = 5.3$ ft,

$d_k = h_2 - h_1 = 5.3 - 3 = 2.3$ ft;

$F_1 = 3837 = 211.5h_2^2 - 2115$, $h_2 = 5.3$ ft,

$d_k = 5.3\,\text{ft} - 3.0\,\text{ft} - 0.5\,\text{ft (tapered toe)} = 1.8\,\text{ft}.$

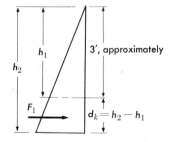

Figure 6–19

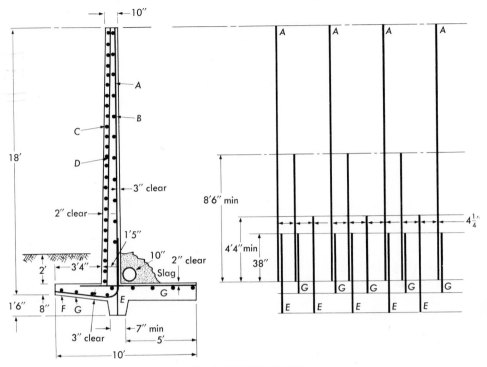

Fig. 6–20. Final design.

ADDITIONAL INFORMATION

A: No. 8 bars at $12\frac{3}{4}''$ c.c.

B: 13 No. 4 bars at 18" c.c.

C: No. 4 bars at 9" c.c.

D: No. 4 bars at 9" c.c.

E: No. 8 bars at $8\frac{1}{2}''$ c.c., variable L

F: No. 8 bars at $8\frac{1}{2}''$ c.c.

G: No. 4 bars at 2" c.c. (spacers)

H: No. 8 bars at 6" c.c., 8' long

We next determine the thickness of shear the key. From the shear, we have

$$d_v = V/vb = 3837/110 \times 12 = 2.9 \text{ in.}$$

The depth required by the bending moment is

$$d_m = \sqrt{3837 \times 1 \text{ ft} \times 12/235.4 \times 12} = 4.1 \text{ in.}$$

$$A_s = \frac{M}{f_s jd} = \frac{3837 \times 1 \times 12}{20,000 \times 0.875 \times 4} = 0.66 \text{ in.}^2.$$

Since some of the dowel embedment can satisfy A_s, we find, using a 3-in. cover, that the thickness of the key is 7 in.

Temperature and shrinkage reinforcement. The quantity of steel needed to compensate for expansion or contraction caused by temperature changes, or by shrinkage and creep is governed partially by the ACI Code (Article 2202f).

Fig. 6–21. Retaining wall for flood control, Wellsville, Ohio, at various stages of construction.

For the stem, we calculate the steel requirements as follows:

Horizontal steel = 0.0025 (vertical × average section of stem).

Therefore

$$A_{sH} = 0.0025 \times 18 \text{ ft } \frac{10 + 17}{2} \text{ in.} \times 12 \text{ in/ft} = 7.29 \text{ in}^2.$$

Let us assume that $\frac{2}{3} A_{sH}$ on the front face is 4.86. Hence we use 25 No. 4 bars at a distance of 9 in. center-to-center. $A_s = 5.00$ in². Also $\frac{1}{3} A_{sH}$ on back face is 2.43. Therefore we use 13 No. 4 bars at a distance of 18 in. center-to-center. $A_s = 2.60$ in². Vertical steel is $(0.0015 \times 1 \text{ ft})[(10 + 17)/2](12 \text{ in.}/1) = 0.243$ in²/ft. Assume that all the vertical steel is placed on the front face since the back face is more than adequately reinforced for temperature by the reinforcement for bending. Hence one may use No. 4 bars 9 in. apart center-to-center. $A_s = 0.266$ in². For toe and heel, $(0.0015 \times 10 \times 14 \text{ in.} \times 12 \text{ in.}/1) = 2.52$ in²/ft. Hence 13 bars are placed approximately 9 in. apart center-to-center. This steel may be usefully arranged in the form of tie bars.

Drainage. It is desirable to decrease the water pressure by providing drainage in back of a wall. This can be accomplished by placing *French drains* (for details, see Fig. 6–20) or holes, called *weep holes,* in the stem near the base. French drains are usually more effective.

PROBLEMS

RETAINING WALLS

Notation: h = stem height, h_w = water depth, H_i = ice thrust, l = base width, t = base thickness, S = surcharge, α = slope of backfill, ϕ = angle of repose, w_s = soil weight, w_c = concrete weight, μ = coefficient of function of concrete on soil, p_s = soil pressure.

Note: The following problems are set up in such a way that the stability analysis of the first group is tied in with the force analysis of the second group, and both aid in the designs called for by the third group. For example, the calculations from Problem 6–1 may be used to determine the forces in Problem 6–6,

which in turn are useful for the design required in Problem 6–11. A similar relationship exists among Problems 6–2, 6–7, and 6–12, etc.

Analysis of Stability:
Sliding, Overturning, and Soil Pressure

Problems 1 through 5. Investigate the stability against sliding, overturning, and foundation soil pressure of the retaining walls described below. Assume a stem thickness of 1 in. for every foot of height, h. The base thickness, t, is uniform for the whole base.

6–1. For the wall in Fig. 6–22, $h =$ 16 ft, $l = 9$ ft, $t = 1$ ft 3 in., $S = 300$ lb/ft^2, $w_c = 150$ lb/ft^3, $w_s = 100$ lb/ft^3, $\phi = 33°$, $\mu = 0.4$, $p_s = 4000$ lb/ft^2.

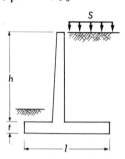

Figure 6–22

6–2. For the wall in Fig. 6–23, $h =$ 15 ft, $l = 9$ ft, $t = 1$ ft 2 in., $\alpha = 30°$, $w_c = 150$ lb/ft^3, $w_s = 110$ lb/ft^3 $\phi =$ 30°, $\mu = 0.45$, $p_s = 5500$ lb/ft^2.

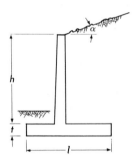

Figure 6–23

6–3. For the wall in Fig. 6–24, $h =$ 18 ft, $l = 11$ ft, $t = 1$ ft 4 in., $w_c = 150$ lb/ft^3, $w_s = 110$ lb/ft^3, $\mu = 0.4$, $\phi =$ 30°, $p_s = 5000$ lb/ft^2, $h_w = 8$ ft.

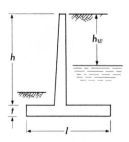

Figure 6–24

6–4. For the wall in Fig. 6–25, $h =$ 16 ft, $l = 10$ ft, $t = 1$ ft 4 in., $w_c = 150$ lb/ft^3, $w_s = 110$ lb/ft^3, $\mu = 0.4$, $\phi =$ 34°, $p_s = 3000$ lb/ft^2, $H_i = 500$ lb/ft^2.

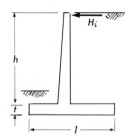

Figure 6–25

6–5. For the wall in Fig. 6–26, $h =$ 20 ft, $l = 11$ ft, $t = 1$ ft 4 in., $w_c = 150$ lb/ft^3, $w_s = 105$ lb/ft^3, $\mu = 0.50$, $\phi =$ 30°, $p_s = 4500$ lb/ft^2, $S = 350$ lb/ft^2, $l_1 = 5$ ft.

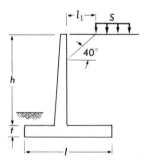

Figure 6–26

Analysis of Internal Forces and Moments

Determine the bending moment and shear forces (M and V) for the stem, toe, and heel near the junction point of base and stem for the given conditions.

6–6. Use the retaining wall in Fig. 6–22 and the dimension and conditions of Problem 6–1.

6–7. Use the retaining wall in Fig. 6–23 and the dimension and conditions of Problem 6–2.

6–8. Use the retaining wall in Fig. 6–24 and the dimension and conditions of Problem 6–3.

6–9. Use the retaining wall in Fig. 6–25 and the dimension and conditions of Problem 6–4.

6–10. Use the retaining wall in Fig. 6–26 and the dimension and conditions of problem 6–5.

Design of Component Parts of Wall

Determine a suitable design for the toe, heel, and stem. The design should indicate the quantity of reinforcing steel required, the cut-off points and the size of the members. Base your design on the conditions given below and the ACI Code specifications.

6–11. Using the data of Problem 6–1 as a starting point, design the wall shown in Fig. 6–22. Neglect the uplift-soil reaction.

6–12. Using the data of Problem 6–2 as a starting point, design the retaining wall shown in Fig. 6–23.

6–13. Using the data of Problem 6–3 as a starting point, design the retaining wall shown in Fig. 6–24.

6–14. Using the data of Problem 6–4 as a starting point, design the retaining wall shown in Fig. 6–25.

6–15. Using the data of Problem 6–5 as a starting point, design the retaining wall shown in Fig. 6–25.

Design of L-shaped Walls

The following five problems concern the design of L-shaped retaining walls. The conditions are those given in Problems 6–1 through 6–5 and Figs. 6–22 through 6–26; however, *the toe is to be omitted.*

6–16. Given: Problem 6–1 and Fig. 6–22. Design an L-shaped wall.

6–17. Given: Problem 6–2 and Fig. 6–23. Design an L-shaped wall.

6–18. Given: Problem 6–3 and Fig. 6–24. Design an L-shaped wall.

6–19. Given: Problem 6–4 and Fig. 6–25. Design an L-shaped wall.

6–20. Given: Problem 6–5 and Fig. 6–26. Design an L-shaped wall.

6–21. Redesign the retaining wall, described in Section 6–4 for a stem height of 21 ft. The allowable soil pressure is 4000 lb/ft^2 and the coefficient of concrete on soil is 0.40. Use 4000 psi concrete and intermediate-grade steel. The surcharge of 300 lb/ft^2 is assumed to act 5 ft back of the retaining wall, as shown in Fig. 6–26.

REFERENCES

1. W. REJMAN, "Stability of Reinforced Concrete Retaining Walls and Abutments," *ACI Journal,* June 1955.
2. KARL TERZAGHI and RALPH B. PECK, *Soil Mechanics in Engineering Practice,* John Wiley and Sons, Inc., New York, 1948.
3. B. K. HOUGH, *Basic Soils Engineering,* Ronald Press Co., New York (1957).

7 FOOTINGS

Concrete canopy, Cincinnati, Ohio. This canopy with a diameter of 30 ft forms a park shelter in Cincinnati.

7-1 INTRODUCTION

A footing is that part of a structure which transmits the load to the underlying soil or rock. The terms *footing* and *foundation* are to a great extent synonymous. The latter usually includes the entire substructure, i.e., all the parts that support the superstructure.

The purpose of the footing is to distribute the load from the substructure to the ground in such a way that the settlement of (a) the total structure and (b) any part of the structure relative to any other part is held to a minimum. Although both types are important, the latter usually proves more damaging.

Soils compress appreciably when subjected to heavy loads. The compressive deformation, however, is a function not only of the magnitude and duration of the load but also of the soil characteristics, which vary greatly from place to place and even within the boundaries of the construction site. Hence many special kinds of foundation are called for by various loads, special underground conditions, and site restrictions, such as boundary limits.

Most footings fall under two general classifications: wall footings and column footings. Figure 7-1(a) shows a portion of a *wall* footing. The wall rests on a continuous strip of reinforced concrete, which is wider than the wall. An *isolated column* footing, Fig. 7-1(b), is one which supports the load from a single

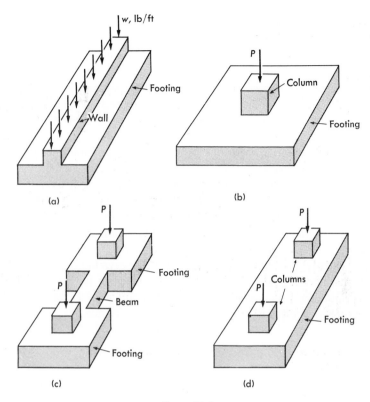

Figure 7–1

column. It may be square, rectangular, or round, and is considered the simplest and usually the most economical type. Two isolated column footings joined by a beam are commonly known as a *cantilever* footing (Fig. 7–1c). If a single mat supports two or more columns, as shown in Fig. 7–1(d), the mat is known as a *combined* footing.

When the soil conditions are poor and the column loads large, and the conditions do not call for a deep foundation, it might prove economical or perhaps necessary to support the whole structure on a single mat or slab. When the soil is incapable of taking the applied bearing loads, concrete caissons or piles are sometimes used to transmit the load down to rock.

7–2   SOILS AS FOUNDATION MATERIALS

It goes almost without saying that the foundation must be adequate if a structure is to be safe and acceptable. In this respect the analysis of the soils which support the load is possibly the most important, and frequently the most difficult, part of the design. The importance of the soil as a foundation material in the design of a structure might well be described by the saying, "A chain is only as strong as its weakest link."

A foundation must fulfill two definite requirements if it is to show satisfactory behavior under load. First, the shearing stresses transmitted to the soil must be smaller than the shearing strength of the soil, by an amount sufficient to give an ample safety factor. Second, the differential settlement must not reach a degree which might disfigure or damage the structure. Depending upon the geographical and environmental conditions, the foundation must often meet a third requirement: it should be placed at adequate depth to prevent frost damage, undermining by scouring, etc.

The foundation material may consist of one or a combination of many types of material, such as rock, gravel, sand, clay, silt, muck, peat, loam, hardpan, and others. In this connection, two questions arise: (1) how does the engineer know when he is confronted with a poor foundation material and (2) if the foundation material is poor, how does he improve the conditions.

The answer to these questions is not easy. Test borings, laboratory analysis, and building codes, combined with the data found in the literature on soil mechanics, usually prove very helpful. But the available information often leaves a gap which must be filled by sound engineering judgment. There is no clear-cut formula for deriving such answers. It is often said that the planning of foundations for structures is more of an art than a science.

7–3 SOIL PRESSURE

The pressure distribution beneath a footing depends on the type of soil immediately under the footing and on the rigidity of the footing itself. Figure 7–2 shows approximated shapes of pressure distributions as determined by experiments and theoretical analysis. Such analysis is found in texts on soil mechanics. Here the soil pressure is considered uniform for centered loading and linearly variable for eccentric loading, as shown in Fig. 7–3.

The pressure shown in Fig. 7–3, usually called the *net* pressure, is the resultant pressure over the base of the footing caused by the column load (axial and bending). It does not include the weight of the footing and of the overburden. The effect of all these factors (i.e., axial and bending column loads, weight of footing, and overburden) is generally classified as *gross* soil pressure.

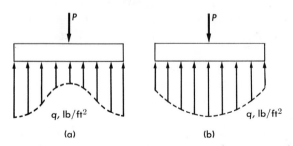

Fig. 7–2. Contact pressure distributions on the base of rigid footings on (a) saturated clay and (b) cohesionless soil.

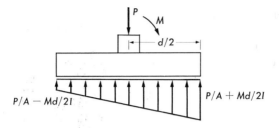

Fig. 7–3. Assumed contact-pressure distribution on the base of a concrete footing.

The weights of the footing and of the overburden are not included in the computation of moment and shear acting on the concrete section. The reason is that the downward weight of the footing and overburden are counteracted by an equal force acting in an upward direction, and thus are essentially canceled out. Nonetheless, the column load, footing weight, as well as any overburden pressure, must, combined, fall within the permissible soil pressure. The footing area must be sufficiently large to ensure that the allowable soil pressure is not exceeded.

7–4 PROPORTIONING OF FOOTINGS FOR UNIFORM SETTLEMENT

The need to prevent differential settlement of footings has already been mentioned. It has also been strongly implied that this is not easy because of varied soil characteristics and uncertain loading conditions. For most soils (rock, gravel, and coarse-sand soils excluded), the settlement is a gradual, continuing rather than an instantaneous process. Since the live load (LL) varies with time, its effect on settlement is less predictable than that of the dead load (DL), which is present at all times. Furthermore, even the sizes of footings have some effect on settlement due to the pressure distributions they cause. However, these size differences are frequently small, and hence this effect may often be omitted for purposes of analysis.

For fine-grained soils, the settlement may be assumed to be proportional to the bearing pressure caused by the DL plus a fraction of the LL. The fraction is usually taken to be the ratio of the time the load is actually applied to the time it is possible to apply it. For example, if the LL is applied for 8 hours out of a possible 24-hour period, the fraction is one-third. Note, however, that while only DL + ⅓(LL) would be used in settlement analysis, the total load (DL + LL) must be used in computing the maximum bearing pressure and in designing the footing.

The proportioning of the bearing areas of several footings is guided by that footing with the greatest percentage of *total* to *applied* loads, that is, (DL + LL)$_{total}$/$(DL + LL)_{applied}$. This footing is commonly referred to as the *critical footing.* The bearing area for this footing, A_{critical}, is then (a) for *bearing,*

$$A_{\text{critical}} = \frac{(DL + LL)_{\text{critical}}}{q_a}, \tag{7-1}$$

where q_a is the allowable bearing pressure, and (b) *for settlement,*

$$q_{\text{critical}} = \frac{(DL + LL)_{\text{critical}}}{A_{\text{critical}}}. \tag{7-2}$$

For any other footing of the system, the area of the footing, A_i, for settlement is

$$A_i = \frac{(DL + LL)_i}{(DL + LL)_{\text{critical}}} A_{\text{critical}}. \tag{7-3}$$

Example 7-1.

Given: The estimated DL and LL, and the application time of the LL on four footings, as listed in the table below. The allowable soil pressure, q_a, is 4 k/ft².

Footing	DL, kip	LL, kip	DL + LL, kip	Time of application of LL, %	DL + LL, kip	$\dfrac{(DL + LL)_{\text{total}}}{(DL + LL)_{\text{applied}}}$
A	250	150	400	40	310	1.290
B	350	200	550	55	460	1.195
C	400	160	560	50	480	1.166
D	300	100	400	37	337	1.187

Find: The areas of the footings that will ensure equal settlement.

SOLUTION: The critical footing is A since it has the largest load ration, 1.29. Thus

$$A_{\text{critical}} = A_A = \frac{(DL + LL)_{\text{critical}}}{q_a} = \frac{400\ \text{k}}{4\ \text{k/ft}^2} = 100\ \text{ft}^2.$$

Assume that

$$A_{\text{critical}} = A_A = 10\ \text{ft} \times 10\ \text{ft} = 100\ \text{ft}^2,$$

$$q_{\text{critical}} = \frac{310\ \text{k}}{100\ \text{ft}^2} = 3100\ \text{lb/ft}^2,$$

$$A_B = \frac{460}{3100} = 148.4\ \text{ft}^2.$$

Use a footing with dimensions

$$(12\ \text{ft } 3\ \text{in.})(12\ \text{ft } 3\ \text{in.}); \qquad A_B = 150\ \text{ft}^2.$$

$$A_C = \frac{480}{3100} = 154.8\ \text{ft}^2.$$

Use a footing with dimensions

$$(12 \text{ ft } 6 \text{ in.})(12 \text{ ft } 6 \text{ in.}); \qquad A_C = 156.25 \text{ ft}^2.$$

$$A_D = \frac{337}{3100} = 108.7 \text{ ft}^2.$$

Use a footing with dimensions

$$(10 \text{ ft } 6 \text{ in.})(10 \text{ ft } 6 \text{ in.}); \qquad A_D = 110.25 \text{ ft}^2.$$

Note that the areas for *B, C, D* give maximum pressures that are less than the allowable pressure of 4 k/ft². For example,

$$A_A = \frac{400}{100} = 4000 \text{ lb/ft}^2, \qquad A_C = \frac{560}{156.25} = 3584 \text{ lb/ft}^2,$$

$$A_B = \frac{550}{150} = 3666.66 \text{ lb/ft}^2. \qquad A_D = \frac{400}{110.25} = 3628 \text{ lb/ft}^2.$$

7–5 WALL FOOTINGS

As the name implies, a wall footing supports a wall. In most cases, the load that the wall transmits to the footing may be considered uniform over the length of the wall. It follows, therefore, that the entire footing is given a uniform width, except in those cases where the soil characteristics vary appreciably over the length of the wall. Unlike the column footings which are subjected to bending in two directions, the wall footing only experiences bending in one direction, in a plane perpendicular to the face of the wall.

To analyze the footing, let us take a typical one-foot strip cut from the footing, as shown in Fig. 7–4. This projection is treated as a cantilever beam loaded with the net upward soil pressure. The bending moment to be used in the design

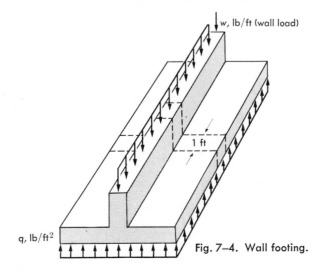

Fig. 7–4. Wall footing.

of wall footings shall be the moment computed at the face of the wall for footings supporting a concrete wall, and the moment computed halfway between the middle and the edge of the wall, for footings under masonry walls (Article 2304b, ACI Code).

The shear to be used as a measure of diagonal tension for footings on soil shall be determined at a distance $d/2$ measured from the corresponding face of the wall (see Article 1207b, ACI Code).

Example 7–2. Design

Given: A 16-in. masonry wall carries a load of 25 kip/lin. ft;

$$f_c' = 3000 \text{ psi}, \qquad q_a = 4 \text{ k/ft}^2, \qquad v = 110 \text{ psi}, \qquad f_s = 18,000 \text{ psi},$$
$$\text{and} \quad u = 160 \text{ psi}.$$

Find: Design a reinforced concrete footing.

SOLUTION: Let us assume that the footing has a weight of 150 lb/ft². Then the net bearing pressure is

$$q_{net} = 4000 - 150 = 3850 \text{ lb/ft}^2.$$

The width of the footing is

$$\frac{25,000}{3850} = 6.50 \text{ ft.}$$

The critical bending moment is at a section ¼ × 16 in. inside the face of the wall. Thus the cantilevered length considered is

$$31 + \tfrac{16}{4} = 35 \text{ in.} = 2.92 \text{ ft.}$$

From Fig. 7–5, we have

$$M_{max} = \frac{(2.92)^2}{2} \times 3850, \qquad M_{max} = 16,412 \text{ ft/lb.}$$

Using this result for M_{max}, we compute d:

$$d = \left(\frac{M}{Kb}\right)^{1/2} = \left(\frac{16,412 \times 12}{208 \times 12}\right)^{1/2} = (78.903)^{1/2}.$$

$$d = 8.9 \text{ in.}, \quad \text{say 9 in.}$$

(The factor 208 is taken from Table 3 of Appendix B.) We now check the diagonal

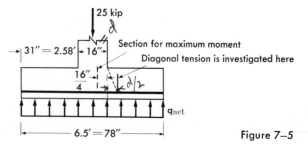

Figure 7–5

tension. The critical section for the diagonal tension is a distance of $d/2$ in. away from the face of the wall. We next determine the depth required, and find

$$d = \frac{V}{bjv} = \frac{(2.58 - 0.75)3850}{12 \times 0.88 \times 110} = 8.0 \text{ in.}$$

Thus d may be assumed to be 9 in. as governed by the moment. Hence

$$A_s = \frac{M}{f_s jd} = \frac{16{,}412 \times 12}{18{,}000 \times 0.88 \times 9} = 1.38 \text{ in}^2/\text{ft of wall.}$$

Next we compute the required $\sum_0$.

$$\sum_0 = \frac{V \text{ at face of wall}}{ujd} = \frac{2.58 \times 3850}{160 \times 0.88 \times 9} = 7.84 \text{ in/ft of wall.}$$

From Table 2 of Appendix B, we find that we need 3 No. 7 bars: $A_s = 1.76 \text{ in}^2$, and $\sum_0 = 8.25 > 7.84$ and thus is satisfactory. The spacing of the bars is 12 in. $\div$ 3 bars $= 4$ in. center-to-center.

Answers: Assuming an overall depth of 13 in., we find that the cover is 13 in. $-$ 9 in. $- \frac{1}{2}$ diameter of one No. 7 bar $= 3.56$ in.; use 3 No. 7 bars spaced 4 in. center-to-center. Note that due to the weight of the footing a base thickness of 13 in. gives only a negligible variation in the assumed pressure of 150 lb/ft^2.

Example 7–3.   Design

Given: The wall-footing data of Example 7–2.

Find: Design of a plain footing.

SOLUTION: Refer to ACI Code, Article 2307b. The tensile stress in concrete must be less than or equal to $1.6\sqrt{f_c'}$, say 87.5 psi. Let us assume that the weight of the footing is 400 lb/ft^2. (This is equivalent to a thickness of approximately $2\frac{2}{3}$ ft, say 32 in.) Then $q_{net} = 4000 - 400 = 3600$ lb/ft^2. The width of the footing is $25{,}000/3600 = 6.94$ ft, say 7 ft.

We now refer to Fig. 7–6 to determine the moment:

$$M = \frac{(3.17)^2}{2} \times 3600 = 18{,}060 \text{ ft-lb.}$$

From $\sigma = M_c/I$, $M = (f_t)bh^2/6$, where f_t is the allowable tensile stress in concrete, or

$$(18{,}060) \times 12 = \frac{87.5 \times 12h^2}{6},$$

$$h = 35 \text{ in.}$$

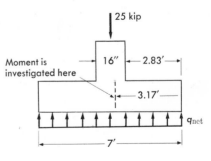

Figure 7–6

Although the thickness of 35 in. is slightly greater than that assumed (32 in.) and thus the net pressure, q_{net}, is slightly less than the 3600 psf used, the difference does not justify a reevaluation.

7–6 ISOLATED COLUMN FOOTINGS

A footing which supports a single column is usually referred to as an isolated column footing. Its most common form is that of a flat slab, either square or rectangular, of uniform thickness, but it may also be stepped or sloped as shown in Fig. 7–7(b) and (c), respectively, in order to save concrete near the outer edges where the stresses are small. The savings in the concrete, however, are often offset by a higher cost of the more complicated forms.

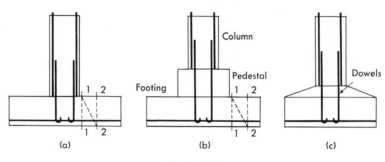

Figure 7–7

In designing or analyzing column footings, one must investigate the various stresses existing in any one section. These are:

(a) the stresses in concrete and reinforcing steel due to bending;
(b) the bond stress between steel and concrete;
(c) the diagonal tension stress;
(d) the bearing stress from the column; and
(e) soil pressure (see Article 7–3).

For isolated footings of uniform thickness and for sloped ones (Fig. 7–7c), the bending moment is computed at the face of the column (ACI Code, Article 2304b). These critical sections are indicated by 1–1 in the figure.

For the bond stress, we shall base our computations at the same critical sections that were prescribed for the bending moment; in addition, we must consider the sections at all other vertical planes where changes of section or reinforcement occur (ACI Code, Article 2305b). For two-way footings, the older codes permitted the use of 85% of the static shear for calculating bond stresses. (Article 1205e, 1956 ACI Code). A similar reduction was permitted in calculating steel stresses (Article 1204e, 1956 ACI Code). However, investigations at the University of Illinois published in 1948 show that this reduction has no physical significance and that it should not be made. Therefore, we shall work with the 100% static shear. Figure 7–8 shows the critical section for computing bond and bending stresses.

The shear stresses in footings are investigated at a section $d/2$ from the face of the column (see Fig. 7–7). For footings reinforced in two directions (two

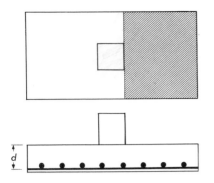

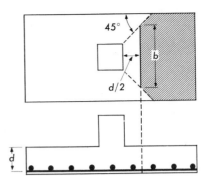

Fig. 7–8. Critical section for bending and bond.

Fig. 7–9. Critical section for diagonal tension.

steel layers, one in each direction), this depth may be taken as the average depth of the two layers (Fig. 7–8). Furthermore, the area used to determine the shear stress as a measure of diagonal tension is approximately represented by the shaded area (Fig. 7–9) within the two lines projected from the face of the column at 45° with the horizontal, and at a distance of $d/2$ from the face of the column.

The shear stress may be determined from the formula $v = V/bjd$, where b is as given in Fig. 7–9, and V is the shear force for the shaded area. Since for a rectangular footing (other than one having square sides), the shear force is different for each of the two directions, it is advisable to compute the shear stresses in each direction unless the critical direction is obvious.

The design must provide safeguards against excessive bearing stresses on the footings or pedestals caused by the columns. The bearing stress on the footing at the base of the column or pedestal should not exceed the allowable compressive stress of the concrete in the column. This means that dowel bars (see Fig. 7–7), i.e., vertical reinforcing bars embedded in the footing and column, should be used to transfer, by bond, the load from the column reinforcement into the footing. Steel plates serve the same purpose for steel columns placed on a concrete footing or pedestal.

As defined in Chapter 4, a pedestal (Fig. 7–7b) is an upright compression member whose height does not exceed three times its least lateral dimension. To avoid shear failure between pedestal and footing, the footing and the pedestal should be poured monolithically whenever feasible.

The pedestal may provide embedment for extra-long dowels, the lengths of which are controlled by the bond stresses, etc. The inclusion of these dowels permits the designer to use an appreciably smaller depth for the footing for a given load, due to a smaller cantilever projection of the footing. When footings are at different levels, pedestals may be used as the means of bringing the bases of all columns to the same level. As a result, it may be possible to have the same design and common length for all columns.

Example 7-4.   *Design and Analysis*

Given: A concrete column having a diameter of 20 in. transmits a 400-kip load to a footing. $f_c' = 3000$ psi for the column, and for the footing, the allowable soil pressure is 4000 lb/ft², $n = 10$, and $v = 110$ psi.

Find: A suitable design for the footing.

SOLUTION: Assume that the DL of the footing is 300 lb/ft², that is, the footing has a thickness of 2 ft. The net soil pressure is $4000 - 300 = 3700$ lb/ft². Hence the required area is

$$\frac{\text{column load}}{q_{\text{net}}} = \frac{400,000}{3700} = 108 \text{ ft}^2.$$

Let us assume that we have a square footing of side B. Then

$$B = \sqrt{108} = 10.4 \text{ ft, say 10 ft 6 in.,}$$

$$q_{\text{net}} = \frac{400,000}{(10.5)^2} = 3625 \text{ lb/ft.}$$

Next, let us suppose that the overall depth of the footing is 24 in. and that the average depth of the steel is 21 in. Note that for round columns, we base our analysis on a square-column section having the same area as the round column.

We next calculate the shear stress (Fig. 7-10):

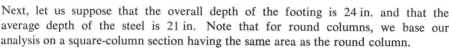

$$a = \sqrt{\frac{\pi D^2}{4}} = \sqrt{\frac{\pi(20)^2}{4}} = 17.8 \text{ in.}$$

$$g = \frac{B}{2} - \frac{a}{2} - \frac{d}{2},$$

$$B = 10 \text{ ft 6 in.} = 126 \text{ in.}$$

Hence

$$g = \frac{126}{2} - \frac{17.8}{2} - \frac{21}{2} = 43.6 \text{ in.} = 3.63 \text{ ft;}$$

$$b = a + d,$$

$$b = 17.8 \text{ in.} + 21 \text{ in.} = 38.8 \text{ in.} = 3.24 \text{ ft.}$$

To determine the required depth of the steel, we proceed as follows.

$$M = q_{\text{net}} \frac{B-a}{2} B \frac{B-a}{4}$$

$$= \frac{1}{8} q_{\text{net}} B (B-a)^2,$$

$$V = q_{\text{net}} \frac{b+B}{2} g,$$

$$V = 3625 \frac{3.24 \text{ ft} + 10.5}{2} \times 3.63$$

$$= 90,500 \text{ lb.}$$

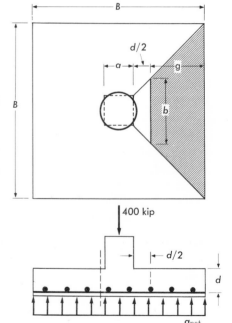

Figure 7-10

If shear governs,

$$d = \frac{V}{jbv} = \frac{90{,}500}{0.88 \times 1 \times 110} = 24.1 \text{ in.}$$

Thus the assumed d, although not quite sufficient, is close enough to the above result that a reevaluation is not necessary. Therefore, let us take $d = 24$ in.

Bending moment:

$$\tfrac{1}{8}q_{net}B(B - a)^2 = \tfrac{1}{8}/3625 \times 10.5(10.5 - 1.48)^2,$$

$$M = 387{,}000 \text{ ft-lb} = 4{,}640{,}000 \text{ in.-lb.}$$

Trial. We check by trial,

$$A_s = \frac{M}{f_s jd} = \frac{4{,}640{,}000}{(18{,}000)(0.88)(24)} = 12.20 \text{ in}^2,$$

and find that we may use 13 No. 9 bars ($A_s = 13.0$ in²) spaced approximately 9 in. apart. The same reinforcement shall be used in both directions.

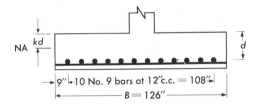

NA   kd

d

9″ ├10 No. 9 bars at 12″c.c. = 108″┤

B = 126″

Figure 7–11

Bending stresses. We assume that d is approximately 24 in. (Fig. 7–11), and calculate the stresses, using a transformed section.

$$\frac{B}{2}(kd)^2 = nA_s(d - kd) = 10 \times 13(24 - kd)$$

$$63(kd)^2 + 130kd - 3120 = 0,$$

$$kd = 6.08 \text{ in;}$$

$$(d - kd) = 17.92 \text{ in.;}$$

$$I_c = \frac{B(kd)^3}{3} + nA_s(d - kd)^2,$$

$$I_c = \frac{126}{3}(6.08)^3 + (10 \times 13(17.92)^2) = 51{,}180 \text{ in}^4;$$

$$f_c = \frac{Mkd}{I} = \frac{4{,}640{,}000 \times 6.08}{51{,}180} = 551 \text{ psi;}$$

$$f_s = \frac{Mn(d - kd)}{I_c} = \frac{4{,}640{,}000 \times 10 \times 17.92}{51{,}180} = 16{,}250 \text{ psi.}$$

Fig. 7–12. Retaining-wall footing.

Bond stresses (calculating V at face of column):

$$u = \frac{V}{\sum_0 jd} = \frac{[(B-a)/2]Bq_{\text{net}}}{\sum_0 jd} = \frac{\frac{1}{2}(9.02 \times 10.5 \times 3.625)}{46 \times 0.88 \times 24} = 177 \text{ psi.}$$

According to ACI Code, Article 1301b, the allowable bond stress is

$$u = 5.0\sqrt{f_c'} = \frac{4.8\sqrt{3000}}{1.25} = 202 \text{ psi.}$$

This is satisfactory.

Bearing stress under column: To compute the bond stress in the dowels, we proceed as follows:

$$\text{Area of column} = \frac{\pi(20)^2}{4} = 314 \text{ in}^2 = 2.18 \text{ ft}^2,$$

$$\text{Area of footing} = 10.5 \times 10.5 = 110.5 \text{ ft}^2.$$

Since $2.18 < 110.5/3$,

$$f_c = 0.375 \times 3000 = 1125 \text{ psi} \qquad \text{(Article 1003, ACI Code).}$$

From the column,

$$f_c = \frac{400.00}{314} = 1275 \text{ psi.}$$

Hence a force of $(1275 - 1125)314 = 47{,}200$ lb has to be taken by the dowels via the bond. (Note the dowels sticking out of the footing in Fig. 7–12.)

Next we compute, for $f_s = 18,000$ psi,

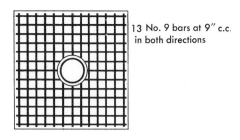

13 No. 9 bars at 9" c.c. in both directions

$$A_{sd} = \frac{47,200}{18,000} = 2.62 \text{ in}^2,$$

and we see that we may use 8 No. 6 bars; $A_s = 3.54$ in²; thus the steel dowel stress is

$$\frac{47,200}{3.54} = 13,350 \text{ lb/in}^2.$$

Hence the minimum length of the dowels in the footing is

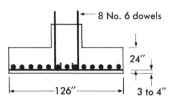

8 No. 6 dowels

24"

126"

3 to 4"

$$\frac{df_s}{4u} = \frac{(0.75)(13,350)}{(4)(240)} = 10.35 \text{ in.},$$

Figure 7–13

where a bond stress of 240 psi is assumed to be satisfactory. For construction purposes, however, the dowels are projected down to the footing reinforcement. Thus, the design is now complete (see Fig. 7–13).

7–7 COMBINED FOOTINGS

In the majority of cases, when a combined footing is chosen in preference to an isolated footing, (1) the bearing capacity of the soil is low, or (2) the combined footing offers greater stability.

One way of compensating for a low bearing capacity of the soil is to increase the area of the footing, thus reducing the soil pressure. Since the area of a combined footing is always equal to, or greater than, the sum of the areas of the isolated footings under consideration, the answer to soil problems of this kind might well be a combined footing. Furthermore, if the isolated footings are close to each other, it might prove more economical to combine these into one. Often the excavation, formwork, and general labor saving from a combined footing compensate for the small saving in concrete an isolated footing system might have to offer.

Sometimes a column is located near a building or property line (Fig. 7–14), and hence the footing cannot extend beyond this limit. In such a case an isolated

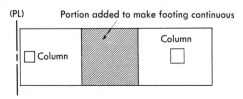

(PL)   Portion added to make footing continuous

Column   Column

Figure 7–14

footing may be a poor choice for the following reasons: (1) it may be unstable in a plane normal to the property line, (2) the pressure it exerts on the soil is uneven and, (3) it may settle at a rate different from that of the other footings. Both, appropriate settlement and stability, are important objectives. Often the most practical means of obtaining these is a combined footing.

There are special cases where a combined footing might also serve as a means of combating hydrostatic pressure.

Example 7–5.   Design

Given: An exterior column (20 in. by 20 in.) abutting a property line carries a 300-kip load. Another interior column (23 in. by 23 in.) carries a 500-kip load. They are 16 ft apart center-to-center. The permissible soil pressure is 6 kip/ft². See Figure 7–15.

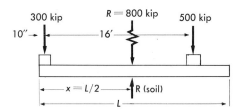

Figure 7–15

Find: A suitable combined footing.

PROCEDURE: Let us assume that $f_c' = 3000$ psi, $v = 110$ psi, $u = 200$ psi, $f_s' = 20,000$ psi, LL + DL $= (300 + 500) + 50$ kip estimated weight of the footing. We find that the total load is 850 kip and the area is $\frac{850}{6} = 142$ ft² (to the nearest ft²).

For uniform soil pressure the center of the footing must coincide with the resultant column load, that is,

$$x \cdot 800 = 0.83 \times 300 + (0.83 + 16)500,$$

where 10 in. $= 0.83$ ft,

$$x = 10.83 \text{ ft} = 10 \text{ ft } 10 \text{ in.}$$

$$\text{L} \times \text{width} = 142 \text{ ft}^2,$$

and hence the width is

$$\frac{142}{2x} = \frac{142}{21.66} = 6.56 \text{ ft}, \qquad \text{say 6 ft 6 in.}$$

From Fig. 7–16, we have

$$q_{\text{net}} = \frac{800 \text{ k}}{(21.66 \times 6.5)} = 5.68 \text{ k/ft}^2,$$

$$q_{\text{net}}/\text{lin. ft} = 36.9 \text{ k/lin. ft},$$

For flexure, we obtain

$$d = \sqrt{M/Kb}.$$

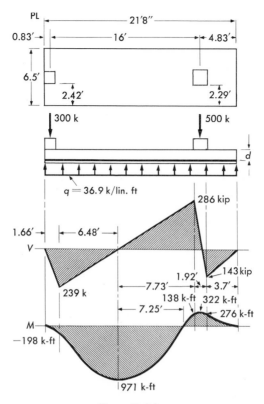

Figure 7–16

From Table 3, Appendix B, we have $K = 235.4$ or 235, approximately. Hence

$$d = \sqrt{971,000 \times 12/235(6.5 \times 12)} = \sqrt{636};$$
$$d = 25 \text{ in., approximately.}$$

We check our assumption regarding the dead load based on 25 in. + 5 in. (approximate cover), and find that

$$DL = 2.5 \text{ ft} \times 6.5 \times 21.66 \times 0.150 = 52.8 \text{ k.}$$

Since we assumed a DL of 50 k, our result is satisfactory.
    For diagonal shear:

$$v = \frac{V}{bjd} = \frac{286,000}{78(0.86)(25)} = 171 \text{ psi.}$$

Since the permissible shear stress v is 110 psi, it follows that stirrups would have to be used. The design of the reinforcement for diagonal tension is explained in Sections 3–6 through 3–9. The use of stirrups is frequently not practical. A more practical solution might be to increase the thickness of the footing for the critical shear portion. A total thickness of $^{171}\!/_{110} \times 25 = 39$ in. would suffice for a short length of the heavier column, and a 25-in. thickness is satisfactory for the other. From here on, the design is similar to that of a beam.

Bottom steel. The following requirements have to be satisfied.

$$A_s = \frac{M}{f_s jd} = \frac{322,000 \times 12}{20,000 \times 0.86 \times 39} = 6.54 \text{ in}^2,$$

$$\Sigma_0 = \frac{V}{ujd} = \frac{286,000}{200 \times 0.86 \times 39} = 42.6 \text{ in.}$$

According to Table 2, Appendix B, we may use 24 No. 5 bars; $A_s = 7.44$ and $\Sigma_0 = 47.0$ are satisfactory. The spacing considerations will be left as an exercise for the student. (For determination of cut-off length, see Chapter 3.)

Top steel. We assume that the allowable bond stress for the bars is 200 psi. The following requirements have to be met:

$$A_s = \frac{971,000 \times 12}{20,000 \times 0.86 \times 25} = 27.2 \text{ in}^2,$$

$$\Sigma_0 = \frac{239,000}{200 \times 0.86 \times 25} = 55.8 \text{ in.}$$

According to Table 2, Appendix B, 22 No. 10 bars may be used; $A_s = 28 \text{ in}^2$, $\Sigma_0 = 87.8$. Both results are satisfactory.

Transverse steel. One conservative design approach for the transverse steel (i.e., steel bars perpendicular to the longitudinal axis of the footing) is to assume that the bending moment in the transverse direction is carried by a transverse beam under each column (see Fig. 7–17).

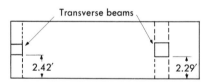

Figure 7–17

Steel under a 300-k column. To determine the steel required, we proceed as follows.

$$w = \frac{300 \text{ k}}{6.5 \text{ ft}} = 46.2 \text{ k/lin. ft of transverse beam.}$$

$$M \text{ at face of column} = \frac{46.2 \times (2.42)^2}{2} = 135 \text{ k-ft,}$$

$$A_s = \frac{M}{f_s jd} = \frac{135,000 \times 12}{20,000 \times 0.86 \times 25} = 3.77 \text{ in}^2,$$

$$\Sigma_0 = \frac{V}{ujd} = \frac{46,200 \times 2.42}{200 \times 0.86 \times 25} = 26 \text{ in}^2.$$

We may use 11 No. 6 bars; $\Sigma_0 = 26.6 \text{ in.}$, $A_s = 4.84 \text{ in.}^2$

Steel under a 500-k column:

$$w = \frac{500}{6.5} = 72.2 \text{ k/lin. ft,}$$

$$M = \frac{77.2(2.29)^2}{2} = 202 \text{ k-ft,}$$

$$A_s = \frac{202,000 \times 12}{20,000 \times 0.86 \times 39} = 3.62 \text{ in}^2,$$

$$\Sigma_0 = \frac{77,000 \times 2.29}{200 \times 0.86 \times 39} = 26 \text{ in.}$$

We may use 11 No. 6 bars; $A_s = 4.84$ in², and $\Sigma_0 = 26$ in.

The results obtained meet the specifications. The steel should be placed in such a way that maximum symmetry with the centerline of the column is achieved. (The steel detailing is left as an exercise for the student.)

7-8 CANTILEVER FOOTINGS

A cantilever footing is similar to a combined footing in that both consist of two separate column footings "connected" into one. When property-line restrictions call for a combined footing as mentioned in Section 7–7, and when the "separate" footings are fairly far apart, it might prove more economical to join the two footings by a narrow but stiff section (a beam) designed to take bending. Such a footing is known as a cantilever footing (Fig. 7–18).

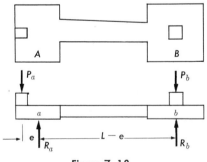

Figure 7–18

From the point of view of analysis, it is simplest to assume that the beam does not induce any soil pressure underneath it except the pressure necessary to carry the weight of the beam itself. This may be accomplished in two ways: the area on which the beam acts may be covered by loose soil, or sometimes straw which would later decay and thus free the footing from the soil, or one may form the beam free from the soil, an effective but perhaps a little more expensive way of accomplishing the same result.

Assuming that the footings A and B (Fig. 7–18) take the loads from the columns and that the soil pressure distribution is uniform for both, we find that the resultant soil pressures under A and B fall at the respective centroids of the two areas under pressure, as indicated in the figure. By taking moments of the forces (excluding dead load) about the points a and b, we have

$$R_a = \frac{L}{L-e}\,P_a \quad \text{and} \quad R_b = P_b - \frac{P_a e}{L-e}.$$

These results show that footing A is larger than is necessary to support P_a alone at a given uniform soil pressure, and footing B is smaller. In other words,

$$\text{Area of } A = \frac{R_a}{q} = \frac{LP_a}{q(L-e)},$$

$$\text{Area of } B = \frac{R_b}{q} = \frac{P_b(L-e) - P_a e}{q(L-e)} = \frac{(P_b L) - e(P_b + P_a)}{q(L-e)},$$

where q is the allowable soil pressure.

A shear and moment diagram might facilitate the design of the beam.

7–9 FOOTINGS ON PILES

If the soil underneath the substructure is weak and, in general, unsuitable for the use of spread footings or mats, it becomes necessary to transmit the load to a lower, firmer stratum that has sufficient bearing capacity to support the loads applied to it. Piles are used for this purpose (see texts on foundations).

The design of footings that rest on piles is similar to those resting directly on soil, with some special exceptions:

(a) *Shear.* In computing the external shear on any section through a footing supported on piles, we shall assume that the entire reaction from any pile whose center is located 6 in. or more outside the section produces shear on the section, and that the reaction from any pile whose center is located 6 in. or more inside the section produces no shear on the section. For intermediate positions of the pile center, the portion of the pile reaction assumed as producing shear on the section shall be based on straight-line interpolation between the full value at 6 in. outside the section and zero value at 6 in. inside the section.

(b) *Moment and bond.* The critical section for bending is the same as for footings resting directly on soil. In these analyses, the pile reactions are assumed to be concentrated forces acting at the centers of the piles.

(c) *Size of footing.* The number and spacing of the piles govern the size of the footing. The number of piles required depends, of course, on the external load applied (vertical and horizontal) and the bearing capacity of the pile. The spacing is based on the soil conditions and upon common practice and good judgment. For friction piles, the spacing is usually 3 ft or more. The spacing for end-bearing piles is occasionally less. (See Fig. 7–19.)

Fig. 7–19. The footing load is transmitted through the piles (in this case, metal casings were driven down and then filled with concrete) to a strata substantially firm to take the bearing load of the pile.

In designing a pile footing, one should make sure that the load is evenly distributed among all piles. This is not always accomplished, especially when bending moments, by horizontal or eccentric vertical loads, are induced in the systems. But the variations in loads should be kept to a minimum. The design would be especially unsatisfactory if any of the piles were placed in tension by such a moment.

PROBLEMS

FOOTINGS

Design the footings for the conditions specified in the following problems, in accordance with the ACI Code requirements. Show the steel arrangement and the soil pressure distribution.

Notation: P = axial column loads, kip; w = uniform wall load, kip/lin. ft; p_s = allowable soil pressure, lb/ft²; l, a, b = distances as shown; f_c' = ultimate concrete strength, psi; D = dimension (thickness) of column or wall, in.; M = overturning moment ft-lb.

7-1. Design an isolated square footing, Fig. 7–20, given that $P = 175$ kip, $D = 15$ in., $p_s = 3500$ lb/ft², $f_c' = 3000$ psi, intermediate-grade steel.

7-2. Design an isolated square footing, Fig. 7–20, given that $P = 175$ kip, $D = 15$ in., $p_s = 5000$ lb/ft², $f_c' = 3000$ psi, intermediate-grade steel.

7-3. Design an isolated square footing, Fig. 7–20, given that $P = 215$ kip, $D = 20$ in., $p_s = 4000$ lb/ft², $f_c' = 3000$ psi, intermediate-grade steel.

7-4. Design an isolated square footing, Fig. 7–20, given that $P = 215$ kip, $D = 21$ in., $p_s = 4000$ lb/ft², $f_c' = 3000$ psi, $M = 50,000$ ft-lb, intermediate-grade steel.

7-5. Design an isolated square footing, Fig. 7–20, given that $P = 150$ kip, $D = 19$ in., $p_s = 6000$ lb/ft², $f_c' = 3000$ psi, $M = 80,000$ ft-lb, intermediate-grade steel.

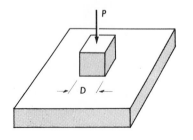

Fig. 7-20. Isolated square footing.

7-6. Design a wall footing, Fig. 7–21, given that $w = 10$ kip/ft, $D = 12$ in., $p_s = 3000$ lb/ft², $f_c' = 2500$ psi, no reinforcement.

7-7. Design a wall footing, Fig. 7–21, given that $w = 15$ kip/ft, $D = 16$ in., $p_s = 3500$ lb/ft², $f_c' = 2500$ psi, no reinforcement.

7-8. Design a wall footing, Fig. 7–21, given that $w = 25$ kip/ft, $D = 20$ in., $p_s = 3000$ lb/ft², $f_c' = 3000$ psi, intermediate-grade steel.

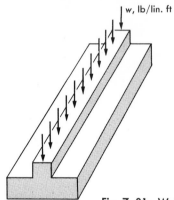

w, lb/lin. ft

Fig. 7-21. Wall footing.

7-9. Design a cantilever footing, Fig. 7–22, given that $P_1 = 200$ kip, $P_2 = 400$ kip, $D_1 = 16$ in., $D_2 = 28$ in., $p_s = 4500$ lb/ft², $f_c' = 3000$ psi, $L = 29$ ft, $a_{max} = 3$ ft (b is not restricted), intermediate-grade steel.

7-10. Design a cantilever footing, Fig. 7–22, given that $P_1 = 200$ kip, $P_2 = 400$ kip, $D_1 = 16$ in., $D_2 = 28$ in., $p_s = 4500$ lb/ft², $f_c' = 3000$ psi, $L = 29$ ft, $b_{max} = 3$ ft (a is not restricted), intermediate-grade steel.

7-11. Design a cantilever footing, Fig. 7–22, given that $P_1 = 250$ kip, $P_2 = 350$ kip, $D_1 = 16$ in., $D_2 = 28$ in., $p_s = 4500$ lb/ft², $f_c' = 3000$ psi, $L = 29$ ft, $a_{max} = 3$ ft (b is not restricted), intermediate-grade steel.

7–12. Design a cantilever footing, Fig. 7–22, given that $P_1 = 250$ kip, $P_2 = 350$ kip, $D_1 = 16$ in., $D_2 = 28$ in., $p_s = 4500$ lb/ft², $f_c' = 3000$ psi, $L = 29$ ft, $b_{max} = 3$ ft (a is not restricted), intermediate-grade steel.

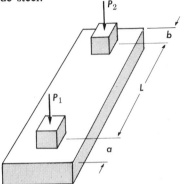

Fig. 7–22. Cantilever footing.

7–13. Design a combined column footing, Fig. 7–23, given that $P_1 = 200$ kip, $P_2 = 400$ kip, $D_1 = 16$ in., $D_2 = 28$ in., $p_s = 3000$ lb/ft², $f_c' = 3000$ psi, $L = 29$ ft, $a_{max} = 3$ ft (b is not restricted), intermediate-grade steel.

7–14. Design a combined column footing, Fig. 7–23, given that $P_1 = 200$ kip, $P_2 = 400$ kip, $D_1 = 16$ in., $D_2 = 28$ in., $p_s = 3000$ lb/ft², $f_c' = 3000$ psi, $L = 29$ ft, $b_{max} = 3$ ft (a is not restricted), intermediate-grade steel.

7–15. Design a combined column footing, Fig. 7–23, to rest on piles when all the load is to be taken by the piles and the allowable load/pile = 60 kip. Given: $P_1 = 200$ kip, $P_2 = 400$ kip, $D_1 = 16$ in., $D_2 = 28$ in., $f_c' = 3000$ psi, $L = 29$ ft, $a_{max} = 3$ ft (b is not restricted), intermediate-grade steel.

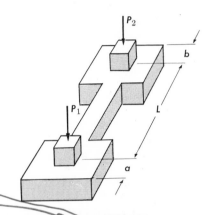

Fig. 7–23. Combined column footing.

7–16. Design a combined column footing, Fig. 7–23, to rest on piles when all the load is to be taken by the piles and the allowable load/pile = 60 kip. Given: $P_1 = 200$ kip, $P_2 = 400$ kip, $D_1 = 16$ in., $D_2 = 28$ in., $f_c' = 3000$ psi, $L = 29$ ft, $b_{max} = 3$ ft (a is not restricted), intermediate-grade steel.

REFERENCES

1. FRANK W. RICHART, "Reinforced Concrete Wall and Column Footings," *ACI Journal,* Oct. 1948 and Nov. 1948.
2. PAUL JAKOWLEW-HERBACZEWSKI, "Concrete Footings for Walls and Columns," *ACI Journal,* Dec. 1951.
3. EIVIND HOGNESTAD, "Shearing Strength of Reinforced Concrete Column Footings," *ACI Journal,* Nov. 1953.

8 TWO-WAY AND FLAT SLABS

Apartment building, Columbus, Ohio. Note the spiral cantilever slab serving the parking garage.

8–1 TYPES OF SLABS

The discussion in Chapter 2 was confined to slabs that are reinforced against bending in one direction only. These slabs, usually referred to as *one-way* slabs (Fig. 8–1), were treated as shallow beams. In this chapter, we shall study slabs supported on all four sides and those supported at four corners. Slabs supported on all sides are known as *two-way* slabs (Fig. 8–3) and are usually square or rectangular in shape. Those supported only at the corners are called *flat* slabs (Fig. 8–12). Both types have two-way reinforcement against bending, although sometimes four-way reinforcement is found for certain designs, i.e., reinforcement in both perpendicular and diagonal directions. Triangular or circular shapes or slabs supported only along two adjacent sides are less common.

182

Fig. 8–1. One-way slab.

(a)

(b)

Fig. 8–2. (a) Waffle slab. (b) Pan-joist slab.

The type of slab chosen for a particular design may depend on factors such as appearance, utility, and economy. Usually economy plays an important role in the choice of floor systems. Hence, when deciding the type of slab construction to be adopted, the designer should give careful consideration to such matters as site conditions, size of building, labor and material costs, and possible changes of construction techniques. For instance, flat-plate or waffle-slab systems require the least total floor depth, thus reducing gross story height and bringing about savings in the materials needed for walls, columns, and all other vertical elements, as well as in heating and air conditioning costs. Also, the columns of a flat-plate or waffle system (Figs. 8–2a and 8–14) may be placed in an irregular or staggered pattern, thus offering greater architectural flexibility.

8–2   TWO-WAY SLABS

As mentioned above, slabs of this type are supported at all four edges by beams or girders and have reinforcement in two perpendicular directions. The analysis of these slabs is usually highly indeterminate. The mathematical determination of the moments and shear results in complex expressions that are seldom useful in slab analyses. The Code provides established procedures for analysis and design of such slabs which, although highly empirical, have proved acceptable over the years.

The amount of load distributed in each direction depends on several factors among which are: stiffness of the slab, the ratio of one side to that perpendicular to it, the relative rigidity (with respect to deflection) of the beams or girders supporting the slab, and the type of support conditions (continuous, simply supported, etc.). When the slab is square, and the support conditions are identical for all four sides, the load taken by each direction can be assumed to be equal to one-half of the total. If the slab has a rectangular shape, then for the same support conditions, more load is distributed to the shorter than to the longer span.

Fig. 8–3. Two-way slab.

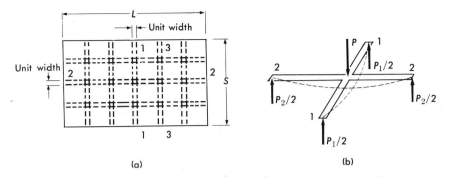

Fig. 8–4. Slab transformed into grid of perpendicular beams.

The uneven load distribution for a rectangular slab may be partially explained as follows: Let us take a rectangular slab of length L and width S, and let us assume that the slab consists of a series of simply supported *cross beams*. The degree of deflection of any two cross beams must be the same at the point of intersection. Hence we can estimate the percentage of the total load carried by each beam by letting the deflections equal each other. For example, in Fig. 8–4(a), let $L = 2S$, and assume a load P is applied at the intersection of beams 1–1 and 2–2, Fig. 8–4(b). The loads taken by the beams are P_1 and P_2, respectively, where $P_1 + P_2 = P$. The deflection at the centerline for the respective beams is

$$\delta_2 = \frac{P_2 L^3}{48EI}, \qquad \delta_1 = \frac{P_1 S^3}{48EI}.$$

Setting $\delta_1 = \delta_2$, we have

$$P_1 = P_2 \left(\frac{L}{S}\right)^3 = P_2 \left(\frac{2S}{S}\right)^3 = 8P_2.$$

If $L = 3S$, then

$$P_1 = P_2 \left(\frac{3S}{S}\right)^3 = 27P_2.$$

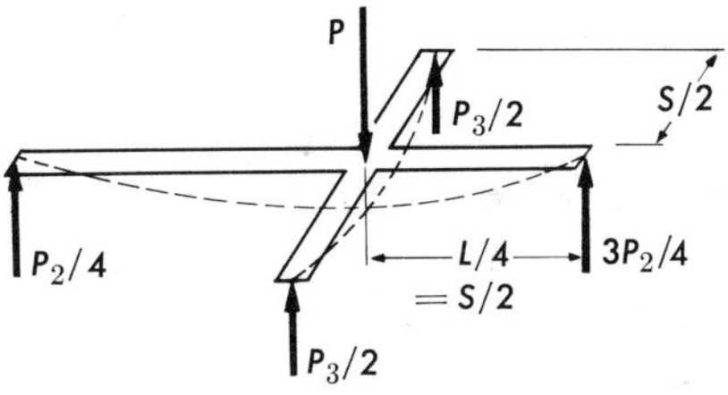

Figure 8–5

For square slabs, $L = S$, and $P_1 = P_2$, etc.

Now take beams 2–2 and 3–3 as shown in Fig. 8–5, and compare those with beams 1–1 and 2–2 in Fig. 8–4(b).

$$P_3 = \frac{9}{16} \left(\frac{L}{S}\right)^3,$$

$$P_3 = \frac{9}{16} \left(\frac{2S}{S}\right)^3 P_2 = 4.5P_2, \qquad \text{when } L = 2S.$$

The comparison shows that the portion of the total load P taken by the longer beam increases near the ends, but is still appreciably less than that of the short-span beam. Therefore, when the long side is twice or more the short side, it is customary to treat the slab as a one-way slab spanning in the short direction.

The above analysis was by no means exact. It could be refined by introducing a finer grid than that used in Fig. 8–4(a) and by considering torsional stiffness of these beams as deflection takes place. The result would still be inexact since the interaction of these cross beams and deformations (including deformations which behave according to the Poisson-ratio concept) are difficult to take into account. All these considerations add to the mathematical complexity of the analysis, and there is little, if any, "return" for the effort, since the solutions are only as good as the assumed conditions and the materials involved. Analysis of a "diagonal" grid instead of a rectangular one gives results which are somewhat closer to those reported by tests and more complex mathematical analysis. But since a diagonal grid implies a diagonal arrangement of the reinforcement, which is not particularly convenient from the standpoint of bar lengths and spacing, one is still left with the need for a better method.

Tests have shown that these two-way slabs do not actually collapse when some of the steel yields, since the load is transferred to an adjacent portion which has not yet yielded. Thus, before collapse or failure occurs, a large percentage of the steel has actually been called upon to assume the stress.

8–3 TWO-WAY SLABS DESIGNED BY ACI METHOD 2

The ACI Code, Chapter 20 and Appendix A, lists three methods for designing two-way slabs. Each method provides a means for estimating the maximum moments (positive and negative) and maximum shears. Here we will discuss Method 2, perhaps the more commonly used method of the group.

The slab panel is divided into a middle strip and column strips, as shown in Fig. 8–6. The maximum positive bending moment is assumed to occur in the middle strip, and the maximum negative moment in the column strips over the

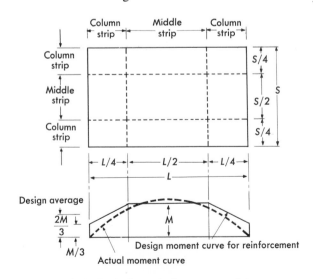

Fig. 8–6. Typical panel of a two-way slab.

TABLE 8–1   Moment Coefficients

Moments	Short span						Long span, all values of m
	Values of m						
	1.0	0.9	0.8	0.7	0.6	0.5 and less	
1. Interior panels Negative moment at:							
Continuous edge	0.033	0.040	0.048	0.055	0.063	0.083	0.033
Discontinuous edge	—	—	—	—	—	—	—
Positive moment at midspan	0.025	0.030	0.036	0.041	0.047	0.062	0.025
2. One edge discontinuous Negative moment at:							
Continuous edge	0.041	0.048	0.055	0.062	0.069	0.085	0.041
Discontinuous edge	0.021	0.024	0.027	0.031	0.035	0.042	0.021
Positive moment at midspan	0.031	0.036	0.041	0.047	0.052	0.064	0.031
3. Two edges discontinuous Negative moment at:							
Continuous edge	0.049	0.057	0.064	0.071	0.078	0.090	0.049
Discontinuous edge	0.025	0.028	0.032	0.036	0.039	0.045	0.025
Positive moment at midspan	0.037	0.043	0.048	0.054	0.059	0.068	0.037
4. Three edges discontinuous Negative moment at:							
Continuous edge	0.058	0.066	0.074	0.082	0.090	0.098	0.058
Discontinuous edge	0.029	0.033	0.037	0.041	0.045	0.049	0.029
Positive moment at midspan	0.044	0.050	0.056	0.062	0.068	0.074	0.044
5. Four edges discontinuous Negative moment at:							
Continuous edge	—	—	—	—	—	—	—
Discontinuous edge	0.033	0.038	0.043	0.047	0.053	0.055	0.033
Positive moment at midspan	0.050	0.057	0.064	0.072	0.080	0.083	0.050

support. The expression for the moments is given by

$$M = CwS^2, \tag{8-1}$$

where C = moment coefficient for two-way slabs as given in Table 8–1,
w = total uniform load per square foot, including the weight of the slab,
S = length of short span for two-way slabs. The span shall be considered as the center-to-center distance between supports or the clear span plus twice the thickness of the slab, whichever is the smaller.

The average moment per foot of width in the *column strip* may be computed by setting C equal to two-thirds of the value used for the *middle strip*. The average bending moment of the column strip may be assumed to vary from a maximum at the edge of the middle strip, where its value equals that of the middle strip, to a minimum of one-third of the average value of the middle strip at the edge of the panel. Figure 8–6 shows the portions defined as middle and column strips, and long and short spans.

The minimum thickness of a slab is the largest of the values found from shear and moment consideration or from Code requirements. Article 2002e of the ACI Code limits the thickness of the slab to no less than $3\frac{1}{2}$ in. or not less than the perimeter of the slab divided by 180. (Article 2104d stipulates different thickness restrictions for *flat* slabs.) Expressing the thickness in equation form yields

$$t = d + \text{bar diameter} + \text{cover, or } \quad t = \frac{2(L \text{ ft} + S \text{ ft})12 \text{ in./ft}}{180} \quad \text{or } \quad t = 3\tfrac{1}{2} \text{ in.,}$$

whichever is the largest.

It is convenient to measure d to the centroid of the areas of the two crossed rows of bars, as shown in Fig. 8–7. It is thus not necessary for the designer to specify whether the short or the long steel span has to be placed first. Note, however, that the shorter span is the more critical, so that it is desirable to have the greater value of d for that steel. Based on the moment and shear calculations ($d_m = \sqrt{M/Kb}$ for $b = 12$ in., a balanced design, and $d = V/bjv$, respectively) the value of d required leads to a conservative design for the bottom reinforcement.

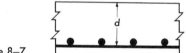

Figure 8–7

The distribution of the slab load for shear in the slab and for the design of the supporting beams is assumed uniform within the tributary areas of the panel bounded by the intersection of 45-degrees lines from the corners with the median line of the panel parallel to the long side (Fig. 8–8). The load taken by the short beams, *AD* or *BC,* is

$$W_s = \frac{wS^2}{4}, \qquad (8\text{–}2)$$

and that taken by the long beams is

$$W_L = \frac{wS^2}{4} \frac{2 - m}{m}, \qquad (8\text{–}3)$$

where $m = S/L$.

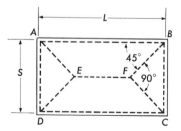

Fig. 8–8. Distribution of slab loads to beams.

To determine the maximum bending moment in the supporting beams, we use the uniform load per foot of beam which, for short spans, is:

$$W_s = \frac{wS}{3},\qquad\qquad(8\text{--}4)$$

and for long spans:

$$W_L = \frac{wS}{3}\,\frac{3-m^2}{2}.\qquad\qquad(8\text{--}5)$$

Example 8–1.

Given: A typical interior slab has to carry a LL of 200 lb/ft². Assume that $f_c' = 3000$ psi, $f_s = 20,000$ psi, and $v = 90$ psi.

Find: An acceptable design for the slab. Use the empirical method 2 in accordance with the ACI Code.

PROCEDURE: According to Fig. 8–9, S is either 15 ft or $S = 15$ ft $- 1$ ft $+ 2t$ ft whichever is the smaller. To approximate S and L let us assume that $t = 5$ in. (This will be checked later.) Therefore

$$
\begin{aligned}
S &= 15\text{ ft} - 1\text{ ft} + 2(5/12)\text{ ft.} = 14.83\text{ ft,}\\
L &= 17\text{ ft} - 1\text{ ft} + 2(5/12)\text{ ft.} = 16.83\text{ ft,}\\
m &= S/L = 0.88.
\end{aligned}
$$

Checking the value of t based on deflection, we find

$$t = \frac{2(L+S)}{12/180},$$

$$t = \frac{2(16.83 + 14.83)}{180} \times 12$$

$$= 4.22\text{ in.} > t_{min} = 3\tfrac{1}{2}\text{ in.,}$$

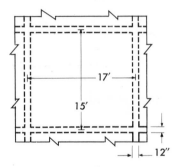

Fig. 8–9. Typical interior panel.

which is satisfactory. We check the t based on shear, given that $t = d + $ bar diameter $+$ cover. Assuming that we have No. 4 bars, a ¾-in. cover, $d = V/bjv$, and a 1-ft strip, we find

$$
\begin{aligned}
V &= [200 + (5/12)150]14.83/2 = 1950,\\
d &= V/bjv = 1950/12 \times 0.88 \times 90 = 2.05\text{ in.,}\\
t &= 2.05 + \tfrac{1}{2} + 0.75 = 3.30\text{ in.} < t_{min} = 3.5\text{ in.}
\end{aligned}
$$

Hence we either use $t = 4.22$ in. or we agree that t determined from the bending moment is the controlling factor. Then

$$\text{LL} + \text{DL} = 200 + (5/12)150 = 263\text{ lb/ft}^2,$$

Therefore

$$M = CwS^2 = C(263)(14.83)^2 \times 12 = 694,000C\text{ in-lb.}$$

TABLE 8–2

		Short span							Long span			
m	Type of moment	C	M	d_m	t_m	t_u, in.	A_s	S_{pg}, in.	C	M	A_s	S_{pg}, in.
0.88	Negative	0.0416	28,870	3.20	4.45	4.5	0.513	4.58	0.033	22,900	0.407	5.89
0.88	Positive	0.0312	21,652	2.77	4.02	4.5	0.444	5.40	0.025	17,350	0.356	6.74

The value of C is given in Table 8–1, under "Case 1. Interior panels." The procedure is presented in tabular form in Table 8–2; the individual steps are explained in detail as needed.

Sample calculations, negative moment, short span (Table 8–2). Analysis of a 1-ft strip.

$$C = 0.040 + 0.02/0.10 \, (0.048 - 0.040) = 0.0416, \quad \text{(from Table 8-1)},$$

$$d_m = \sqrt{M/kb} = \sqrt{694{,}000C/236 \times 12} = \sqrt{245C} = 15.66\sqrt{C}$$
$$= 15.66 \sqrt{0.0416} = 3.20 \text{ in.},$$

$$t_m = d_m + \tfrac{1}{2}\text{-in. bar diameter} + \tfrac{3}{4}\text{-in. cover} = 15.66\sqrt{C} + 1.25 \text{ in.}$$
$$= 3.20 + 1.25 = 4.45 \text{ in.},$$

$t_u = t$ used = the largest of the values of t determined from moment, shear, or required by Code minimum of $3\tfrac{1}{2}$ in. For our case $t_u = 4.45$ in., say 4.5 in.,

$$A_s = M/f_s j d_m = 694{,}000C/20{,}000 \times 0.88 d_m = 39.43C/d_m \text{ in.}^2/\text{ft}$$
$$= 39.43 \times 0.0416/3.20 = 0.513 \text{ in.}^2,$$

min A_s required by Code $= 0.0020bd = 0.024d = 0.0916$ in.^{2},

$S_{pg} =$ spacing of No. 4 bars $= 0.20$ in $\times$ 12 in.$/A_s = 4.58$ in.

The Code limits the maximum spacing to $3t$ (Article 2002e).

The quantity of steel required is calculated according to the formula

$$\text{Number of No. 4 bars} = \frac{\text{Total strip width}}{\text{spacing}}.$$

Note that one-third of the steel area must be carried through the segments of the slab which do not need it for carrying the moment as such. One may safely assume the point of inflection (zero moment) at $\tfrac{1}{8}$ to $\tfrac{1}{6}$ of the clear span. Two-thirds of the bars needed for the positive moment may be bent up at this point to take the negative moment. Also note that two-thirds of the steel must be placed in the middle strips (one-third in each of the two column strips). The steel requirements are as follows (Fig. 8–10):

Short span, middle strip:

Negative moment steel	No. 4 bars	$7.5 \times 12/4.58 = 20$ bars,
Positive moment steel	No. 4 bars	$7.5 \times 12/5.40 = 17$ bars.

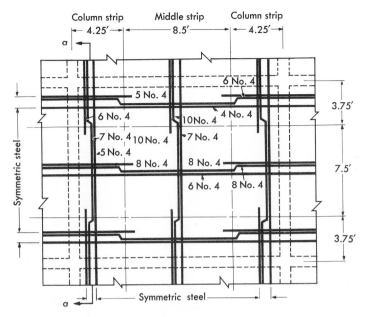

Fig. 8–10. Bar arrangement, symmetrical for the respective sides.

Long span, middle strip:

       Negative moment steel   No. 4 bars $8.5 \times 12/5.89 = 16$ bars,

       Positive moment steel   No. 4 bars $8.5 \times 12/6.74 = 14$ bars.

Note that if No. 4 bars are used throughout, the spacing arrangement will increase the number of bars required by analytical spacing calculations. However, the placing and inspection difficulties encountered when steel of varying sizes is used are frequently more troublesome than is the cost of the "extra" steel necessary when bars of the same size are used—in our case No. 4 bars.

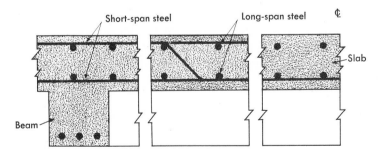

Fig. 8–11. Section *a-a;* typical steel arrangement symmetrical to the right cut.

Since the short span is the more "critical" of the two, the bars reinforcing the short span should be placed near the bottom of the slab surface (Fig. 8–11) in order to increase their moment arm, *d.*

Fig. 8–12. Flat slab.

8–4   FLAT SLABS

The term *flat slab,* Fig. 8–12, refers to concrete slabs that are reinforced in two or more directions and usually do not have beams or girders to transfer the loads directly to supporting columns. Beams may be used for support at the outside of a structure or at openings in the slab; for example, around elevator shafts, stair openings, etc. Except for openings in the slab, flat slabs are supported only at the corners.

Figure 8–13 shows a typical flat-slab support (see also Fig. 8–14). The column diameter is frequently increased at the top to form a *column capital* which will reduce the "punching-through" effect of the column when the slab is fully loaded. *Drop panels* are used whenever additional slab thickness is required

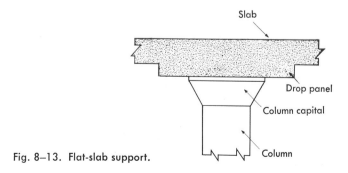

Fig. 8–13. Flat-slab support.

(a)

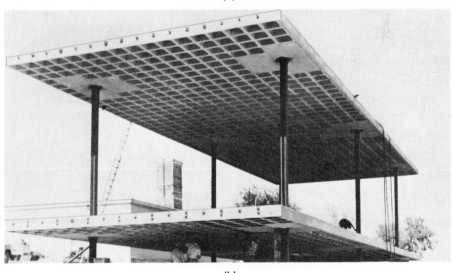

(b)

Fig. 8–14. Note the similarity in supports for the flat-plate slab shown in (a) and the waffle slab shown in (b).

to prevent punch-through failures and to increase the bending resistance of the slab over the support. This type is appreciably heavier (thicker) than the two-way slab supported by beams. It also requires a larger quantity of reinforcing steel than the other type. However, these two apparent disadvantages are more than compensated for by several advantages:

(1) *Economical construction.* This is especially true for heavier live loads. The form work is greatly simplified, and thus the construction cost is substantially reduced.

(2) *Greater clear height.* Eliminating the beams and girders increases the clear height. Conversely, for a given clear height, the overall building height is reduced.

(3) *More pleasant appearance.*

(4) *Functional improvement,* in particular, better fire protection and easier installation of facilities such as lighting, heating pipes, sprinkler systems, etc.

As for two-way slab, or perhaps more so, the analysis of flat slabs is highly indeterminate, and hence an exact analysis is virtually impossible. The ACI Code provides empirical but dependable design specifications based on mathematical analysis and modified to comply with tests results.

8–5   STATICAL ANALYSIS OF SQUARE FLAT SLABS FOR MOMENT

Figure 8–15 shows a square interior flat slab panel of span L, carrying a uniform unit load w. The load produces a negative moment, M_n, over the supports and a positive moment, M_p, along the x–x and y–y sections of zero shear. Assuming that the reaction is uniformly distributed around the edges of the quadrant, we find that the resultant reaction acts at a distance of c/π from the left edge, as shown in Fig. 8–15. Taking moments about the left side yields

$$M_n + M_p + (W/2)(c/\pi) - \left(\frac{w\pi c^2}{8}\right)\frac{c}{\pi} - \frac{W}{2}\frac{l}{4} - \frac{w\pi c^2}{8}\frac{2c}{3\pi} .$$

Substituting wl^2 for W, we have

$$M_n + M_p + \frac{wl^2 c}{2\pi} - \frac{w\pi c^2}{8}\frac{c}{\pi} = \frac{wl^3}{8} - \frac{wc^3}{12} .$$

Letting $M_s = M_n + M_p$, we obtain

$$M_s = \frac{wl^3}{8} + \frac{wc^3}{8} - \frac{wc^3}{12} - \frac{wl^2 c}{2\pi} = \frac{wl^3}{8}\left[1 - \frac{4c}{\pi l} + \frac{1}{3}\left(\frac{c}{l}\right)^3\right].$$

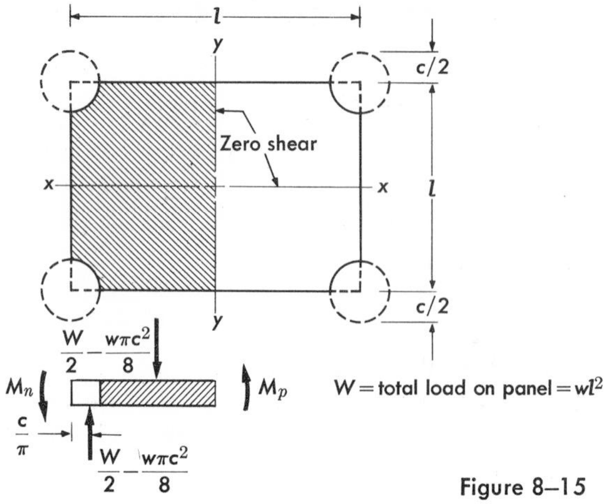

Figure 8–15

The above expression may be reduced as follows. Let

$$\left(1 - \frac{2c}{3l}\right)^2 = 1 - \frac{4c}{3l} + \frac{4c^2}{9l^2} \approx 1 - \frac{4c}{\pi l} + \frac{c^3}{3l^3},$$

when the ratio of (c/l) is small. Thus,

$$M_s = 0.125Wl(1 - 2c/3l)^2.$$

The above formula agrees more closely with tests results if the coefficient 0.125 is replaced by 0.09F:

$$M_0 = 0.09FWl(1 - 2c/3l)^2, \tag{8–6}$$

where $F = 1.15 - c/l$ but not less than 1. This is the formula adopted by the Code.

For a rectangular panel of length l and short span b, the bending moments to be taken by the long-span steel and the short-span steel are, respectively,

$$M_L = 0.09FWl\left(1 - \frac{2c}{3l}\right)^2, \tag{8–6}$$

and

$$M_b = 0.09FWb\left(1 - \frac{2c}{3b}\right)^2. \tag{8–7}$$

Note that the greatest moment is taken by the *long* span—in sharp contrast to the two-way slab where the greatest load is carried by the *short* span.

8–6   DESIGN CONSIDERATION FOR FLAT SLABS

The design of a flat slab consists of (1) proportioning the concrete so that slab thickness, column caps, drop panels, etc., meet the ACI Code specifications governing bending, shear, and diagonal tension, whichever may apply, and (2) selecting the reinforcing steel to meet the Code requirements for bending and bond.

The Code lists two techniques for designing flat slabs: elastic analysis and empirical method. The latter will be discussed here. It makes use of the moment coefficients recommended by the Code. The procedure is explained step by step in Example 8–2. For the present we give a partially condensed version of some of the specifications.

A. *General limitations.* (1) The construction shall consist of at least three continuous panels in each direction.

(2) The ratio of length to width of the panels shall not exceed 1.33.

(3) The grid pattern shall consist of approximately rectangular panels.

(4) The successive span lengths in each direction shall differ by not more than 20% of the longer span.

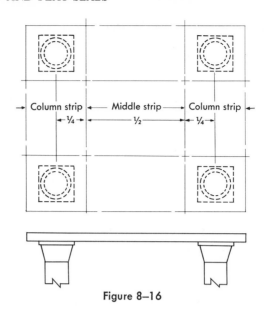

Figure 8–16

B. *Slab thickness.* The slab thickness, span l being the longest side of the panel, shall be at least:

(1) $t_1 = l/36 \geq 5$ in. or $t_1 = 0.028l(1 - 2c/3l)\sqrt{(w'/f_c'/2000)} + 1\frac{1}{2}$ without drop panels; $w' = $ LL $+$ DL per square foot.

(2) $t_2 = l/40 \geq 4$ in. or $t_2 = 0.024l(1 - 2c/3l)\sqrt{w'/f_c'/2000} + 1$ with drop panels; t is given in inches, c and l in feet.

(3) Where the exterior supports provide only negligible restraint for the slab, the values of t in steps 1 and 2 for the exterior panel shall be increased by at least 15%.

C. *Drop panel.* (1) The maximum total thickness of the slab at the drop panel used in computing the negative steel area for the column strip is less than or equal to $1.5t_2$.
(2) The side or diameter of the drop panel shall be at least 0.33 times the span in the parallel direction.

D. *Bending moment coefficients.* The numerical sum of the positive and negative bending moments in the direction of either side of a rectangular panel shall be assumed to be not less than

$$M_0 = 0.09WlF(1 - 2c/3l)^2, \tag{8–6}$$

where $F = 1.15 - c/l$ but not less than 1, and c is defined by Articles 2104c and 2104f3 of the ACI Code.

The distribution of the total moment M_0 (Eq. 8–6) to various design sections is given by Table 8–3, and is further "translated" by Fig. 8–17(a) and (b), which will help the reader to visualize the data of the table.

TABLE 8–3 Moments in Flat Slab Panels in Percentages of M_0

Strip	Column head	Side support type	End support type	Exterior panel			Interior panel	
				Exterior negative moment	Positive moment	Interior negative moment	Positive moment	Negative moment
Column strip	With drop		A	44				
			B	36	24	56	20	50
			C	6	36	72		
	Without drop		A	40				
			B	32	28	50	22	46
			C	6	40	66		
Middle strip	With drop		A	10				
			B	20	20	17*	15	15*
			C	6	26	22*		
	Without drop		A	10				
			B	20	20	18*	16	16*
			C	6	28	24*		
Half column strip adjacent to marginal beam or wall	With drop	1	A	22				
			B	18	12	28	10	25
			C	3	18	36		
		2	A	17				
			B	14	9	21	8	19
			C	3	14	27		
		3	A	11				
			B	9	6	14	5	13
			C	3	9	18		
	With-drop	1	A	20				
			B	16	14	25	11	23
			C	3	20	33		
		2	A	15				
			B	12	11	19	9	18
			C	3	15	25		
		3	A	10				
			B	8	7	13	6	12
			C	3	10	17		

(cont.)

TABLE 8–3 Moments in Flat Slab Panels in Percentages of M_0 (cont.)

Percentage of panel load to be carried by marginal beam or wall in addition to loads directly superimposed thereon	Type of support		
	Side support parallel to strip	Side or end edge condition of slabs of depth t	End support at right angles to strip
0	1	Columns with no beams	
20	2	Columns with beams of total depth $1\frac{1}{4}t$	A
40	3	Columns with beams of total depth $3t$ or more	B
		Reinforced concrete bearing walls integral with slab	
		Masonry or other walls providing negligible restraint	C

* Increase negative moments 30% of tabulated values when middle strip is continuous across support of type B or C. No other values need be increased.

Note: For intermediate proportions of total beam depth to slab thickness, values for loads and moments may be obtained by interpolation.

E. *Arrangement of slab reinforcement.* (1) The spacing of the bars at critical sections shall not exceed 2 times the slab thickness.

(2) In exterior panels, except for bottom bars adequately anchored in the drop panel, all positive reinforcement perpendicular to the discontinuous edge shall extend to the edge of the slab and have embedment, straight or hooked, of at least 6 in. in spandrel beams, walls, or columns where provided. All negative reinforcement perpendicular to the discontinuous edge shall be bent, hooked, or otherwise anchored in spandrel beams, walls, or columns.

(3) The area of reinforcement shall be determined from the bending moments at the critical sections, but shall not be less than 0.0020 bd at any section.

(4) Required splices in bars may be made wherever convenient, but preferably away from points of maximum stress. The length of any such splice shall be at least that given by Article 805 of the Code.

Example 8–2.

Given: A flat slab 8 panels wide and 12 panels long. It carries a uniform live load of 200 lb/ft². The panels are square, placed 22 ft apart center-to-center of the columns. Assume that $f_c' = 3000$ psi, $f_s = 20,000$ psi, $n = 10$, $v = 90$ psi, $u = 300$ psi.

Find: An acceptable design for a typical *interior* panel.

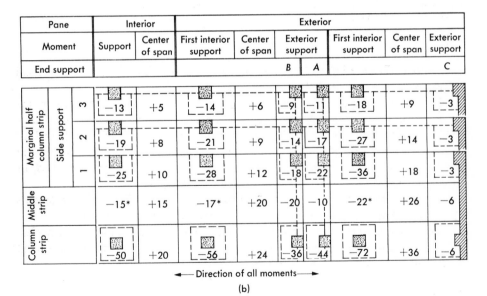

Table (a)

Panel		Interior		Exterior						
Moment		Support	Center of span	First interior support	Center of span	Exterior support		First interior support	Center of span	Exterior support
End support						B	A			C
Marginal half column strip — Side support	3	−12	+6	−13	+7	−8	−10	−17	+10	−3
	2	−18	+9	−19	+11	−12	−15	−25	+15	−3
	1	−23	+11	−25	+14	−16	−20	−33	+20	−3
Middle strip		−16*	+16	−18*	+20	−20	−10	−24*	+28	−6
Column strip		−46	+22	−50	+28	−32	−40	−66	+40	−6

◄—Direction of all moments—►

(a)

Table (b)

Pane		Interior		Exterior						
Moment		Support	Center of span	First interior support	Center of span	Exterior support		First interior support	Center of span	Exterior support
End support						B	A			C
Marginal half column strip — Side support	3	−13	+5	−14	+6	−9	−11	−18	+9	−3
	2	−19	+8	−21	+9	−14	−17	−27	+14	−3
	1	−25	+10	−28	+12	−18	−22	−36	+18	−3
Middle strip		−15*	+15	−17*	+20	−20	−10	−22*	+26	−6
Column strip		−50	+20	−56	+24	−36	−44	−72	+36	−6

◄—Direction of all moments—►

(b)

Fig. 8–17. (a) Moments in flat slab panels in percentages of M_0 without drops. (b) Moments in flat slab panels in percentages of M_0 with drops.

SOLUTION:

Column capitals and slab thickness. As a trial figure (to be checked later) let us assume that we have a round column capital of about $\frac{1}{5}$ $l = 4.5$ ft diameter $= c$. Then

and

$$t_2 = l/40 = 22 \times 12/40 = 6.6 \text{ in.}$$

$$\left.\begin{array}{l} \\ t_2 = 0.024l(1 - 2c/3l)\sqrt{w'/f_c'/2000} + 1.0; \end{array}\right\} \text{with drop panels}$$

$$w' = LL + DL \text{ per square foot,}$$

$$w' = 200 + (150/12)t_2,$$

$$t_2 = 0.024 \times 22 \left(1 - \frac{2 \times 4.5}{3 \times 22}\right) \sqrt{\frac{200 + 12.5t_2}{3000/2000}} + 1.0,$$

$$t_2 = 0.456\sqrt{133.3 + 8.33t_2} + 1.0.$$

By trial and error, we obtain $t = 7.2$ in. This value will be used.

Bending moments. From Eq. (8–6), $M_0 = 0.09 \ WlF \ (1 - 2c/3l)^2$. Hence

$$W = wl^2 - w\frac{\pi c^2}{4}$$

[see explanation following Eq. (8–7)]. The weight of the drop panel outside the capital may be neglected, and thus we obtain

$$W = (200 + 150 \times 7.2/12)\left[(22)^2 - \frac{\pi(4.5)^2}{4}\right] = 136,000 \text{ lb,}$$

$$F = 1.15 - c/l = 1.15 - 4.5/22 = 0.95.$$

We shall round this result to 1. Since $l = b$ for square panels,

$$M_0 = M_l = M_0 = 0.09 \times 136,000 \times 22 \left(1 - \frac{2 \times 4.5}{3 \times 22}\right)^2 = 201,000 \text{ ft-lb.}$$

Column strip moments. The negative moment is

$$-M_c = -0.5 \times 201,000 = -100,500 \text{ ft-lb}$$

[see Table 8–3 or Fig. 8–17 (b)], and the positive moment is

$$+M_c = +0.2 \times 201,000 = 40,200 \text{ ft-lb.}$$

Middle strip moment. The negative moment is

$$-M_m = -0.15 \times 201,000 = -30,150 \text{ ft-lb,}$$

and the positive moment is

$$+M_m = +0.15 \times 201,000 = 30,150 \text{ ft-lb.}$$

To compute the thickness based on flexure, shear, and diagonal tension, we begin by assuming that the drop panel has dimensions $\frac{1}{3} \times 22$ ft $= 7.33$ ft in each direction.

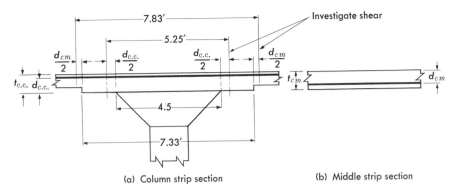

(a) Column strip section   (b) Middle strip section

Fig. 8–18. Column-strip thickness.

For flexure, Article 2102c (1) of the ACI Code permits only ¾ the width of section to be used in $d = \sqrt{M/Kb}$. For the negative moment on the column strip, $K = 236$ (Table 3, Appendix B). Hence

$$d_{c.c.} = \sqrt{\frac{100{,}500 \times 12}{236 \times 7.33 \times 12 \times \frac{3}{4}}} = 8.8 \text{ in.}$$

Therefore, $t_{c.c.} = 8.8$ in. + cover + bar diameter = $8.8 + 0.75 + 0.5$; estimated = 10.05 in., say 10.00 in. This thickness is shown in Fig. 8–18(a).

Since $+M_c = 0.2\, M_0 > M_m$, the positive moment in the column strip will be used to determine the slab thickness between drops. From the moment, M_c, the effective depth, and thickness of the slab we have

$$d_{cm} = \sqrt{\frac{40{,}200 \times 12}{236 \times 7.33 \times 12 \times \frac{3}{4}}} = 5.56 \text{ in., } \quad \text{say 6 in.}$$

Thus

$$t_{cm} = 5.56 + 0.75 + 0.5 = 6.81 \text{ in.}$$

Since this is less than the value of $t_2 = 7.2$ in. prescribed by the Code, we shall use the Code specification. We next check the slab thickness for shear at $d_{cm}/2$ from the edge of the drop panel (see Fig. 8–18a):

$$v = V/bjd,$$

where

$$V = 290[(22)^2 - (7.83)^2] = 122{,}200 \text{ lb,}$$
$$b = 7.83 \times 12 \times 4 = 376 \text{ in.,}$$
$$d = 6; \quad j = 0.88.$$

Thus

$$v = \frac{122{,}200}{376 \times 0.88 \times 6} = 62 \text{ psi,}$$

which is satisfactory since it is less than 90 (ACI Code, Article 2102c2). To check the slab thickness for shear at $d_{c.c.}/2$ from the edge of the capital (see Fig. 8–18a), we compute

$$V = 290\left[(22)^2 - \frac{\pi}{4}(5.25)^2\right] = 134{,}000 \text{ lb},$$

$$b = \text{circumference} = \pi D = \pi(5.25 \times 12) = 198 \text{ in.},$$

$$d \cong 8.8; \qquad j = 0.88.$$

Thus

$$v = \frac{134{,}000}{198 \times 0.88 \times 8.8} = 8.75 \text{ psi},$$

which is again less than 90, and hence satisfactory. The area of steel can now be determined. For clarity the calculations are represented below in tabular form ($A_s = M/f_s jd$), and because of the symmetry, the values are identical for both directions.

Strip	Location	Moment coeffi-cient	Moment, in-k	d used, in.	A_s, in. Required	Minimum required*	Number of selected No. 5 bars†	Bars, area	Spacing Used, in.	2t maximum permitted, ‡ in.
Column	Top	0.50	1207	7.75	8.8	—	29	8.99	4.6	—
	Bottom	0.20	482	5.75	4.72	—	16	4.96	8.1	14.4
Middle	Top	0.15	362	5.75	3.53	1.89	12	3.72	11	14.4
	Bottom	0.15	362	5.75	3.53	1.89	12	3.72	11	14.4

* Minimum $A_s = 0.0020\,bd$, where $b = 22/2 = 11$ ft $= 132$ in.
† The choice of No. 5 instead of No. 4 bars does not warrant rechecking t.
‡ $2t$ is the maximum spacing permitted by the Code.

Before showing the final dimensions, let us investigate the bond. Let us assume that the point of inflection is located at ⅕l from the center of column. Thus, if one imagines each column to support the load outside the region shown by the shaded area in Fig. 8–19, the load

$$V = 290\, l^2[1 - (2/5)^2] = 290(22)^2 \times 0.84 = 117{,}900 \text{ lb}.$$

Therefore, in each direction, $V/4 = 29{,}470$ lb; the "bottom" steel located within the 8.8-ft side consists of $(12/8.1) \times 8.8 \simeq 13$ No. 5 bars. For this, $\sum_0 = 25.5$. Thus

$$\mu = V/\textstyle\sum_0 jd = \frac{29{,}470}{25.5 \times 0.88 \times 5.75} = 228 \text{ psi}.$$

Since 228 < 300 psi, our result is satisfactory.

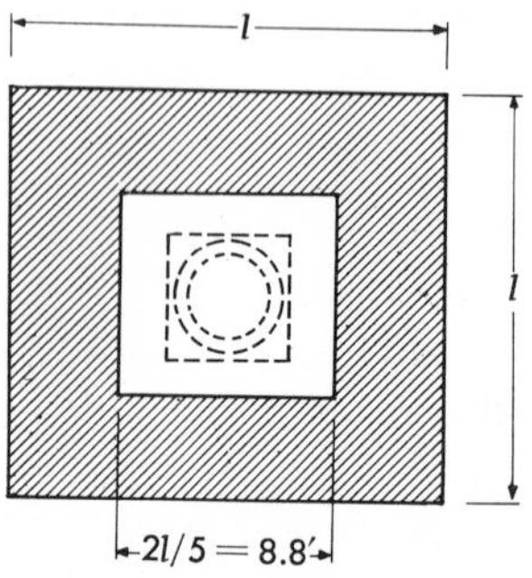

Fig. 8–19. Area loaded for bond investigation.

Columns. The code limits minimum dimensions for a column to 10 in. Also the moment of inertia, I_c, shall be:

$$I_c = t^3 H/[6.5 + (W_{DL}/W_{LL})]$$

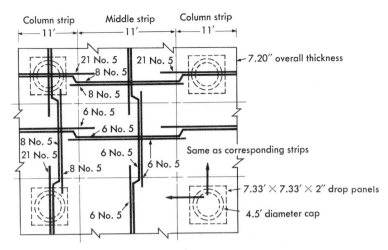

Fig. 8–20. Sketch of dimensions and steel arrangement.

(I_c must be greater than or equal to 1000 in^2), where

t = slab thickness (in our case, 7.20 in.),
H = story height, ft,
W_{LL} and W_{DL} = 200 lb/ft^2 and 90 lb/ft^2, respectively;

it is assumed that $H = 10$ ft. Then

$$I_c = (7.20)^3(10)[0.5 + (90/200)] = 4010 \text{ in}^4 > 1000 \text{ in}^4,$$

which is satisfactory. For a round column,

$$D = (64I_c/\pi)^{1/4} = [(64 \times 4010)/3.14]^{1/4} = 16.9 \text{ in.}$$

This is merely the minimum. The column must still satisfy the conditions governing columns subjected to either axial or eccentric loads as discussed in previous chapters. Also, if there is no column above the slab, the value of I_c of the column below the slab shall be $(2-2.3h/H)$ times that given by the formula with a minimum of 1000 in^4 (ACI Code, Article 2104b).

8–7 LIFT SLABS

These are specially constructed flat-plate slabs. The columns are fixed in place before casting begins. Sleeves or collars which fit loosely around the column are embedded in the concrete. The bottom level is poured first, and this serves as the pouring bed for the following levels, and so on, until all slabs are poured. When cured, the slabs are lifted by hydraulic jack to the desired level where the collar is fixed to the column. Figure 8–21(a) and (b) shows the slabs during the lifting operations. Lifting the slab so that equal increments are maintained at every support is important in order to prevent the generation of excessive stresses in the slab.

Fig. 8–21. Lift slabs at various stages of lifting operations.

The analysis of a lift slab is not covered by the code. It should be pointed out that this type of slab might well lack the rigidity at the column joint that a monolithic slab might exhibit. For this reason, approaching the design of such a slab empirically is likely to produce unreliable or perhaps even misleading results. Perhaps a more realistic approach is the elastic-analysis method explained in the ACI Code.

PROBLEMS

The slab shown in Fig. 8–22 has 5 panels in each direction, with spans as indicated. Because of symmetry, only one-quarter of the total slab is shown. The edge of the slab is on beam supports. The various problems call for design and analysis of both flat and two-way slabs. This combination will provide the reader with the opportunity to familiarize himself with the design of both types of slab and to compare the two with respect to size and economy. The dashed lines represent the centerlines of the rows of columns (or beams for two-way slabs). The

assignment may refer to the whole slab or only to certain panels.

Two-Way Slabs: Design and Analysis

For Problems 8–1 through 8–12, assume that the slab is supported by beams having stems 12 in. wide, whose centerlines are given by the dashed lines in Fig. 8–22.

8–1. Design the corner panel, A, of the slab for a LL of 150 lb/ft², DL = weight of the slab, $f_c' = 3000$ psi, intermediate-grade steel. Show the arrangement of the reinforcement.

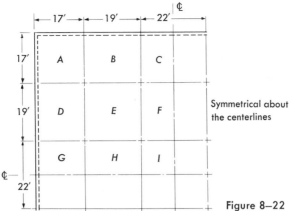

Figure 8–22

8–2. Design the exterior panel, *D*, for LL = 150 lb/ft², DL = weight of slab, $f_c' = 3000$ psi, intermediate-grade steel. Show the arrangement of the reinforcement.

8–3. Design the exterior panel, *G*, of the slab for LL = 150 lb/ft², DL = weight of slab, $f_c' = 3500$ psi, intermediate-grade steel. Show the arrangement of the reinforcement.

8–4. Design the interior panel, *E*, of the slab for LL = 150 lb/ft², DL = weight of slab, $f_c' = 3000$ psi, intermediate-grade steel. Show the arrangement of the reinforcement.

8–5. Design the interior panel, *F*, of the slab for LL = 150 lb/ft², DL = weight of slab, $f_c' = 3000$ psi, intermediate-grade steel. Show the arrangement of the reinforcement.

8–6. Design the interior panel, *I*, of the slab for LL = 150 lb/ft², DL = weight of slab, $f_c' = 3000$ psi, intermediate-grade steel. Show the arrangement of the reinforcement.

8–7. Design the corner panel, *A*, of the slab for LL = 200 lb/ft², DL = weight of slab, $f_c' = 3500$ psi, intermediate-grade steel. Show the arrangement of the reinforcement.

8–8. Design the exterior panel, *D*, of the slab for LL = 200 lb/ft², DL = weight of slab, $f_c' = 3500$ psi, intermedi-

ate-grade steel. Show the arrangement of the reinforcement.

8–9. Design the exterior panel, *G*, of the slab for LL = 200 lb/ft², DL = weight of slab, $f_c' = 3500$ psi, intermediate-grade steel. Show the arrangement of the reinforcement.

8–10. Design the interior panel, *E*, of the slab for LL = 200 lb/ft², DL = weight of slab, $f_c' = 3500$ psi, intermediate-grade steel. Show the arrangement of the reinforcement.

8–11. Design the interior panel, *F*, of the slab for LL = 200 lb/ft², DL = weight of slab, $f_c' = 3500$ psi, intermediate-grade steel. Show the arrangement of the reinforcement.

8–12. Design the interior panel, *I*, of the slab for LL = 200 lb/ft², DL = weight of slab, $f_c' = 3500$ psi, intermediate-grade steel. Show the arrangement of the reinforcement.

Flat Slabs: Design and Analysis

For Problems 8–13 through 8–24, assume that the slab is supported only by columns at the intersections of the dashed lines. Where necessary, assume that there are drop panels and column capitals.

8–13. Design the corner panel, A, of the slab for LL $= 150$ lb/ft^2, DL $=$ weight of slab, $f_c' = 3000$ psi, intermediate-grade steel. Show arrangement of the steel.

8–14. Design the exterior panel, D, of the slab for LL $= 150$ lb/ft^2, DL $=$ weight of slab, $f_c' = 3000$ psi, intermediate-grade steel. Show arrangement of the steel.

8–15. Design the exterior panel, G, of the slab for LL $= 150$ lb/ft^2, DL $=$ weight of slab, $f_c' = 3000$ psi, intermediate-grade steel. Show arrangement of the steel.

8–16. Design the interior panel, E, of the slab for LL $= 150$ lb/ft^2, DL $=$ weight of slab, $f_c' = 3000$ psi, intermediate-grade steel. Show arrangement of the steel.

8–17. Design the interior panel, F, of the slab for LL $= 150$ lb/ft^2, DL $=$ weight of slab, $f_c' = 3000$ psi, intermediate-grade steel. Show arrangement of the steel.

8–18. Design the interior panel, I, of the slab for LL $= 150$ lb/ft^2, DL $=$ weight of slab, $f_c' = 3000$ psi, intermediate-grade steel. Show arrangement of the steel.

8–19. Design the corner panel, A, of the slab for LL $= 200$ lb/ft^2, DL $=$ weight of slab, $f_c' = 3500$ psi, intermediate-grade steel. Show arrangement of the steel.

8–20. Design the exterior panel, D, of the slab for LL $= 200$ lb/ft^2, DL $=$ weight of slab, $f_c' = 3500$ psi, intermediate-grade steel. Show arrangement of the steel.

8–21. Design the exterior panel, G, of the slab for LL $= 200$ lb/ft^2, DL $=$ weight of slab, $f_c' = 3500$ psi, intermediate-grade steel. Show arrangement of the steel.

8–22. Design the interior panel, E, of the slab for LL $= 200$ lb/ft^2, DL $=$ weight of slab, $f_c' = 3500$ psi, intermediate-grade steel. Show arrangement of the steel.

8–23. Design the interior panel, F, of the slab for LL $= 200$ lb/ft^2, DL $=$ weight of slab, $f_c' = 3500$ psi, intermediate-grade steel. Show arrangement of the steel.

8–24. Design the interior panel, I, of the slab for LL $= 200$ lb/ft^2, DL $=$ weight of slab, $f_c' = 3000$ psi, intermediate-grade steel. Show arrangement of the steel.

REFERENCES

1. J. DiStasio and M. P. Van Buren, "Slabs Supported on Four Sides," *ACI Journal,* Jan.–Feb. 1936.
2. Henry D. Dewell and Harold B. Hammill, "Flat Slabs and Supporting Columns and Walls Designed as Indeterminate Structural Frames," *ACI Journal,* Jan.–Feb. 1938.
3. Joseph A. Wise, "Circular Flat Slabs, With Central Column," *ACI Journal,* Jan.–Feb. 1938.
4. Ralph W. Kluge, "Impact Resistance of Reinforced Concrete Slabs," *ACI Journal,* Apr. 1943.
5. Paul Rogers, "Two-Way Reinforced Concrete Slabs," *ACI Journal,* Sept. 1944.
6. R. L. Bertin, Joseph DiStasio, and M. P. Van Buren, "Slabs Supported on Four Sides," *ACI Journal,* June 1945.
7. C. P. Siess and N. M. Newmark, "Rational Analysis and Design of Two-Way Concrete Slabs," *ACI Journal,* Dec. 1948.
8. Eivind Hognestad, "Yield-Line Theory for the Ultimate Flexural Strength of Reinforced Concrete Slabs," *ACI Journal,* Mar. 1953.
9. John F. Brotchie, "General Method for Analysis of Flat Slabs and Plates," *ACI Journal,* July 1957.

9 PRESTRESSED CONCRETE

Lake Pontchartrain bridge, Louisiana, 23.8 mi long and 28 ft wide, prestressed. Completed January 1957.

9–1 INTRODUCTION

Since the tensile strength of concrete is much lower than the compressive strength, the use of the material for reinforced concrete structures is subject to many inherent physical limitations.

(a) In conventionally reinforced concrete beams subjected to bending moments only about one-third of the area (that above the neutral axis) is assumed to take the bending moment. The other two-thirds is not only wasted but is actually a burden in the sense that it adds to the dead weight of the structure.

(b) Because of the "extra heavy" beam necessary to carry the load, a conventionally reinforced concrete beam may, quite conceivably, be *limited* in the *span length,* since the dead-load moment is a direct function of the square of the span.

(c) When subjected to high shear loads, the depth of a conventionally reinforced beam might be governed by the shear stress as a measure of diagonal tension. In view of the inability of concrete to take tensile load, this tension may again be a factor limiting the span of a "conventional" beam since the unwanted weight is there, but the material is not effective.

208

(d) It was pointed out frequently that cracks, especially large cracks, in the portion below the neutral axis are undesirable. However, stretching a structural-grade steel bar beyond a certain limit results in excessive deformation, which in turn permits larger cracks. Hence the working stresses of steel are limited, regardless of the actual strength of the steel. Thus, for example, the working stress might be 25,000 to 30,000 psi, which is only a small fraction of the ultimate stress of some high-strength steels. When one realizes that the modulus of elasticity is the same for both structural and high-strength grades, then it becomes obvious that the *deformation* caused by stretching beyond a certain limit, and not the stresses, governs the magnitudes of the cracks.

From the above it is obvious that neither high-strength steels nor high-strength concretes are called for in conventional design.

The development of the prestress concept was a partial answer to these limitations. However one should not interpret the previously mentioned disadvantages of conventionally designed structures to mean that in all instances prestressed concrete would be more applicable or desirable than ordinary concrete. Prestressed concrete also has disadvantages (to be discussed in the following sections), but these are frequently outweighed by the advantages. It has been consistently emphasized throughout the text that good judgment should always be employed for good design.

9–2 PRINCIPLES OF PRESTRESSING

Figure 9–1 shows three stress cases and the respective loads causing them. In all cases the material is assumed to be elastic. When subjected to moment, a section of a beam might be stressed as shown in Fig. 9–1(a). The same beam is assumed to be stressed uniformly over the section when subjected to a load through the centroid of the area (Fig. 9–1b). If the load is applied eccentrically a distance e from the centroidal axis, the resulting stress is a combination of bending and direct compression, as shown by Fig. 9–1(c).

Now superimposing (a) and (c) in Fig. 9–1 changes the stress distribution even further, as is indicated by Fig. 9–2. In this case, the stress caused by M is combined with that induced by the eccentric load P, the result being a uniform

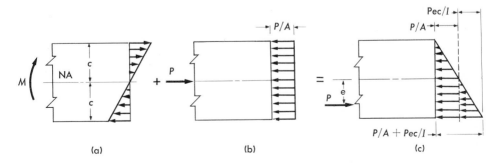

Figure 9–1

compressive stress, which, for several reasons, is a marked improvement over the situation shown in Fig. 9–1(a): the danger of tension cracks is reduced or even eliminated, a more efficient cross section is realized (a greater percentage of concrete may be stressed), and a higher-grade steel (higher stresses) may be used. Also, the use of higher-strength concrete might prove economical.

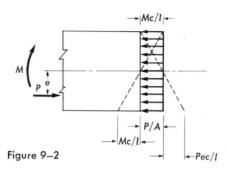

Figure 9–2

The stress condition illustrated in Fig. 9–2 may be obtained by prestressing, i.e. by pretensioning or posttensioning a concrete beam. The prestressing force in the longitudinal reinforcement provides the force P. The moment M comes from the externally applied transverse load and the dead weight.

9–3   METHODS OF PRESTRESSING BEAMS

Beams are prestressed by stretching high-strength steel wire, wire strands, or bars. This may be accomplished by either pretensioning or posttensioning.

Pretensioning refers to the process of placing the longitudinal reinforcement in tension before the concrete is cast. The bars or wire strands are stretched between fixed anchors and held in this state. The concrete is then poured around the steel, cured, and hardened. Then the reinforcement is released, usually by cutting it. In the meantime, a bond has formed between the steel and the concrete, which prevents the steel from contracting to its original length, thus inducing an initial compressive stress in the concrete.

Pretensioning is usually carried out in a plant, rather than on the building site. Economy of fabrication dictates this arrangement. Basically, the pouring bed, as it is frequently called, consists of two fixed heads or abutments. The wire is fixed at one abutment and stretched at the other, usually by hydraulic jacks, as illustrated in Fig. 9–3(a). Figure 9–3(b) shows an actual pouring bed, and the wire strand anchored to the abutment. Providing the bed with heating facilities for accelerated curing, making it long enough for simultaneous multiple-beam pours, and using high-early cements are some of the factors which make for efficient operation.

Wire or wire strand, rather than bars, is customarily used for pretensioning. This choice is dictated by two reasons: (1) a better bond is developed on wire

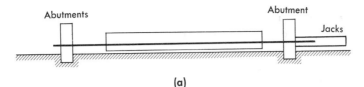

(a)

(b)

Fig. 9–3. Pouring bed for prestressed beams.

or wire strand than on bars because the ratio of surface area to cross sectional area is greater for wire than for bars; (2) since wire or wire strand can be shipped on spools, it permits a long pour (several beams) with much greater ease than bars do.

Posttensioning. In this method, the longitudinal reinforcement is not bonded with the concrete. If it is in place when the concrete is poured, the wire or rods may be greased or "wrapped" to prevent bonding, or the reinforcement may be introduced after the concrete is poured and set, by providing a conduit path (tubes, hoses, etc.) through which the reinforcing may be treaded. The reinforcing is then stretched and anchored at the ends of the beam by wedges (cylindrical ones are commonly used) or nuts. When released, the stretched wires tend to contract and in this manner compress the concrete.

The posttension system of fabrication is more laborious and less adaptable to mass production than the pretensioning process, but it does have some advantages over the other: it is less influenced by early creep and shrinkage of the concrete because the "stretching" can be delayed until a substantial portion of shrinkage has taken place or, under special circumstances, the steel may be even restretched to correct losses of prestress due to creep and shrinkage before the beams are used.

9–4 SOME PRETENSION LOSSES

Part of the initial pretension load in the steel is lost as a result of elastic deformation, creep (sometimes referred to as plastic strain), and shrinkage. Steels may also experience permanent deformations from creep, but at ordinary temperatures, these losses are small compared with those in the concrete. For this reason, they are often ignored in design.

Elastic deformation. When the load from the reinforcement is transferred to the concrete, as is the case, for example, when the wire strand is cut, the concrete is placed in compression. This compressive force causes a deformation in the concrete which may be assumed to follow Hooke's law up to a point (usually less than the yield point), and within this limit, the deformation is assumed to be elastic.

While the concrete creeps, the load in the steel is reduced accordingly. In other words, there occurs a loss in pretension due to the elastic deformation of the materials which, however, is compensated for in the design by "adding" an estimated amount of pretension. The following example illustrates the pretension losses due to elastic deformation.

Example 9–1. *Analysis*

Given: The steel reinforcement for a prestressed slab (Fig. 9–4) was pretensioned to a stress f_{s0}. The ratio of the cross-sectional area of steel to that of concrete is $\frac{1}{30}$; $n = 8$. Assume that there is no eccentricity.

Find: (a) Final stresses in concrete and steel in terms of f_{s0}. (b) Loss of pretension stress due to elastic deformation.

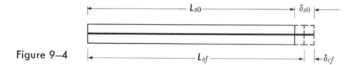

Figure 9–4

SOLUTION: We base our calculations on Fig. 9–4 and the following notation:

$$L_{s0} = \text{original length of steel before pretension,}$$
$$L_{sf} = \text{final length of steel after pretension release,}$$
$$\delta_{s0} = \text{elongation of steel caused by pretension,}$$
$$\delta_{cf} = \text{contraction of concrete after pretension,}$$
$$f_{sf} = \text{final steel stress after pretension release,}$$
$$f_{rf} = \text{final concrete stress.}$$

We have $\delta_{sf} = \delta_{s0} - \delta_{cf}$. From the expression

$$\delta = \frac{P}{A}\frac{L}{E} = f\frac{L}{E},$$

we find

$$f_{sf}(L/E_s) = f_{s0}(L/E_s) - f_{cf}(L/E_c) \quad \text{or} \quad f_{sf} = f_{s0} - (E_s/E_c)f_{cf}.$$

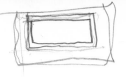

Substituting the given values, $E_s/E_c = 8$; $f_{cf} = \frac{1}{30} f_{sf}$ in the equation above, and using $(fA)_{\text{concrete}} = (fA)_{\text{steel}}$, we have

$$f_{sf} = f_{s0} - 8 \cdot \frac{1}{30} f_{sf}, \qquad f_{sf} = \frac{30}{38} f_{s0} = \frac{15}{19} f_{s0}.$$

Thus our answers are (a) $f_{sf} = \frac{15}{19} f_{s0}$; $f_{cf} = \frac{1}{30} \cdot \frac{15}{19} f_{s0} = \frac{1}{38} f_{s0}$, and (b) loss of pretension stress is $\frac{4}{19} f_{s0}$.

Creep. When subjected to a sustained load, concrete experiences an increasing and cumulative deformation. Similarly, concrete subjected to a repeated application of loads, such as that induced by fatigue cycles, will deform beyond the instantaneous elastic strain. This type of plastic deformation is commonly referred to as *creep,* although the term "plastic flow" is occasionally used to describe this phenomenon.

Creep is perhaps the most important loss that must be taken into consideration in the design of prestressed beams. Its magnitude depends on many variables, not all of which are known or clearly understood. Experiments over the last 30 years have shown that the magnitude of the sustained load, the time of loading, the material itself, and the environmental conditions (including curing and temperature) are factors which affect the magnitude and rate of creep (time and rate are interrelated).

Because of all these variables, the magnitude of creep cannot be easily expressed in terms of absolute magnitudes. Yet the designer needs absolute values. Some investigators have reported creep magnitudes as high as four times those of elastic strain.

It is difficult, if not actually impossible, to differentiate between creep and shrinkage (shrinkage is discussed in the next paragraph) for a specimen subjected to load. The results most frequently reported cover both creep and shrinkage subsumed under the term "plastic flow."

The author carried out tests on both conventionally reinforced and prestressed (pretensioned and posttensioned) concrete beams under sustained load and under repeated load applications (fatigue type). The results showed a deformation beyond the elastic strain amounting up to three times the instantaneous "elastic strain." Figure 9–5 shows a typical creep curve for beams tested under

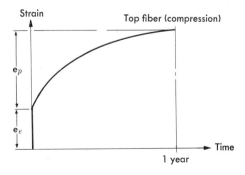

Fig. 9–5. Creep from beams under sustained load.

sustained load. The total creep amounted to approximately $\frac{3}{4}$ μin. for each inch of stress. The author believes that for concrete that is well vibrated and for which high-early cement is used, the creep (including shrinkage) can be safely and reasonably approximated by $\epsilon_c = \frac{3}{4} \times 10^{-6}$ in/in/psi.

The rate of creep is high during the early stages of loading and then decreases with time. In most instances it is safe to assume that 80 to 90% of the expected creep will occur in the first 6 months of load time. The rest will occur over a much longer period.

Shrinkage. Shrinkage is the deformation caused by the capillary forces that arise from temperature changes, chemical reaction, and water content in the concrete. Its rate of occurrence is somewhat similar to that of creep although the magnitudes of the two phenomena are different. As in the case of creep, most of the shrinkage occurs during the first six months. However, the magnitude of shrinkage deformation is appreciably less than that of creep.

Shrinkage is affected by many variables, and its magnitude is reported to vary from 200×10^{-6} in/in to 600×10^{-6} in/in. For design purposes, a value of 200 to 300 μin. may be used. Investigators and designers alike agree on the need for additional information on this subject, as well as on creep.

Example 9–2.

Given: For a prestressed concrete beam subjected to bending, we have

$$f_c' = 5500 \text{ psi}, \qquad f_s' = 225{,}000 \text{ psi},$$
$$E_c = 5.5 \times 10^{-6} \text{ psi}, \qquad E_s = 27 \times 10^{-6} \text{ psi}.$$

Find: Approximate loss of pretension stress.

PROCEDURE: Let us assume a working stress of $f_c = 2000$ psi and $f_s = 150{,}000$ psi.

It is quite unlikely that $f_c = 2000$ psi at all times. It is more probable that the average sustained stress is less than 50% of that, i.e., 1000 psi. Even this value might not be the average, but rather the value reached by the maximum stressed fiber, i.e., the extreme fiber. At any rate, our analysis is a guess, at best.

Let the probable deformation be Δf_c. Then

$$\Delta f_c = \text{elastic strain} + \text{creep} + \text{shrinkage} + \text{negligible steel creep},$$
$$\Delta f_c = 1000 \text{ psi}/E_c + \tfrac{3}{4} \times 1000 \times 10^{-6} + 350 \times 10^{-6},$$

where $E = 5.5 \times 10^6$ psi,

$$\Delta f_c = (182 + 750 + 350) \times 10^{-6} = 1282 \times 10^{-6},$$
$$\Delta f_s = E_s \times 1282 \times 10^{-6} = 30 \times 10^{+6} \times 1282 \times 10^{-6} = 38{,}460 \text{ psi}.$$

Even with rather high estimates of sustained stress, the loss of prestress is less than 30% of the working stress of steel. Thus, a loss of 20 to 25% may be a more realistic assumption.

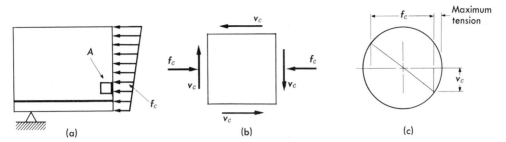

Fig. 9–6. Stresses acting on an element subjected to prestressing. (a) Assumed stress distribution for a prestressed section at full load. (b) Element A. (c) Mohr circle for stress on element A.

9–5 SHEAR AND DIAGONAL TENSION

As mentioned previously in this chapter, one of the advantages of a pre-stressed-beam design is the elimination of diagonal cracks that occur as a result of diagonal tension. Since the prestressed beam is so designed that some compression acts over the entire depth at all times, diagonal tension stresses are likely to be very small. This could be shown as follows: Let us assume that a small element A is taken out from a portion of the beam, say near the support where the shear and pretension stresses are likely to be the greatest under full load (DL and LL). Let v_c be the shear stresses on this element and f_c, the net compressive stress at full load. These stresses are shown to act on the element in Fig. 9–6(b). When a Mohr circle for this stress condition is constructed, Fig. 9–6(c), we see that the maximum tensile stress becomes

$$f_t = \sqrt{v_c{}^2 + (f_c/2)^2} - f_c/2.$$

As f_c approaches zero, f_t approaches a maximum, which is v_c (v_c is a maximum at that support of a simple-span beam where V is the greatest). Unless the reinforcement depth is adjusted with moment, the pretension stress in the concrete is reduced most where the bending moment is a maximum, thus making f_c a minimum at the "lower" depth of the beam, i.e., near the reinforcement.

The magnitudes of f_c and v_c for a prestressed beam may be calculated as follows. Let us assume that for the beam shown in Fig. 9–7, the centroid of the

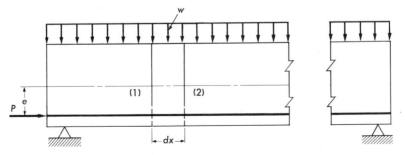

Fig. 9–7. Prestressed beam.

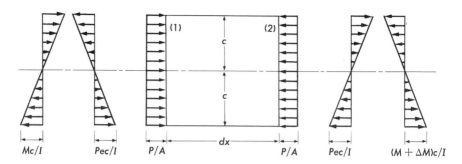

Fig. 9–8. Flexure stress on two faces of an element of length dx.

pretensioned reinforcement is eccentric, with e as shown. Let us take an increment of length dx, from that beam, as shown in Fig. 9–7. The bending stresses on faces (1) and (2) caused by the eccentric load P and by the bending moment from the load are shown in Fig. 9–8. The moment diagram for DL and LL gives M_1 and M_2 as the bending moments at faces (1) and (2), respectively, or $M_2 = M_1 + dM$. Thus the flexure stress is $f_c = P/A \pm Pey/I \pm My/I$. The flexure stresses on the two faces are also shown in Fig. 9–8. The difference of the two forces, dF, caused by dM (Fig. 9–9a) must be taken up by the shear force induced through the shear stress:

$$v_c\, b\, dx = dF = \int_{y_2}^{c_2} \left(\frac{dMy}{I}\right) dA = \frac{dM}{I} \int_{y_2}^{c_2} y\, dA,$$

from which

$$v_c = \frac{dM}{dx}\frac{1}{Ib} \int_{y_2}^{c_2} y\, dA = \frac{V}{Ib} \int_{y_2}^{c_2} y\, dA,$$

where $V = dM/dx$. We now set $\int_{y_2}^{c_2} y\, dA$, the statical moment about the neutral axis of the area below (or above) the level at which the shear stress v_c is desired, equal to Q. Then

$$v_c = \frac{VQ}{Ib}.$$

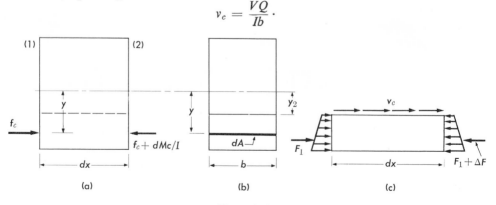

Figure 9–9

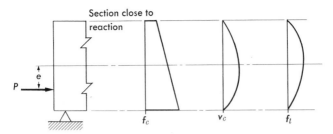

Fig. 9–10. Relationship of compressive, shear, and diagonal tension stresses as represented by the equations given in this article.

(For a rectangular cross section, the greatest value of v_c occurs at $d/2$, as can be seen from a plot of the above equation.

The code does not specify the permissible value for v_c. However, a value considerably above that given for shear as a measure of diagonal tension is considered safe. A shearing stress $v_c = 0.1f_c'$ is generally considered safe and acceptable.

The increase in the shearing stress may mean a substantial reduction in the web thickness of the beam, i.e., the prestressed beam section may be designed as an I-beam instead of a rectangular section. This not only reduces the volume of concrete and makes for easier handling due to the decrease in weight, but permits longer spans since the dead weight is reduced. Furthermore, a rectangular section usually requires more reinforcement because the pretension force needed for a given pretension stress distribution is greater for rectangular than for I-beams. Yet the moment of inertia does not vary at the same rate.

Web reinforcement for pretensioned beams is rarely required. However, for thin webs, a small amount of reinforcement may be warranted near the ends of the beam, i.e., near the supports if there exists the possibility of "slippage" of the strand (anchorage failure resulting in a reduction of pretension at that point). A thicker web at supports is also a possibility that should be kept in mind.

The various stresses, bending, shear, and diagonal tension over the cross section of a beam, are illustrated in Fig. 9–10.

9–6   DESIGN OF PRETENSIONED BEAMS

Given: LL + DL = 450 lb/lin. ft (not including weight of beam), span = 40 ft, $f_c' = 6000$ psi, $f_{su} = 250,000$ psi, $n = 6$ (use ⅜ in. strand, $A = 0.08$ in²).

Design: a beam suitable to carry the load given.

PROCEDURE. We shall assume that the design provides an I-section (to be examined later), that the working stresses for concrete and steel are 2250 psi and 150,000 psi, respectively, and that there is a 20% loss of pretension caused by shrinkage, elasticity, slippage, and creep (both steel and concrete). Only the center section of the span shall be investigated, and the results used for the whole span.

Fig. 9–11. Pretensioning of wire strand with a hydraulic jack.

For trial purposes, make the following assumptions (author's own rule of thumb): We have a relatively light load, $d \cong 0.5L$ to $1L$ and $b/d \cong \frac{1}{2}$, where only the magnitude of L is taken, in feet; d and b are in inches. The flange thickness equals the strand diameter plus spacing of rows and cover, and the web thickness equals the strand diameter plus cover.

For our case, let us assume

$$d = 0.5 \times 40 = 20 \text{ in.}, \qquad b = 10 \text{ in.}$$

Let us assume that the web houses some of the longitudinal reinforcement, let us say two rows of strands in the lower flange. We have

Web thickness $= 1\frac{1}{2}$-in. cover $+ \frac{3}{8}$-in. cover $+ 1\frac{1}{2}$-in. strand $= 3\frac{3}{8}$, or approximately 3.5 in.

Flange thickness $= 1\frac{1}{2}$ in. $+ \frac{3}{8}$ in. $+ 1$ in. $+ \frac{3}{8}$ in. $+ 1\frac{1}{2}$ in. $= 4\frac{3}{4}$ in.

Neglecting the steel, we find that the cross sectional area (Fig. 9–12) is

$$A = 10 \times 20 - (10 - 3.5)10.5 = 131.75 \text{ in}^2,$$

$$\text{weight} = (A/144)150 \cong 138 \text{ lb/lin. ft},$$

$$I = \frac{10 \times 20^3}{12} - \frac{(10 - 3.5)(10.5)^3}{12} = 6039 \text{ in}^4.$$

$$\text{Total load} = 450 + \text{weight} = 588 \text{ lb/ft},$$

$$M \text{ at } \text{\cent} = \frac{588(40)^2}{8} = 117,600 \text{ ft-lb} = 1,411,200 \text{ in-lb}.$$

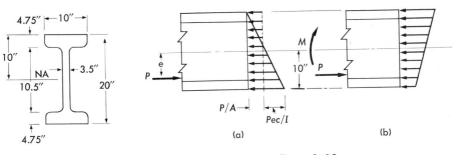

Figure 9–12   Figure 9–13

We now check the section. The permissible moment based on $f_c = 2250$ psi is

$$M = \frac{f_c I}{c} = \frac{2250 \times 6039}{10} = 1{,}358{,}775 \text{ in-lb},$$

and we see that M_{actual} is 4% greater than the permissible moment. Note that our calculation was based on the assumption that the section did not contain any steel. When steel is included, I increases slightly. Therefore, the section obtained will be tentatively accepted with the proviso that it will be checked later.

When the cable is cut, and before the transverse load is applied, the stress diagram over the section is as shown in Fig. 9–13(a). Zero stress at the top is usually desired under this condition, since tension on that face might cause cracks. Hence we find at the top:

$$0 = \frac{P}{A} - \frac{Pec}{I} = P\left(\frac{1}{A} - \frac{ec}{I}\right),$$

and since $P \neq 0$,

$$\frac{I}{A} - ec = 0, \quad \text{or} \quad e = \frac{I}{Ac} = \frac{6039}{131.75 \times 10} = 4.58 \text{ in.}$$

At the bottom we assume that after M is applied, $f_{\text{bottom}} = 100$ psi compression, a nominal stress slightly greater than zero. Therefore

$$f_{\text{bottom}} = \frac{P}{A} + \frac{Pec}{I} - \frac{Mc}{I} = P\left(\frac{1}{A} + \frac{ec}{I}\right) - \frac{Mc}{I},$$

$$100 = P\left(\frac{1}{131.75} + \frac{45.8}{6029}\right) - \frac{1{,}411{,}200 \times 10}{6029},$$

$$P = \frac{100 + 2340}{(0.759 + 0.759) \times 10^{-2}} = 160{,}670 \text{ lb.}$$

If there is no loss due to creep, shrinkage, elasticity, etc., then

$$A_s = \frac{160{,}670}{150{,}000} = 1.0711 \text{ in}^2.$$

At a 20% loss, A_s is increased to $1.0711/0.80 = 1.3388$ in².

If a $\frac{3}{8}$ in. strand is used, $A_s = 0.08$ in², the number of strands required is $1.3388/0.08 = 16.75$, say 17 strands. Ten strands will be placed in the bottom flange as shown in Fig. 9–14. The remaining 7 will be placed in the web. The center of gravity of the 7 must be such that the center of gravity of all 17 strands is 4.58 in. $= e$ from the neutral axis. The distance from line 0 to the center of gravity is 10 in. $- 4.75/2$ in. $- 4.58$ in. $= 3.05$ in., say 3 in. Thus

$$3.0 \text{ in.} = \frac{7 \times \bar{y}_7}{17}; \qquad \bar{y}_7 = 7.28 \text{ in.}$$

Now compare the transformed area and the moment of inertia of the new section with the original one. The neutral axis shifts only a negligible amount with the strands in place. The center of gravity (c.g.) of the 7 strands is 10 in. $-$ 7.28 in. $- 4.75/2$ in. $= 0.35$ in. from the neutral axis (NA) of the section. Thus, for simplicity, place one strand at about NA, the other 6 at a distance of about 1.75 in. apart, as shown in Fig. 9–14. The transformed area is $A = 131.75 + 5 \times 0.08 \times 17 = 138.55$ in², approximately, where 5 represents $(n - 1)$.

$I = 6039 + \{2[(1.75)^2 + (3.5)^2 + (5.25)^2]$
$\qquad + 5[(7.10)^2 + (8.74)^2]\} 0.08 \times 5,$

$I = 6039 + 278 = 6317 \text{ in}^4.$

The increase in percent is

$$A = \frac{(138.55 - 131.75)}{131.75} \times 100 = 5.2\%,$$

$$I = \frac{(6310 - 6029)}{6029} \times 100 = 4.3\%.$$

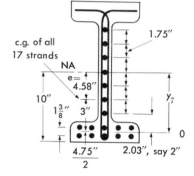

Figure 9–14

The difference that these changes make in the calculations is not considered enough to warrant a rerun. Note, however, that the new value of I is sufficiently greater that the allowable moment is slightly increased over the applied one.

If the eccentricity of the steel is kept constant for the whole length of the beam, the stress diagram is not the same at the mid-span as it is at the ends, since the moments at the center are different from those at the ends. Decreasing the eccentricity, e, of the strands is not always advisable. Careful attention should be given to anchorage, and consequently slippage, the section modulus and stress, all related to e, when the variable eccentricity is considered.

We now continue our calculations, and find that the horizontal shear stress at the end is $v_c = VQ/Ib$, and at mid-depth,

$$Q = (10 \times 10 \times 10/2) - 5.25 \times 6.5 \times (6.5/2) = 390 \text{ in}^3,$$
$$V = \text{reaction} = \tfrac{1}{2}(\text{total LD}) = 588 \times 20 = 11,760 \text{ lb},$$
$$I = 6317 \text{ in}^4, \qquad b = 3.5 \text{ in},$$
$$v_c = \frac{11,760 \times 390}{3.5 \times 6317} = 207 \text{ psi}.$$

which is less than $0.1f_c'$, and hence acceptable, since $0.1f_c'$ is considered a reasonable value for a prestressed section.

The diagonal tension is

$$f_t = \sqrt{v_c{}^2 + (f_c/2)^2} - f_c/2,$$
$$f_t = \sqrt{(207)^2 + (1170/2)^2} - (1170/2) = 44 \text{ psi} \quad \text{(satisfactory)},$$

where 1170 is approximately the compressive stress at mid-depth obtained from M_c/I or $f_c = [(1{,}411{,}200 \times 10/6317) + 100]/2 = 1170$ psi.

For cracks to occur at the bottom at mid-span, the moment has to become greater than 1,411,200 in-lb., that is, the 100-psi bottom stress (compression under full load) + tensile stress must be overcome. Assuming the tensile strength of the concrete to be 10% of the compressive strength (see Chapter 1, Article 1–8), we find that the additional moment required to overcome the stress of 100 psi + 0.1 × 600 psi = 700 psi is (from $f = MC/I$):

$$\text{Additional } M = fI/c = 700 \times 6317/10 = 442{,}190 \text{ in-lb.}$$

Thus the moment causing the cracks is

$$1{,}411{,}200 \text{ in-lb} + 442{,}190 \text{ in-lb} = 1{,}853{,}390 \text{ in-lb.}$$

This result could also be expressed in terms of the safety factor, that is:

$$\text{SF} = \frac{1{,}853{,}390}{1{,}411{,}200} = 1.32.$$

To tie in place the strands passing through the web, it is advisable to use No. 3 bars approximately 2 ft apart center-to-center: they serve as ties (or spacers) for the strands and at the same time as web reinforcement (see detail shown in Fig. 9–14).

The Code specifies that the required ultimate load on a member determined in accordance with structural analysis and proportioning of members (ultimate-strength design) shall not exceed the ultimate flexural strength which is given for

(1) rectangular sections, or flanged sections in which the neutral axis lies within the flange, by

$$M_u = \phi[A_s f_{su}\, d(1 - 0.59q')] = \phi[A_s f_{su}(d - a/2)],$$

where

$$a = \frac{A_s f_{su}}{0.85 f_c' b};$$

and (2) flanged sections in which the neutral axis falls outside the flange, by

$$M_u = \phi\left[A_{sr} f_{su}\left(1 - \frac{0.59 A_{sr} f_{su}}{b'\, d f_c'}\right) + 0.85 f_c'(b - b')t(d - 0.5t)\right],$$

where

$$A_{sr} = A_s - A_{sf}, \quad \text{and} \quad A_{sf} = \frac{0.85 f_c'(b - b')t}{f_{su}}.$$

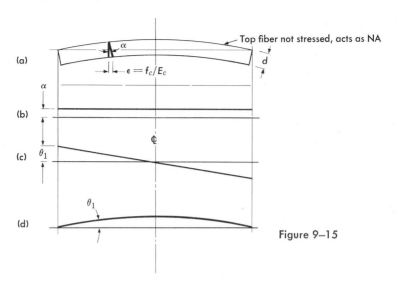

Figure 9–15

9–7   DEFLECTION OF PRESTRESSED BEAMS

Due to prestressing, a beam bends upward, and due to the transverse loads, DL and LL, it bends downward. The net deflection may be calculated by superimposing these two loads.

The upward deflection caused by pretensioning is due to the difference in the elastic deformation of the two faces (top and bottom) and to the plastic deformation (creep and shrinkage). Let us assume that immediately after prestressing, the deformation is purely elastic and that it varies as a function of stress assumed approximately zero at the top and a maximum at the bottom. Let us assume further that the eccentricity is constant for the entire length of the beam. This makes the strain the same for any section of the beam. The curvature in Fig. 9–15(a) is highly exaggerated. Therefore $\tan \alpha = \alpha = \epsilon/d = f_c/dE_c = a$ is constant for the whole beam, for the assumed constant eccentricity. The magnitude of α at any one point on the span is represented in Fig. 9–15(b). The slope of the deflection curve at, say the left support, and the deflection at the center of the span may be found by means of the area-moment theorems, or by integration, etc. (see a text on theory of structures). Using the moment-area theorems and taking moments about the left end of one-half the area under the α-diagram, we find that the deflection at the centerline due to the prestressing force P_r is

$$\delta_{\math₵ P_r} = \alpha \frac{L}{2} \frac{L}{4} = \frac{f_c}{dE_c} \frac{L^2}{8} \times 144 \text{ in}^2/\text{ft}^2,$$

$$\delta_{P_r} = \frac{18L^2 f_c}{E_c d} \quad \text{(inches)}. \tag{9–1}$$

Similarly, due to the uniformly distributed DL, the beam tends to bend downward. At the centerline,

$$\delta_{\mathfrak{C}DL} = \frac{5wL^4}{384EI} \times 1728 \text{ in}^3/\text{ft}^3,$$

$$\delta_{DL} = \frac{45}{2} \frac{wL^4}{EI} \quad \text{(inches)}. \tag{9-2}$$

By combining Eqs. (9-1) and (9-2) and converting the units to make the deflection read in inches, we see that

$$\delta_{\mathfrak{C} P_r + DL} = \frac{9L^2}{2E_c} \left(\frac{4f_c}{d} - \frac{5wL^2}{I} \right) = \text{in}, \tag{9-3}$$

where

L = span length, ft,

f_c = maximum prestress, psi,

w_{DL} = uniform DL, lb/lin. ft,

d = depth of section, in,

E_c = modulus of elasticity of concrete, psi,

I = moment of inertia of section, in^4.

Note that creep (possibly shrinkage) results in an additional upward deflection for which we can make merely a rough estimate since the magnitudes of these quantities and the variation of E_c with time and stress can only be approximated at any given time. Multiplying the elastic deflection (Eq. 9-1) by 3 might be an arbitrary approach to this estimate.

Example 9-3.

Given: Beam designed in Article 9-6, i.e. $L = 40$ ft, $f_c = 2250$ psi, $d = 20$ in. Assume that $E = 5 \times 10^6$ psi.

Find: The approximate deflection at the centerline of the span for the conditions given.

PROCEDURE: From Eq. (9-1) the deflections are

$$\text{Elastic, upward } \delta_{\mathfrak{C}} = \frac{36L^2 f_c}{2E_c d} = \frac{36 \times (40)^2 \times 2250}{2 \times 5 \times 10^6 \times 20},$$

$$\delta_{\mathfrak{C}} = 0.648 \text{ in.}$$

Assume plastic $\delta = 2\delta$ elastic $= 1.296$ in., approximately, total upward $\delta = 1.944$ in. From Eq. (9-2, we find that due to the LL and DL (combined),

$$\delta_{\mathfrak{C}} = \frac{wL^4}{384EI} 1728 = \frac{45}{2} \frac{wL^4}{EI}$$

$$= \frac{45}{2} \frac{588(40)^4}{5 \times 10^6 \times 6310} = 1.072 \text{ in.} \quad \text{(downward)},$$

$$\text{Net } \delta_{\mathfrak{C}} = 1.944 - 1.072 = 0.872 \text{ in.} \quad \text{(upward)}.$$

Fig. 9-16. Double-T prestressed section.

Using Eq. (9–3), which includes elastic and plastic deformations, we have

$$\delta_{\mathbb{C}} = \frac{9}{2} \frac{L^2}{E_c} \left(\frac{3 \times 4f_c}{d} - \frac{5wL^2}{I} \right) = 0.872 \text{ in. (upward).}$$

The term $(3 \times 4fc)/d$ includes elastic and plastic coefficients.

PROBLEMS

PRESTRESSED CONCRETE

In the following problems, design the cross sections by pretensioning Roebling strands (⅜ in. strand); $A_s = 0.08$ in², ultimate stress = 250,000 psi, working stress $f_s = 150,000$ psi. Wherever feasible, keep the ratio of beam depth to width approximately 2 to 1.

Notation: L = span length, ft; LL = live load, lb/in. ft; P = concentrated load, lb; DL = dead load (excluding the weight of the beam) lb/lin. ft; f_c' = ultimate stress of concrete, psi; f_c = working stress of concrete, psi.

9–1. Design a rectangular cross section for: LL = 650 lb/lin. ft, L = 18 ft, DL = 200 lb/lin. ft, $f_c' = 5000$ psi, $f_c = 2000$ psi.

9–2. Design an I-cross section for: LL = 650 lb/lin. ft, L = 18 ft, DL = 200 lin. ft, $f_c' = 5000$ psi, $f_c = 2000$ psi.

9–3. Design a simply supported slab for: LL = 75 lb/ft², L = 12 ft, DL = 30 lb/ft², $f_c' = 5000$ psi, $f_c = 2000$ psi.

9–4. Design an I-cross section for: LL = 300 lb/lin. ft, L = 36 ft, DL = 250 lb/lin. ft, $f_c' = 5500$ psi, $f_c = 2250$ psi.

9–5. Design an I-cross section for: LL = 300 lb/lin. ft,   L = 36 ft,   DL = 250 lb/lin. ft, $f_c' = 5500$ psi, $f_c = 2250$ psi, $P = 8$ kip at centerline of span.

9–6. Design an I-cross section for: LL = 300 lb/lin. ft,   L = 36 ft,   DL = 250 lb/lin. ft, $f_c' = 5500$ psi, $f_c = 2250$ psi.

9–7. Design an I-cross section for: LL = 300 lb/lin. ft,   L = 42 ft,   DL = 250 lb/lin. ft, $f_c' = 5500$ psi, $f_c = 2250$ psi.

9–8. Design an I-cross section for: LL = 300 lb/lin. ft,   L = 42 ft,   DL = 250 lb/lin. ft, $f_c' = 5500$ psi, $f_c = 2250$ psi.

9–9. Design an I-cross section for: LL = 300 lb/lin. ft,   L = 48 ft,   DL = 200 lb/lin. ft, $f_c' = 5500$ psi, $f_c = 2250$ psi.

9–10. Design an I-cross section for: LL = 300 lb/lin. ft,   L = 48 ft,   DL = 200 lb/lin. ft, $f_c' = 5500$ psi, $f_c = 2250$ psi.

REFERENCES

1. HERMAN SCHORER, "Prestressed Concrete Design Principles and Reinforcing Units," *ACI Journal,* June 1943.
2. P. W. ABELES, "Fully and Partly Prestressed Reinforced Concrete," *ACI Journal,* Jan. 1945.
3. HOWARD R. STALEY and DEAN PEABODY, JR., "Shrinkage and Plastic Flow of Prestressed Concrete," *ACI Journal,* Jan. 1946.
4. GUSTAVE MAGNEL, "Creep of Steel and Concrete in Relation to Prestressed Concrete," *ACI Journal,* Feb. 1948.
5. ALFRED L. PARME and GEORGE H. PARIS, "Designing for Continuity in Prestressed Concrete Structures," *ACI Journal,* Sept. 1951.
6. JACK R. JANNEY, "Nature of Bond in Pretensioned Prestressed Concrete," *ACI Journal,* May 1954.
7. D. F. BILLET and J. H. APPLETON, "Flexural Strength of Prestressed Concrete Beams," *ACI Journal,* June 1954.
8. NORMAN W. HANSON and PAUL H. KAAR, "Flexural Bond Tests of Pretensioned Prestressed Beams," *ACI Journal,* Jan. 1959.

10 THIN SHELL ROOFS

Folded plate and shell roofs provide the cover for the Grandstand of Sciota Downs Raceway, Columbus, Ohio. *Description:* 5 hyperbolic paraboloid inverted umbrellas each 60 × 116 ft, 36-in. diameter columns, thickness 4½ and 5 in., ribs and edge beams on top, tilted 12 ft, front edge 65 ft above ground. 100 × 160 ft, 5 peaks with cantilevered edges, 4-in. thickness, supported on 2 rows of columns, 45-ft cantilever in front. Mezzanine roof: 282 ft × 26 ft 8 in., 10 peaks plus cantilevered edges, 4-in. thickness, supported on two rows of columns.

10-1 INTRODUCTION

One of the most common shell structures is the chicken egg. The remarkable strength of this shell may be quite convincingly demonstrated by squeezing an egg in the palm of one's hand. When one squeezes evenly, and does not "punch" at any one spot, it is quite likely that the egg will not break. However, once the egg is broken, the resistance of the shell to bending can be shown to be relatively weak. The shell is too thin to have any section modulus that can take the bending. Its strength comes from the curvature or shape, rather than from the mass of the material.

The strength, beauty, simplicity and economy of construction, and the capability of providing large areas free of obstructions have made the shell roof a noticeable if not prominent factor in roof construction. It was not until about 1920 that the first experimental modern reinforced concrete shell roof was built at the Zeiss works in Germany, and it was not until about 30 years ago (1933) that the first shell roof was built in the United States. By now nearly a thousand such roofs of various shapes and sizes have been built throughout the world.

An exact analysis of concrete shells is a difficult, if not impossible, task because the design must take into consideration not only all the variables in loading and

Fig. 10–1. Winter Garden Ice Skating and Sports Arena, Provo, Utah. *Description:* The double-curve concrete shell (3½ in. thick) was formed over a man-made mound containing 40,000 yd³ of earth. The cost of the 160 × 240 ft arena, including footing, was approximately $2.32/ft² of floor area. About 21 miles of reinforcing steel bar were used in the construction.

Fig. 10–2. Benedictine Priory Church, St. Louis, Missouri. *Description:* The building has a 134-ft diameter. The lower-tier arches rise 21 ft, the upper-tier arches rise an additional 12 ft, and a 33-ft tower tops the central altar. The shell thickness ranges from 3 to 6 in.

Fig. 10–3. Hamilton Township High School Gymnasium, Franklin County, Ohio. *Description:* 97 ft × 105 ft, 200-ft radius (out to out) 95 ft × 103 ft, 195-ft radius, thickness 4 in. at crown, 5 in. at bottom, rise 5 ft 8¾ in. from top of column to crown.

Fig. 10–4. Exposition Palace, Paris, France.

physical make-up of the structure but also the physical properties of the materials used and their composite action under load. To help in the design of cylindrical shell roofs the American Society of Civil Engineers published Manual No. 31, *Design of Cylindrical Shell Roofs* (1952). The Portland Cement Association's Structural and Railway Bureau has a series of pamphlets covering quite satisfactorily the analysis of and design alternatives for several types of shells. In fact, through the courtesy of Portland Cement Association, some of the Bureau's work has been reproduced here almost in its entirety.

10–2 HYPERBOLIC PARABOLOID SHELLS

The double curvature in this type of shell makes possible the transfer of loads to the supports entirely by direct forces, resulting in a uniformly stressed shell. This feature frequently permits the use of shells as thin as one inch, or less, although the average thickness is probably closer to three inches, a thickness sometimes dictated by reinforcement coverage as well as stresses. In addition, the forming is relatively simple, as explained in the following paragraph. These are two important factors making for economical construction. Furthermore, the beauty of the shape is another advantage which should be considered in decisions regarding the merit of the shell.

Fig. 10–5. Gault Aviation Hangar, Corpus Christi, Texas. *Description:* Approximately 150 × 210 ft and up to a rise of 38 ft the shell thickness varies from 2½ to 3½ in. The cost was approximately $1.00/ft² of floor area.

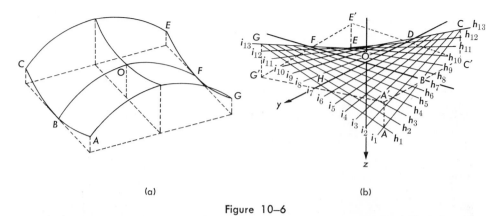

(a)   (b)

Figure 10–6

(a) *Surface construction.* The surface of a hyperbolic paraboloid may be constructed by intersecting several systems of a limited number of straight lines and then covering these lines with a skin (plywood, metal sheathing, etc.) to develop the warped surface that will resemble a "true" hyperbolic paraboloid. In a true hyperbolic paraboloid, a doubly curved surface may be generated either by sliding a vertical parabola having upward curvature over another with downward curvature, as shown in Fig. 10–6(a), or by warping a parallelogram, as shown in Fig. 10–6(b).

By sliding a straight line which remains parallel to the xz-plane at all times but pivots on line HD and rests on line AC one generates the surface shown in Fig. 10–6(b). Note that the grid shown in Fig. 10–6(b) consists of a system of

Fig. 10–7. Bellarmine Chapel, Xavier University, Cincinnati, Ohio. *Description:* Hyperbolic paraboloid saddle-shaped roof 126 ft between abutments.

Fig. 10–8. Benedictine High School Gymnasium, Cleveland, Ohio. *Description:* 1 hyperbolic paraboloid 100 × 100 ft, four-corner shell, 19-ft rise, 5-in. thickness.

straight lines, an interesting feature, especially for those confronted with the "forming" task in actual construction.

A part or a combination of parts of such a curved surface may be used to develop various roof forms. This is a particularly attractive feature since it permits freedom of expression and the imaginative use of shapes in design. Some shapes of this kind are shown in Fig. 10–9.

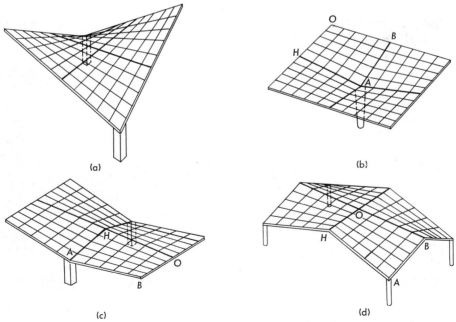

(a)

(b)

(c)

(d)

Figure 10–9

Fig. 10–10. Peoples Savings and Loan Association, Toledo, Ohio. *Description:* Groined vault, 24 ft square, circular arc, 6-ft rise.

(b) *Geometry of surface rectangular in plan.*   Since the approach to defining the surface in terms of x-, y-, and z-coordinates is basically the same for roofs skewed in plan as it is for those rectangular in plan, only the latter will be used to illustrate the procedure. Let us assume a basic quadrant, $OHAB$ (Fig. 10–9b) and isolate this quadrant as shown in Fig. 10–11.

From similar triangles, $A'HA$ and dHd', we have

$$c = x(h/a).$$

Also from a triangle $d'Ed$, we have

$$c = (z/y)b.$$

Equating the two expressions, we obtain

$$(z/y)b = x(h/a),$$

from which

$$z = xy(h/ab). \qquad (10\text{–}1)$$

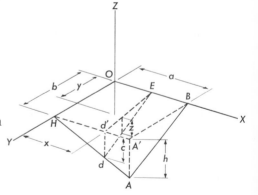

Figure 10–11

This equation is in a convenient form for those interested in "forming" for the roof. The quantity h/ab is a constant for a specific design. Thus the value of z is

$$z = kxy. \qquad (10\text{–}1a)$$

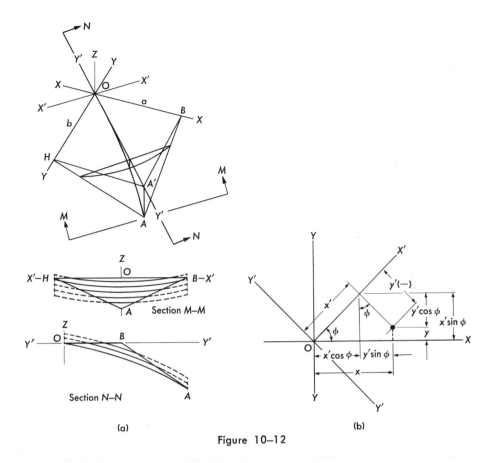

Figure 10–12

From this equation one may easily obtain the straight lines shown in Fig. 10–6(b).

A more convenient form of this result may be obtained by rotating the axes x and y through an angle $\phi = 45°$ to obtain the new axes x' and y' positioned with respect to the x- and y-axes as shown in Fig. 10–12(a). From Fig. 10–12(b), the values of x and y in terms of the new coordinates x' and y' obtained by the transformation are

$$x = x' \cos \phi + (-y' \sin \phi) = \left(\frac{1}{\sqrt{2}}\right)(x' - y')$$

and

$$y = x' \sin \phi - (-y' \cos \phi) = \left(\frac{1}{\sqrt{2}}\right)(x' + y')$$

for $\phi = 45°$.

Substituting these expressions in Eq. 10–1(a), we obtain

$$z = k\left(\frac{1}{\sqrt{2}}\right)^2 [(x' - y')(x' + y')] = \frac{k}{2}(x'^2 - y'^2). \qquad (10\text{–}2)$$

This equation defines the surface of the hyperbolic paraboloid in terms of x' and y'.

We may obtain the equation of any parabola lying parallel to either the $x'z$- or $y'z$-plane by making either y' or x' a constant.

When y' is constant, say $y' = k_y$, then

$$z = \frac{k}{2}(x'^2 - k_y^2). \tag{10–3}$$

Let

$$z' = z + \frac{k}{2}k_y^2 = \frac{k}{2}x'^2; \tag{10–3a}$$

this is the equation of a parabola lying in a plane parallel to the $x'z$-*plane*.

Similarly, when x' is a constant, say $x' = k_x$, then

$$z = \frac{k}{2}(k_x^2 - y'^2). \tag{10–4}$$

Let

$$z' = z - \frac{k}{2}k_x^2 = \frac{k}{2}y'^2; \tag{10–4a}$$

this is the equation of a parabola lying in a plane parallel to the $y'z$-plane.

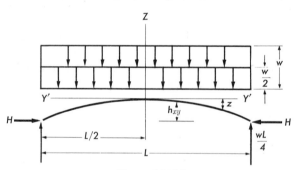

Figure 10–13

(c) *Stresses.* To determine the forces and stresses related to this type of shell, assume that a uniform load, w, acts on a hyperbolic paraboloid shell, as shown in Fig. 10–13. In reality, one notes that the slope of the surface steepens near the supports, and thus the assumption of a uniform load is not strictly correct. However, this variation is insignificant, and therefore our assumption is a reasonable one.

Since the shell consists entirely of two sets of arches, one set perpendicular to the other and all having the same shape, the total load may be assumed equally divided in two directions, each direction carrying $w/2$, as shown in Fig. 10–13.

The moment throughout a parabolic arch supporting only a uniform load equals zero. Thus, letting the sum of the moments about the center of the span equal zero, we may determine the value of the horizontal reaction H, i.e.,

$$\sum M_{L/2} = 0,$$

$$\frac{wL}{4}\frac{L}{2} - \frac{w}{2}\frac{L}{2}\frac{L}{4} - Hh_{xy} = 0,$$

from which

$$H = \frac{-wL^2}{16h_{xy}}. \qquad (10\text{--}5)$$

The equation of any arch in the direction shown is $z' = -(k/2)(y')^2$. When $y' = L/2$, then $z' = -h_{xy}$ and therefore $z' = h_{xy} = (k/2)(L/2)^2 = kL^2/8$. From $k = h/ab$, we have $h_{xy} = hL^2/8ab$. Substituting in Eq. (10–5) yields

$$H = -\frac{wa\dot{v}}{2h}, \qquad (10\text{--}6)$$

which is the compressive (or tensile) thrust in the shell supporting a uniform load.

The net result of the interaction of the sets of arch elements is that they create only shearing forces parallel to the edges of the shell. Edge beams are provided at every edge of the shell to "absorb" these shearing forces and provide the necessary and sufficient support to take care of the horizontal reaction H described above. Example 10–1 will illustrate the function of, and reinforcement for, the edge beams.

That only shearing forces parallel to the edges exist in the shell can be shown by taking a corner of the shell of Fig. 10–6(b) and isolating it as shown in Fig. 10–14(a). Edges HO and OB are horizontal, and AH and AB are sloped. Edge beams are present along the edges.

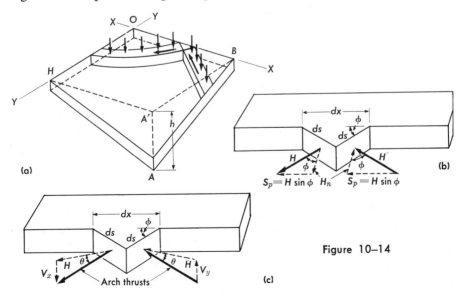

Figure 10–14

Two parabolic arches, one perpendicular to the other, are taken as shown in Fig. 10–14(a), and their effect on the edge beams is analyzed. The forces exerted by the two arches are illustrated in the magnified sketches of Fig. 10–14(b) and (c).

The normal components of the horizontal forces H of the two arches are equal in magnitude but opposite in direction. Thus they do not exert a force normal to the edge beams. The components of H parallel to the edge beam, S_p, are additive since they act in the same direction. Letting the intensity of the shear per unit length along the beam be represented by S, and taking the sum of the forces in the x-direction, we obtain

$$S\,dx = 2H \sin \phi\, ds, \quad \text{or} \quad S = 2H \sin \phi\, \frac{ds}{dx} = 2H \sin \phi \cos \phi.$$

For $\phi = 45°$, and $H = wab/2h$,

$$S = \frac{2wab}{2h}\left(\frac{1}{\sqrt{2}}\right)^2 = \frac{wab}{2h}. \tag{10–7}$$

Comparing Eqs. (10–6) and 10–7), we see that $|H| = |S|$, which proves that the horizontal reaction H shown in Fig. 10–13 is provided by the edge beams. Thus the shell must be reinforced only to sustain this force.

Figure 10–14(c) shows the arch thrusts resolved into a horizontal component H and two vertical components, V_x and V_y, from the two arches, the latter making an angle in the *vertical* plane. In terms of H, the combined vertical component, V, at any point due to the thrust in the two arches is

$$V = \Sigma H \tan \phi = H\frac{dz}{dy'} + H\frac{dx}{dx'} = H\left(\frac{dz}{dy'} + \frac{dz}{dx'}\right). \tag{10–8}$$

From Eqs. (10–4) and (10–3), respectively,

$$\frac{dz}{dy'} = -ky', \qquad \frac{dz}{dx'} = +kx'.$$

Therefore

$$V = Hk(-y' + x'). \tag{10–9}$$

When the edge is horizontal, for example OH, $x' = y'$. Therefore on a horizontal edge, $V = 0$. On a sloping edge such as AB, $y = x' - a\sqrt{2}$ (see Figs. 10–11 and 10–12). Substituting for y' in Eq. (10–9), we have

$$V = Hka\sqrt{2}. \tag{10–10}$$

Substituting the equivalent *magnitudes* for H and k,

$$H = \frac{wab}{2h}, \qquad k = \frac{h}{ab},$$

changes Eq. (10–10) to

$$V = \frac{wab}{2h}\frac{h}{ab}a\sqrt{2} = \frac{wa}{\sqrt{2}}. \tag{10–11}$$

This force, V, acts on the surface of length ds shown in Fig. 10–14(c). The intensity, V', of this force per unit length of the edge beam is

$$V' = V \cos \phi; \tag{10–12}$$

for $\phi = 45°$

$$V' = \frac{wa}{2}. \tag{10–12a}$$

Example 10–1

Given: Roof dimension in plan 50 ft × 50 ft, live load = 30 lb/ft², $f_s = 20{,}000$ psi, $f_c' = 3000$ psi.

Find: A suitable design of a hyperbolic paraboloid shell roof, as shown in Fig. 10–9(b).

PROCEDURE: The stresses in the concrete of a shell are quite low. Therefore, as explained previously, from the standpoint of construction and material (such as size of the coarse aggregate, etc.) the thickness of the shell is governed perhaps more by considerations of adequate reinforcement and cover, and by practical dimensions than by stress. A thickness of 3 in. is assumed. Also, the edge-beam dimensions are chosen to be 8 in. × 6 in., as shown in Fig. 10–15, and their weight is converted into an approximately uniform load.

Thus the DL of the shell is

$$\tfrac{3}{12}150 = 37.5 \text{ lb/ft}^2,$$

and the weight of the beams is

$$\frac{8 \times 6}{144} 150 = 50 \text{ lb/ft of beam}.$$

The approximately distributed weight is

$$\frac{50 \text{ lb} \times 200 \text{ ft}}{(50 \text{ ft})^2} = 4 \text{ lb/ft}^2.$$

Hence

$$\text{DL} + \text{LL} = 30 + 37.5 + 4$$
$$= 71.5 \text{ lb/ft}^2, \text{ say } 72 \text{ lb/ft}^2.$$

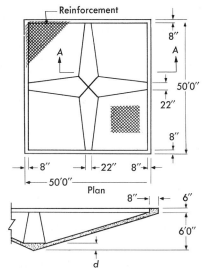

Section A–A

Figure 10–15

The horizontal thrust per foot created by the parabolic arches of this load is positive in one curvature and negative in the other.

Using Eq. (10–6), and assuming a vertical rise of $h = 6$ ft, we have

$$H = \pm \frac{wab}{2h} = \pm \frac{72 \times (50/2)^2}{2 \times 6}, \qquad \text{where} \qquad a = b = \tfrac{50}{2},$$

$$H = \pm 3750 \text{ lb/ft}.$$

Since the tensile strength of concrete is small, the tensile force in the parabolic arches under tension must be taken by the steel reinforcement. Thus, $A_s = {}^{3750}\!/_{20000} =$ 0.19 in²/ft.

The compressive stress in the concrete is

$$f_c = 3750/(3 \times 12) = 102 \text{ psi.}$$

This is a low stress, and for this purpose alone, no reinforcement would be necessary. However, a nominal amount should be used to take care of temperature variation, shrinkage, etc. The reinforcement used here is placed *diagonally* (the direction of the tension arch), with that needed for tension anchored in the edge beams, as shown in Fig. 10–15. Although the size of the bars is not designated, the area, A_s, as well as suitable diameters, must be taken into account.

The total *force* in any of the edge beams is equal to the sum of the shear forces acting along the length of the beam. For the horizontal edge members, it starts with zero at the corners and increases to a maximum value at the center (Fig. 10–16).

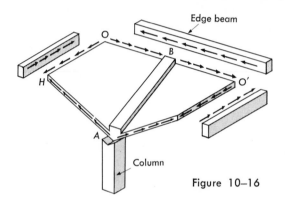

Figure 10–16

The maximum force will be developed at half the length of the 50-ft edge beam and is equal to $H_{tot} = 3750 \times 25 = 94,000$ lb.

The area A_s required for each edge beam at the *center* is

$$A_s = \frac{94,000}{20,000} = 4.7 \text{ in}^2.$$

When detailing the steel, the designer should take care that the centroid of the reinforcement coincide with the line of application of the shear forces so as to eliminate eccentricity; otherwise, due allowance should be made for it. Also, note that the steel may be reduced near the corners, where the load is smaller.

The sloped edge members are in compression. The compression force is developed by shearing force acting on both sides of the members:

$$P = 2H_{tot}\frac{25.7}{25} = 2 \times 94,000 \frac{25.7}{25} = 193,000 \text{ lb,}$$

where 25.7 is the length of the member, i.e. $\sqrt{(25)^2 + (6)^2}$.

The method of analysis and the allowable stresses to be used for determining the area of the sloped member in the valley of the shell may raise doubt in the minds of

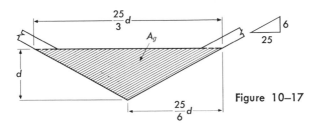

Figure 10–17

some designers. However, for average spans, the area obtained from column fomulas is believed to be a suitable approximation and shall be used here. Assuming for the *"column"* $p_g = 0.02$ and $f_s = 18,000$ psi, we have

$$A_g = \frac{P}{0.18 f_c' + 0.8 f_s p_g} = \frac{193,000}{540 + 288},$$

$$A_g = 233 \text{ in}^2.$$

To comply with the requirements of the geometry involved, i.e. two intersecting surfaces, the distance d shown in section A–A of Fig. 10–15 and magnified in Fig. 10–17 may be approximated as follows.

The cross-sectional area A_g may be expressed in terms of d,

$$233 = A_g = \tfrac{25}{3} d d \tfrac{1}{2} = \tfrac{25}{6} d^2,$$

$$d = \sqrt{\tfrac{6}{25} A_g} = \sqrt{\tfrac{6}{25} 233} = 7.4 \text{ in}.$$

A depth of 9 in. will be used at this point. This provides the added strength that may be needed for unsymmetrical loading conditions, conditions not encountered in our loading assumptions, but nevertheless possible. The width of the top force of the sloped member in the valley is $(\tfrac{25}{3} \cdot 9) - 2(\tfrac{6}{25} \cdot 25.7) = 49.3$ in., say 50 in. At the top, near the edge beam, a width of 22 in. was chosen (see Fig. 10–15).

Fig. 10–18. Golden Bear Restaurant, University of California, Berkeley, California.

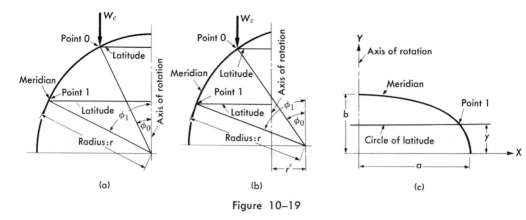

Figure 10–19

10–3   CIRCULAR DOMES

Another shell roof is the dome. One may obtain a dome surface by revolving an arc of a circle or of an ellipse or of other curved geometric figures. For a spherical dome (Fig. 10–19a), the center of the circle is on the axis of rotation.

If the center of the circle is outside the axis of rotation, revolving a circular arc gives a conoidal dome, Fig. 10–19(b). Revolving an ellipse about its minor axis produces an elliptical dome, Fig. 10–19(c). The approaches to their design are similar, and therefore only spherical domes (Fig. 10–20) will be discussed here.

Fig. 10–20. The Elks Club (Lodge 888), Long Beach, California. *Description:* Eighteen radiating arches support the white concrete dome, which is 4 in. thick, covers about 18,000 ft² and rises 34 ft above the second floor at the center. The shell roof was built at a cost of about $2.50/ft² of floor area.

Fig. 10–21. St. John's Byzantine Rite Catholic Church and School, Parma, Ohio. *Descrip-tion*: 20 barrels, radius 6 ft 10 in., chord 15 ft 2 in., 3½ in. thick, 60-ft span plus 6-ft cantilever each end. 12 barrels, 10-ft chord, radius 4 ft 6¼ in., 3 in. thick. Also precast dome 28-ft diameter, rise 14 ft 5 in., 4 in. thick.

Typically, the shell for this type of roof is also considered too thin to develop any bending moment, but thick enough not to buckle. For purposes of analysis, the domes considered here will be assumed to be symmetrical in shape and load-ing with respect to the axis of rotation, i.e., the load is constant along any circle of latitude or hoop. Also, even symmetry of supports should be preserved during the process of forming and construction, and during removal of the forms. When the shell has lantern openings through the top or edge members, these are as-sumed symmetrical with respect to the axis of rotation.

(a) *Surface area and loads for spherical domes.* The derivation will be general enough to include the lantern opening and a sloped edge, point 1, in Fig. 10–22. We begin by calculating the area. The area generated by the arc length, $r \, d\phi$, when rotated 360° is

$$dA = r \, d\phi \, 2\pi r \sin \phi,$$

where $r \sin \phi$ represents the *centroid* of the arc element. The total surface, A, generated by the arc $\widehat{01}$ is

$$A = \int_{\phi_0}^{\phi_1} r \, d\phi \, 2\pi r \sin \phi = 2\pi r^2 [-\cos \phi]_{\phi_0}^{\phi_1},$$

$$A = 2\pi r^2 (\cos \phi_0 - \cos \phi_1). \tag{10–13}$$

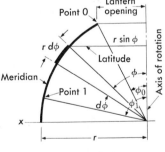

Figure 10–22

If there is no lantern opening, i.e., point 0 lies on the axis of rotation, then $\cos \phi_0 = 1$, and

$$A = 2\pi r^2 (1 - \cos \phi_1). \tag{10–13a}$$

Similarly, if there is no lantern opening and point 1 is moved down to the x-axis, i.e., the tangent to the meridian is vertical, then $\cos \phi_0 = 1$, and

$\cos \phi_1 = 0$. Thus

$$A = 2\pi r^2. \tag{10-13b}$$

Assuming the unit load, w, to be the same for all elements, we obtain the total load, W_u, on the dome between points 0 and 1:

$$W = wA = 2\pi r^2 w(\cos \phi_0 - \cos \phi_1). \tag{10-14}$$

If the unit load increases from zero at point 0 at a uniform rate of load, w' per radian, the unit load at the element $r d\phi$ equals $w'(\phi - \phi_0)$.

The total load described by rotating arc 01 about the axis shown is

$$W = \int_{\phi_0}^{\phi_1} r \, d\phi 2\pi r \sin \phi [w'(\phi - \phi_0)].$$

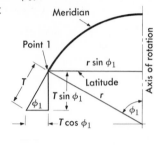

Evaluating, we have

$$W = 2\pi r^2 w'[\sin \phi_1 - \sin \phi_0 - \cos \phi_1(\phi_1 - \phi_0)]. \tag{10-15}$$

Figure 10-23

(b) *Stresses.* A general point, such as point 1 in Fig. 10-23, is usually subjected to two internal forces: (1) meridional thrust, T, tangential to the meridian, and (2) hoop force, H, tangent to the circle of latitude.

Let W represent the total downward load, above the latitude through point 1, and T, the thrust per unit length of circumference of the circle through point 1. Then

$$\Sigma F_y = 0,$$

Upward resisting force = downward load W,

$$(T \sin \phi_1)(\text{circumference}) = (T \sin \phi_1)(2\pi r \sin \phi_1) = W,$$

$$T = \frac{W}{2\pi r \sin^2 \phi_1}. \tag{10-16}$$

From $\cos^2 \phi + \sin^2 \phi = 1$,

$$\sin^2 \phi = (1 - \cos^2 \phi) = (1 + \cos \phi)(1 - \cos \phi),$$

and

$$T = \frac{W}{2\pi r(1 - \cos \phi_1)(1 + \cos \phi_1)}. \tag{10-16a}$$

The horizontal component of T, that is, $T \cos \phi$, causes a *ring tension S*. From the familiar formula for thin-wall cylindrical pressure vessels, $S = qr$, where q represents the internal pressure and r represents the radius of the cylinder,

$$S = (T \cos \phi_1)(r \sin \phi_1) = Tr \sin \phi_1 \cos \phi_1.$$

Substituting for T from equation (10–16), we have

$$S = \left(\frac{W}{2\pi r \sin^2 \phi_1}\right) r \sin \phi_1 \cos \phi_1 = \frac{W \cos \phi_1}{2\pi \sin \phi_1}. \qquad (10\text{–}17)$$

This expression predicts the ring tension in edge members. A hoop force, H, tangential to the circle of latitude may be determined in terms of T and the load, w, as follows.

Figure 10–24(a) shows the forces, T, H, and w acting on an element of surface. Both T and H have components perpendicular to the surface. The radial components of T and H lying in the plane of their respective circles can be shown to be equal to the tangential force divided by the radius of curvature of the respective circles, that is, T/r and $H/r \sin \phi_1$. Assume that arc $r \, d\phi$ has unit depth into the page. The total radial component of T is $2(T \sin d\phi/2) \cong 2(T \, d\phi/2)$.

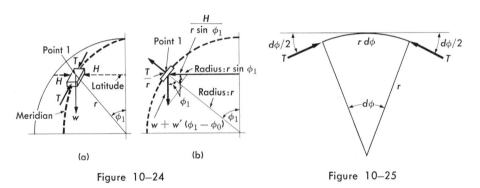

Figure 10–24   Figure 10–25

The radial component per unit length is $2T(d\phi/2)/r \, d\phi$ or T/r. Similarly for H whose circle has a radius $r \sin \phi_1$, the radial component is $H/r \sin \phi_1$. These are shown in Fig. 10–23(b). The summation of forces perpendicular to the surface equals zero. Thus

$$\{T/r + (H/r \sin \phi_1) \sin \phi_1 - [w + w'(\phi_1 - \phi_2)] \cos \phi_1\} = 0,$$

from which

$$H = [w + w'(\phi_1 - \phi_0)]r \cos \phi_1 - T. \qquad (10\text{–}18)$$

This represents the hoop force per unit area of the shell. In the formula, w' represents the rate of increase in load per radian. For example, suppose that the thickness of the dome changes from 4 in. at the top to 5 in. at the base in 0.5 radian. The thickness change is 5 in. $-$ 4 in. $=$ 1 in. This represents $\frac{1}{12} \times$ 150 lb $=$ 12.5 lb/ft² at the base. Therefore,

$$w' = \frac{12.5}{1/2} = 25 \text{ lb/ft}^2.$$

Example 10–2.   *Analysis (and Design)*

Given: Live load $= 30$ lb/ft², radius at base $= 100$ ft, rise of dome $= 25$ ft (no lantern opening), allowable stress in concrete $= 200$ psi.

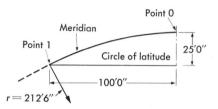

Figure 10–26

Find: For a *uniform* shell thickness of 5 in., (a) thrust forces at top and at base of dome, (b) hoop force at base of dome, and (c) tension in edge member.

PROCEDURE: From Eq. (10–16a),

$$T = \frac{W}{2\pi r(1 - \cos\phi_1)(1 + \cos\phi_1)}, \qquad r^2 = (100)^2 + (r - 25)^2,$$

from which $r = 212.5$ feet. The unit dead load is

$$\tfrac{5}{12}150 = 62.5 \text{ lb/ft}^2, \qquad \text{DL} + \text{LL} = 92.5 \text{ lb/ft}^2.$$

At the top $\phi_1 = 0$, and $\cos\phi_1 = 1$; hence from Eq. (10–14),

$$W = 2\pi r^2 w(1 - \cos\phi_1),$$

$$T_0 = \frac{2\pi r^2 w(1 - \cos\phi_1)}{2\pi r(1 - \cos\phi_1)(1 + \cos\phi_1)} = \tfrac{1}{2}wr,$$

$$T_0 = \tfrac{1}{2} \times 92.5 \times 212.5 = 9830 \text{ lb/ft}^2.$$

At the base:

$$\sin\phi_1 = \frac{100}{212.5} = 0.471; \qquad \cos\phi_1 = 0.882,$$

$$W_{u1} = 2\pi(212.5)^2 \times 92.5(1 - 0.882)$$

$$= 3{,}100{,}000 \text{ lb},$$

$$T_1 = \frac{W}{2\pi r \sin^2 \phi_1}$$

Thus, we get

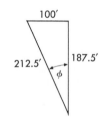

Figure 10–27

$$T_1 = \frac{3{,}100{,}000}{2\pi(212.5)(0.471)^2} = 10{,}460 \text{ lb compression/ft of circle of latitude.}$$

From Eq. (10–18), we obtain the compression H:

$$H = 92.5 \times 212.5 \times 0.882 - 10{,}460 = 6880 \text{ lb/ft} - \text{hoop force.}$$

From Eq. (10–17),

$$S = \frac{3{,}100{,}000 \times 0.882}{2\pi 0.471} = 924{,}000 \text{ lb},$$

which is the tension in the edge member.

The maximum compressive stress occurs at the top of dome where $H = 9830$ lb/ft; thus, taking a 1-ft strip, we find that the stress is $9830\text{ lb}(5\text{ in.}\times 12\text{ in.}) = 164$ psi.

Example 10–3. *Analysis*

Given: The dome of Example 10–2; however, assume that the dome now has a lantern opening of radius 25 ft. Also, there is a total load of 50 kip arranged uniformly around the edge of the opening.

Find: (a) thrust, hoop, and edge-beam forces at point 1, and (b) edge-beam force at lantern opening.

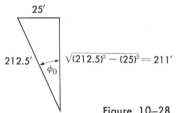

25′

$212.5′$ ϕ_0 $\sqrt{(212.5)^2 - (25)^2} = 211′$

Figure 10–28

PROCEDURE: In this case, point 0 shifts to the edge of the lantern opening (see Fig. 10–22). Point 1 remains the same as in Example 10–2. Then

$$W = 2\pi r^2 w(\cos\phi_0 - \cos\phi_1) + \text{total collar load of 50 kip}$$

$$\cos\phi_1 = \frac{211}{212.5} = 0.993, \qquad \sin\phi_0 = \frac{25}{212.5} = 0.1176,$$

$$\cos\phi_1 = \frac{187.5}{212.5} = 0.882, \qquad \sin\phi_1 = \frac{100}{212.5} = 0.471.$$

Therefore

$$W = 2\pi(212.5)^2 \times 92.5 \times (0.993 - 0.882) + 50{,}000 = 2{,}960{,}000\text{ lb,}$$

and the compression T_1 is:

$$T_1 = \frac{W}{2\pi r \sin^2\phi_1} = \frac{2{,}960{,}000}{2\pi(212.5)(100/212.5)^2} = 10{,}000\text{ lb/ft.}$$

Furthermore, we also have a compression H:

$$H = wr\cos\phi_1 - T_1 = 92.5 \times 212.5 \times 0.882 - 10{,}000 = 7340\text{ lb/ft.}$$

The tension is

$$S_1 = \frac{W\cos\phi_1}{2\pi\sin\phi_1} = \frac{2{,}960{,}000 \times 0.882}{2\pi \times 0.471} = 885{,}000\text{ lb.}$$

Similarly, we obtain a compression S_0:

$$S_0 = \frac{W_0\cos\phi_0}{2\pi\sin\phi_0} = \frac{50{,}000 \times 0.993}{2\pi \times 0.1176} = 67{,}000\text{ lb.}$$

Fig. 10–29. Silver Lake Country Club, Silver Lake, Ohio. *Description:* Span 25 ft, cantilever 4 ft each end, chord 16 ft; 3½ in. thick, 10 in. at ribs, rise 3 ft 9¼ in., radii 3 ft 0 in. and 10 ft 0 in.

10–4   CYLINDRICAL SHELLS

As the name implies, these shells consist of one or a series of cylindrical slabs interconnected to form a roof (see Figs. 10–21 and 10–29). Sometimes this type of roof is also called a barrel shell roof. The shell is supported by "transverse arches," as shown in Fig. 10–30. The radius of this curved slab or the ratio of the radius to the span between transverse supports is usually chosen from the standpoint of utility and esthetics, but in some instances it is determined by the complexity of the mathematical analysis of such a shell. For instance, for a very small ratio of radius to span, we may approximate the analysis by considering beam action; this is a much simpler approach than using the more general procedure outlined in the following discussion.

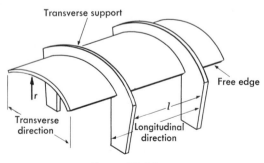

Figure 10–30

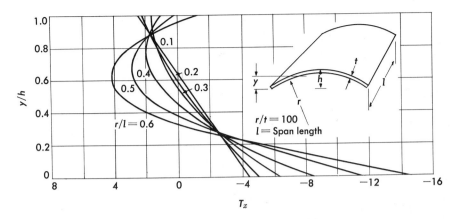

Figure 10–31

An exact mathematical analysis of this three-dimensional structure is quite complicated, but perhaps unnecessary since there are many variables which have to be *assumed*. The American Society of Civil Engineers published Manual No. 31, *Design of Cylindrical Concrete Shell Roofs,* which greatly simplifies the design of such roofs by providing a series of comprehensive tables. Even with this aid, the design procedure for these shells is still quite long and involved. For those particularly interested in the design of such roofs, it would be advisable to refer to the Manual or to the Portland Cement Association's publication, *Design of Barrel Shell Roofs.* One could not cover such a subject adequately in one article, or perhaps even a chapter. Therefore, the presentation here will be limited to a discussion of the behavior and stresses in a shell.

Stresses in a cylindrical shell. Although a shell is a space structure whose internal forces act in three dimensions, its behavior might best be understood by comparing its action under load to that of an ordinary beam. Subjected to load, the shell bends, inducing longitudinal fiber stresses similar to those in a beam. If the ratio of radius of curvature to longitudinal span is small (Fig. 10–30), the distribution of the "flexural" fiber stresses in the shell is linear and similar to those of a beam; that is, we find compression at the top, and tension at the bottom.

As this ratio increases, the distribution of these stresses, T_x, changes from a straight line to a curvilinear form, as shown in Fig. 10–31 for several ratios. Although the variation shown in the figure was calculated for a specific ratio of shell radius to slab thickness 100, the trend is representative of almost all cylindrical shells.

The departure from the linear distribution may be explained as follows. Let us consider a small shell strip of unit width far enough away from the transverse supports not to be affected by their action, as shown in Fig. 10–32(a). Furthermore, let us assume that edge *BD* is the lower edge, and that edge *AC* is at the crown.

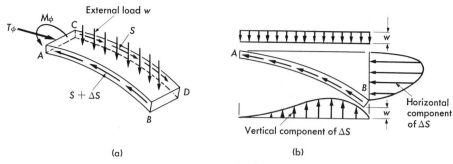

Figure 10–32

The difference between the longitudinal forces T_x on faces AB and CD causes a longitudinal shear determined by the formula $v = VQ/Ib$, where b is taken to be unity. The tangential shear, S, shown on the strip is equal to this longitudinal shear, a fact proved in any text on strength of materials.

The tangential shears on the faces AB and CD are resolved into horizontal and vertical components, and are then added. The net effect, ΔS, is shown in component form in Fig. 10–32(b). The horizontal component of ΔS (as plotted) and the external load create a moment which is clockwise and for most distributed loads, greater than that of the vertical component of ΔS, which is counterclockwise. This means that the transverse resisting moment, M_ϕ, must be equal to the algebraic sum of the moment of the external load and the moment of tangential shear S. When carrying out this operation, one finds that the net moment is always clockwise, and therefore the *resisting* moment M_ϕ is always counterclockwise or negative, as shown in Fig. 10–32(a).

With the net moment clockwise (M_ϕ is counterclockwise), point B would be deflected down and inward relative to A. This induces additional bending in the shell at edge BD, tension on the underside, and compression on the upper surface. Combining this stress for the underside with that of the longitudinal bending results in a stress in excess of those given in ordinary beam flexure, and thus the variation from the straight-line relationship.

In addition to the moment M_ϕ, face AC must provide a normal thrust T_ϕ to satisfy the equilibrium. The value of T_ϕ is equal to the vector sum of the unbalanced vertical and horizontal forces acting on the free body. As mentioned previously, how to determine these internal forces T_x, T_ϕ, M_ϕ, and how to design for them is a rather involved procedure discussed at length in the *ASCE Manual* No. 31.

PROBLEMS

10–1. Design a roof as shown in Fig. 10–9(b) to cover an area 40 ft × 40 ft in plan. Assume that the live load is 35 lb/ft², that intermediate-grade steel and 3000-psi concrete are used, and that the maximum allowable stress in the concrete is 200 psi. Also, assume that the slope of the roof is ¼.

10–2. For the conditions of Problem 10–1, design a roof as shown in Fig. 10–9(c).

10–3. For the conditions of problem 10–1, design a roof as shown in Fig. 10–9(d).

10–4. For a live load of 35 lb/ft², design a spherical dome roof with the radius of the base equal to 100 ft and a rise of 50 ft. Let us assume that intermediate-grade steel and 3000-psi concrete are used, and that the maximum allowable stress in the concrete is 200 psi. Also assume that there is no lantern opening and that the shell thickness is uniform.

10–5. For the conditions of problem 10–4, design a spherical dome roof with a lantern opening of radius 25 ft.

10–6. For the conditions of Problem 10–4, design a spherical dome roof, given that the slab thickness at the base increases 1 inch over that at the top.

REFERENCES

1. F. E. Wolosowick, "Flexure of Cellular Shells," *ACI Journal,* Dec. 1949.

2. Charles S. Whitney, "Cost of Long-Span Concrete Shell Roofs," *ACI Journal,* June 1950.

3. Felix Candela, "Simple Concrete Shell Structures," *ACI Journal,* Dec. 1951.

4. Anton Tedesko, "Construction Aspects of Thin-Shell Structures," *ACI Journal,* Feb. 1953.

5. Charles S. Whitney, "Reinforced Concrete Thin-Shell Structures," *ACI Journal,* Feb. 1953.

6. Herman Craemer, "Design of Prismatic Shells," *ACI Journal,* Feb. 1953.

7. G. C. Ernst, R. R. Marlette, and G. V. Berg, "Ultimate Load Theory and Tests of Cylindrical Long Shell Roofs," *ACI Journal,* Nov. 1954.

8. Mario G. Salvadori and A. D. Ateshoglou, "Ribless Cylindrical Shells," *ACI Journal,* Jan. 1955.

9. James Chinn, "Cylindrical Shell Analysis Simplified by Beam Method," *ACI Journal,* May 1959.

10. Portland Cement Association's Structural and Railway Bureau's Publications: *Elementary Analysis of Hyperbolic Paraboloid Shells, Design of Circular Domes, Design of Barrel Shell Roofs.*

11. AMERICAN SOCIETY OF CIVIL ENGINEERS MANUAL No. 31, *Design of Cylindrical Concrete Shell Roofs*.

12. ALF PFLUGER, *Elementary Statics of Shells*, F. W. Dodge Corp., New York, N.Y.

13. S. TIMOSHENKO and S. WOINOWSKY-KRIEGER, *Theory of Plates and Shells*, 2nd ed., McGraw-Hill Book Co., Inc., New York, N.Y. (1959).

14. D. YITZHAKI, *The Design of Prismatic and Cylindrical Shell Roofs*, Haifa Science Publishers, Haifa, Israel (1958).

15. J. E. GIBSON and D. W. COOPER, *The Design of Cylindrical Shell Roofs*, 2nd ed., D. Van Nostrand Co., Inc., Princeton, N.J. (1961).

16. ALBIN CHRONOWICZ, *The Design of Shells—A Practical Approach*, Crosby Lockwood and Sons, London (1959).

17. J. E. GIBSON and J. A. L. MATHESON, *Computer Analyses of Cylindrical Shells*, E. and F. N. Spon, Ltd., London (1961).

Shears, Moments, and Deflections for Simply Supported Beams, and Moments for Two- and Three-Span Continuous Beams

Reproduced from AISC Handbook 1963, courtesy American Iron and Steel Institute.

BEAM DIAGRAMS AND FORMULAS
FOR VARIOUS STATIC LOADING CONDITIONS

---

1.   SIMPLE BEAM—UNIFORMLY DISTRIBUTED LOAD

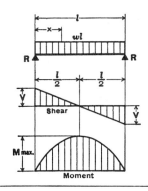

$$R = V \quad \ldots \ldots \ldots \quad = \frac{wl}{2}$$

$$V_x \quad \ldots \ldots \ldots \ldots \quad = w\left(\frac{l}{2} - x\right)$$

$$M \text{ max.} \left(\text{at center}\right) \ldots \ldots = \frac{wl^2}{8}$$

$$M_x \quad \ldots \ldots \ldots \ldots \quad = \frac{wx}{2}(l-x)$$

$$\Delta \text{max.} \left(\text{at center}\right) \ldots \ldots = \frac{5\,wl^4}{384\,EI}$$

$$\Delta_x \quad \ldots \ldots \ldots \ldots \quad = \frac{wx}{24EI}(l^3 - 2lx^2 + x^3)$$

---

2.   SIMPLE BEAM—LOAD INCREASING UNIFORMLY TO ONE END

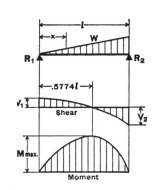

$$R_1 = V_1 \ldots \ldots \ldots \quad = \frac{W}{3}$$

$$R_2 = V_2 \text{ max.} \ldots \ldots \quad = \frac{2W}{3}$$

$$V_x \quad \ldots \ldots \ldots \ldots \quad = \frac{W}{3} - \frac{Wx^2}{l^2}$$

$$M \text{ max.} \left(\text{at } x = \frac{l}{\sqrt{3}} = .5774l\right) \ldots = \frac{2Wl}{9\sqrt{3}} = .1283\,Wl$$

$$M_x \quad \ldots \ldots \ldots \ldots \quad = \frac{Wx}{3l^2}(l^2 - x^2)$$

$$\Delta \text{max.} \left(\text{at } x = l\sqrt{1 - \sqrt{\frac{8}{15}}} = .5193l\right) = .01304\,\frac{Wl^3}{EI}$$

$$\Delta_x \ldots \ldots \ldots \ldots \quad = \frac{Wx}{180EI\,l^2}(3x^4 - 10l^2x^2 + 7l^4)$$

---

3.   SIMPLE BEAM—LOAD INCREASING UNIFORMLY TO CENTER

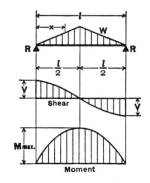

$$R = V \quad \ldots \ldots \ldots \quad = \frac{W}{2}$$

$$V_x \quad \left(\text{when } x < \frac{l}{2}\right) \ldots \ldots = \frac{W}{2l^2}(l^2 - 4x^2)$$

$$M \text{ max.} \left(\text{at center}\right) \ldots \ldots = \frac{Wl}{6}$$

$$M_x \quad \left(\text{when } x < \frac{l}{2}\right) \ldots \ldots = Wx\left(\frac{1}{2} - \frac{2x^2}{3l^2}\right)$$

$$\Delta \text{max.} \left(\text{at center}\right) \ldots \ldots = \frac{Wl^3}{60EI}$$

$$\Delta_x \ldots \ldots \ldots \ldots \quad = \frac{Wx}{480\,EI\,l^2}(5l^2 - 4x^2)^2$$

BEAM DIAGRAMS AND FORMULAS
FOR VARIOUS STATIC LOADING CONDITIONS

4. SIMPLE BEAM—UNIFORM LOAD PARTIALLY DISTRIBUTED

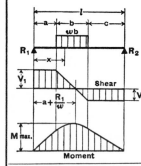

$R_1 = V_1 \left(\text{max. when a} < c\right)$ . . $= \dfrac{wb}{2l}(2c+b)$

$R_2 = V_2 \left(\text{max. when a} > c\right)$ . . $= \dfrac{wb}{2l}(2a+b)$

$V_x \quad \left(\text{when x} > a \text{ and} < (a+b)\right)$. $= R_1 - w(x-a)$

$M \text{ max.}\left(\text{at x} = a + \dfrac{R_1}{w}\right)$ . . . . $= R_1\left(a + \dfrac{R_1}{2w}\right)$

$M_x \quad \left(\text{when x} < a\right)$ . . . . . $= R_1 x$

$M_x \quad \left(\text{when x} > a \text{ and} < (a+b)\right)$. $= R_1 x - \dfrac{w}{2}(x-a)^2$

$M_x \quad \left(\text{when x} > (a+b)\right)$ . . . . $= R_2(l-x)$

5. SIMPLE BEAM—UNIFORM LOAD PARTIALLY DISTRIBUTED
AT ONE END

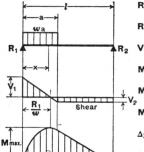

$R_1 = V_1 \text{ max.}$ . . . . $= \dfrac{wa}{2l}(2l-a)$

$R_2 = V_2$ . . . . $= \dfrac{wa^2}{2l}$

$V \quad \left(\text{when x} < a\right)$ . . . . . $= R_1 - wx$

$M \text{ max.}\left(\text{at x} = \dfrac{R_1}{w}\right)$ . . . . . $= \dfrac{R_1^2}{2w}$

$M_x \quad \left(\text{when x} < a\right)$ . . . . . $= R_1 x - \dfrac{wx^2}{2}$

$M_x \quad \left(\text{when x} > a\right)$ . . . . . $= R_2(l-x)$

$\Delta_x \quad \left(\text{when x} < a\right)$ . . . . . $= \dfrac{wx}{24EIl}\left(a^2(2l-a)^2 - 2ax^2(2l-a) + lx^3\right)$

$\Delta_x \quad \left(\text{when x} > a\right)$ . . . . . $= \dfrac{wa^2(l-x)}{24EIl}(4xl - 2x^2 - a^2)$

6. SIMPLE BEAM—UNIFORM LOAD PARTIALLY DISTRIBUTED
AT EACH END

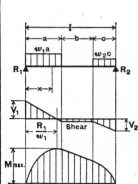

$R_1 = V_1$ . . . . $= \dfrac{w_1 a(2l-a) + w_2 c^2}{2l}$

$R_2 = V_2$ . . . . $= \dfrac{w_2 c(2l-c) + w_1 a^2}{2l}$

$V_x \quad \left(\text{when x} < a\right)$ . . . . . $= R_1 - w_1 x$

$V_x \quad \left(\text{when x} > a \text{ and} < (a+b)\right)$. $= R_1 - R_2$

$V_x \quad \left(\text{when x} > (a+b)\right)$ . . . . $= R_2 - w_2(l-x)$

$M \text{ max.}\left(\text{at x} = \dfrac{R_1}{w_1} \text{ when } R_1 < w_1 a\right)$. $= \dfrac{R_1^2}{2w_1}$

$M \text{ max.}\left(\text{at x} = l - \dfrac{R_2}{w_2} \text{ when } R_2 < w_2 c\right) = \dfrac{R_2^2}{2w_2}$

$M_x \quad \left(\text{when x} < a\right)$ . . . . . $= R_1 x - \dfrac{w_1 x^2}{2}$

$M_x \quad \left(\text{when x} > a \text{ and} < (a+b)\right)$. $= R_1 x - \dfrac{w_1 a}{2}(2x-a)$

$M_x \quad \left(\text{when x} > (a+b)\right)$ . . . . $= R_2(l-x) - \dfrac{w_2(l-x)^2}{2}$

BEAM DIAGRAMS AND FORMULAS
FOR VARIOUS STATIC LOADING CONDITIONS

---

7.   SIMPLE BEAM—CONCENTRATED LOAD AT CENTER

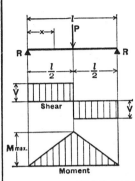

Equivalent Tabular Load . . . . . $= 2P$

$R = V$ . . . . $= \dfrac{P}{2}$

M max. $\left(\text{at point of load}\right)$ . . . . . $= \dfrac{Pl}{4}$

$M_x \quad \left(\text{when } x < \dfrac{l}{2}\right)$ . . . . . $= \dfrac{Px}{2}$

Δmax. $\left(\text{at point of load}\right)$ . . . . . $= \dfrac{Pl^3}{48EI}$

$\Delta_x \quad \left(\text{when } x < \dfrac{l}{2}\right)$ . . . . . $= \dfrac{Px}{48EI}(3l^2 - 4x^2)$

---

8.   SIMPLE BEAM—CONCENTRATED LOAD AT ANY POINT

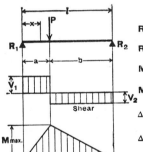

$R_1 = V_1 \left(\text{max. when } a < b\right)$ . . . . $= \dfrac{Pb}{l}$

$R_2 = V_2 \left(\text{max. when } a > b\right)$ . . . . $= \dfrac{Pa}{l}$

M max. $\left(\text{at point of load}\right)$ . . . . $= \dfrac{Pab}{l}$

$M_x \quad \left(\text{when } x < a\right)$ . . . . $= \dfrac{Pbx}{l}$

Δmax. $\left(\text{at } x = \sqrt{\dfrac{a(a+2b)}{3}} \text{ when } a > b\right) = \dfrac{Pab(a+2b)\sqrt{3a(a+2b)}}{27\,EI\,l}$

$\Delta a \quad \left(\text{at point of load}\right)$ . . . . $= \dfrac{Pa^2b^2}{3EI\,l}$

$\Delta_x \quad \left(\text{when } x < a\right)$ . . . . $= \dfrac{Pbx}{6EI\,l}(l^2 - b^2 - x^2)$

---

9.   SIMPLE BEAM—TWO EQUAL CONCENTRATED LOADS
SYMMETRICALLY PLACED

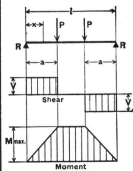

$R = V$ . . . . $= P$

M max. $\left(\text{between loads}\right)$ . . . . . $= Pa$

$M_x \quad \left(\text{when } x < a\right)$ . . . . . . $= Px$

Δmax. $\left(\text{at center}\right)$ . . . . $= \dfrac{Pa}{24EI}(3l^2 - 4a^2)$

$\Delta_x \quad \left(\text{when } x < a\right)$ . . . . . . $= \dfrac{Px}{6EI}(3la - 3a^2 - x^2)$

$\Delta_x \quad \left(\text{when } x > a \text{ and } < (l-a)\right)$ . . $= \dfrac{Pa}{6EI}(3lx - 3x^2 - a^2)$

BEAM DIAGRAMS AND FORMULAS
FOR VARIOUS STATIC LOADING CONDITIONS

---

10.   SIMPLE BEAM—TWO EQUAL CONCENTRATED LOADS UNSYMMETRICALLY PLACED

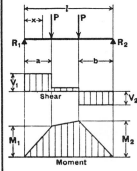

$R_1 = V_1 \left(\text{max. when } a < b \right)$ . . . . . $= \dfrac{P}{l}(l - a + b)$

$R_2 = V_2 \left(\text{max. when } a > b \right)$ . . . . . $= \dfrac{P}{l}(l - b + a)$

$V_x \left(\text{when } x > a \text{ and } < (l-b) \right)$ . . $= \dfrac{P}{l}(b - a)$

$M_1 \left(\text{max. when } a > b \right)$ . . . . . $= R_1 a$

$M_2 \left(\text{max. when } a < b \right)$ . . . . . $= R_2 b$

$M_x \left(\text{when } x < a \right)$ . . . . . . $= R_1 x$

$M_x \left(\text{when } x > a \text{ and } < (l-b) \right)$ . . $= R_1 x - P(x-a)$

---

11.   SIMPLE BEAM—TWO UNEQUAL CONCENTRATED LOADS UNSYMMETRICALLY PLACED

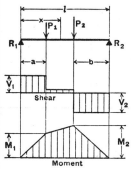

$R_1 = V_1$ . . . . $= \dfrac{P_1(l-a) + P_2 b}{l}$

$R_2 = V_2$ . . . . $= \dfrac{P_1 a + P_2(l-b)}{l}$

$V_x \left(\text{when } x > a \text{ and } < (l-b) \right)$ . . $= R_1 - P_1$

$M_1 \left(\text{max. when } R_1 < P_1 \right)$ . . . $= R_1 a$

$M_2 \left(\text{max. when } R_2 < P_2 \right)$ . . . $= R_2 b$

$M_x \left(\text{when } x < a \right)$ . . . . . . $= R_1 x$

$M_x \left(\text{when } x > a \text{ and } < (l-b) \right)$ . . $= R_1 x - P_1(x-a)$

---

12.   BEAM FIXED AT ONE END, SUPPORTED AT OTHER— UNIFORMLY DISTRIBUTED LOAD

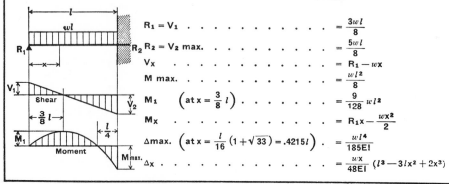

$R_1 = V_1$ . . . . $= \dfrac{3wl}{8}$

$R_2 = V_2$ max. . . . . $= \dfrac{5wl}{8}$

V_x . . . . $= R_1 - wx$

M max. . . . . $= \dfrac{wl^2}{8}$

$M_1 \left(\text{at } x = \dfrac{3}{8}l \right)$ . . . . $= \dfrac{9}{128}wl^2$

M_x . . . . $= R_1 x - \dfrac{wx^2}{2}$

Δ max. $\left(\text{at } x = \dfrac{l}{16}(1 + \sqrt{33}) = .4215l \right)$. $= \dfrac{wl^4}{185EI}$

Δ_x . . . . $= \dfrac{wx}{48EI}(l^3 - 3lx^2 + 2x^3)$

BEAM DIAGRAMS AND FORMULAS
FOR VARIOUS STATIC LOADING CONDITIONS

---

13. BEAM FIXED AT ONE END, SUPPORTED AT OTHER— CONCENTRATED LOAD AT CENTER

Equivalent Tabular Load . . . . $= \dfrac{3P}{2}$

$R_1 = V_1$ . . . . $= \dfrac{5P}{16}$

$R_2 = V_2$ max. . . . . $= \dfrac{11P}{16}$

M max. $\left(\text{at fixed end}\right)$ . . . . . $= \dfrac{3Pl}{16}$

M_1 $\left(\text{at point of load}\right)$ . . . . $= \dfrac{5Pl}{32}$

M_x $\left(\text{when } x < \dfrac{l}{2}\right)$ . . . . . $= \dfrac{5Px}{16}$

M_x $\left(\text{when } x > \dfrac{l}{2}\right)$ . . . . . $= P\left(\dfrac{l}{2} - \dfrac{11x}{.16}\right)$

Δmax. $\left(\text{at } x = l\sqrt{\dfrac{1}{5}} = .4472l\right)$ . . $= \dfrac{Pl^3}{48EI\sqrt{5}} = .009317\dfrac{Pl^3}{EI}$

Δ_x $\left(\text{at point of load}\right)$ . . . . $= \dfrac{7Pl3}{768EI}$

Δ_x $\left(\text{when } x < \dfrac{l}{2}\right)$ . . . . . $= \dfrac{Px}{96EI}(3l^2 - 5x^2)$

Δ_x $\left(\text{when } x > \dfrac{l}{2}\right)$ . . . . . $= \dfrac{P}{96EI}(x-l)^2(11x-2l)$

---

14. BEAM FIXED AT ONE END, SUPPORTED AT OTHER— CONCENTRATED LOAD AT ANY POINT

$R_1 = V_1$ . . . . $= \dfrac{Pb^2}{2l^3}(a+2l)$

$R_2 = V_2$ . . . . $= \dfrac{Pa}{2l^3}(3l^2 - a^2)$

M_1 $\left(\text{at point of load}\right)$ . . . . $= R_1 a$

M_2 $\left(\text{at fixed end}\right)$ . . . . . $= \dfrac{Pab}{2l^2}(a+l)$

M_x $\left(\text{when } x < a\right)$ . . . . . $= R_1 x$

M_x $\left(\text{when } x > a\right)$ . . . . . $= R_1 x - P(x-a)$

Δmax. $\left(\text{when } a < .414l \text{ at } x = l\dfrac{l^2+a^2}{3l^2-a^2}\right) = \dfrac{Pa}{3EI}\dfrac{(l^2-a^2)^3}{(3l^2-a^2)^2}$

Δmax. $\left(\text{when } a > .414l \text{ at } x = l\sqrt{\dfrac{a}{2l+a}}\right) = \dfrac{Pab^2}{6EI}\sqrt{\dfrac{a}{2l+a}}$

Δ_a $\left(\text{at point of load}\right)$ . . . . $= \dfrac{Pa^2b^3}{12EIl^3}(3l+a)$

Δ_x $\left(\text{when } x < a\right)$ . . . . . $= \dfrac{Pb^2x}{12EIl^3}(3al^2 - 2lx^2 - ax^2)$

Δ_x $\left(\text{when } x > a\right)$ . . . . . $= \dfrac{Pa}{12EIl^3}(l-x)^2(3l^2x - a^2x - 2a^2l)$

BEAM DIAGRAMS AND FORMULAS
FOR VARIOUS STATIC LOADING CONDITIONS

15.   BEAM FIXED AT BOTH ENDS—UNIFORMLY DISTRIBUTED LOADS

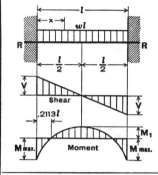

$R = V$ . . . . $= \dfrac{wl}{2}$

V_x . . . . $= w\left(\dfrac{l}{2} - x\right)$

M max. $\left(\text{at ends}\right)$ . . . . . $= \dfrac{wl^2}{12}$

M_1 $\left(\text{at center}\right)$ . . . . . $= \dfrac{wl^2}{24}$

M_x . . . . $= \dfrac{w}{12}(6lx - l^2 - 6x^2)$

Δmax. $\left(\text{at center}\right)$ . . . . . $= \dfrac{wl^4}{384EI}$

Δ_x . . . . $= \dfrac{wx^2}{24EI}(l - x)^2$

16.   BEAM FIXED AT BOTH ENDS—CONCENTRATED LOAD AT CENTER

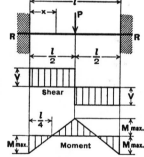

$R = V$ . . . . $= \dfrac{P}{2}$

M max. $\left(\text{at center and ends}\right)$ . . . . $= \dfrac{Pl}{8}$

M_x $\left(\text{when } x < \dfrac{l}{2}\right)$ . . . . . $= \dfrac{P}{8}(4x - l)$

Δmax. $\left(\text{at center}\right)$ . . . . . . $= \dfrac{Pl^3}{192EI}$

Δ_x . . . . $= \dfrac{Px^2}{48EI}(3l - 4x)$

17.   BEAM FIXED AT BOTH ENDS—CONCENTRATED LOAD AT ANY POINT

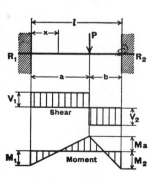

$R_1 = V_1\left(\text{max. when } a < b\right)$ . . . . $= \dfrac{Pb^2}{l^3}(3a + b)$

$R_2 = V_2\left(\text{max. when } a > b\right)$ . . . . $= \dfrac{Pa^2}{l^3}(a + 3b)$

M_1 $\left(\text{max. when } a < b\right)$ . . . . $= \dfrac{Pab^2}{l^2}$

M_2 $\left(\text{max. when } a > b\right)$ . . . . $= \dfrac{Pa^2b}{l^2}$

M_a $\left(\text{at point of load}\right)$ . . . . $= \dfrac{2Pa^2b^2}{l^3}$

M_x $\left(\text{when } x < a\right)$ . . . . . $= R_1x - \dfrac{Pab^2}{l^2}$

Δmax. $\left(\text{when } a > b \text{ at } x = \dfrac{2al}{3a + b}\right)$. $= \dfrac{2Pa^3b^2}{3EI(3a + b)^2}$

Δ_a $\left(\text{at point of load}\right)$ . . . . $= \dfrac{Pa^3b^3}{3EIl^3}$

Δ_x $\left(\text{when } x < a\right)$ . . . . . $= \dfrac{Pb^2x^2}{6EIl^3}(3al - 3ax - bx)$

AMERICAN INSTITUTE OF STEEL CONSTRUCTION

BEAM DIAGRAMS AND FORMULAS
FOR VARIOUS STATIC LOADING CONDITIONS

---

18. CANTILEVER BEAM—LOAD INCREASING UNIFORMLY TO FIXED END

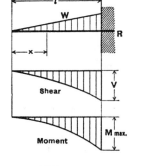

$R = V$ . . . . $= W$

V_x . . . . $= W \dfrac{x^2}{l^2}$

M max. $\left(\text{at fixed end}\right)$ . . . . . $= \dfrac{Wl}{3}$

M_x . . . . $= \dfrac{Wx^3}{3l^2}$

Δmax. $\left(\text{at free end}\right)$ . . . . . $= \dfrac{Wl^3}{15EI}$

Δ_x . . . . $= \dfrac{W}{60EIl^2}(x^5 - 5l^4 x + 4l^5)$

---

19. CANTILEVER BEAM—UNIFORMLY DISTRIBUTED LOAD

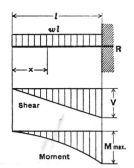

$R = V$ . . . . $= wl$

V_x . . . . $= wx$

M max. $\left(\text{at fixed end}\right)$ . . . . . $= \dfrac{wl^2}{2}$

M_x . . . . $= \dfrac{wx^2}{2}$

Δmax. $\left(\text{at free end}\right)$ . . . . . $= \dfrac{wl^4}{8EI}$

Δ_x . . . . $= \dfrac{w}{24EI}(x^4 - 4l^3 x + 3l^4)$

---

20. BEAM FIXED AT ONE END, FREE BUT GUIDED AT OTHER—UNIFORMLY DISTRIBUTED LOAD

The deflection at the guided end is assumed to be in a vertical plane.

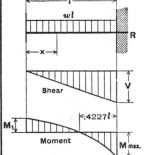

$R = V$ . . . . $= wl$

V_x . . . . $= wx$

M max. $\left(\text{at fixed end}\right)$ . . . . . $= \dfrac{wl^2}{3}$

M_1 $\left(\text{at guided end}\right)$ . . . . $= \dfrac{wl^2}{6}$

M_x . . . . $= \dfrac{w}{6}(l^2 - 3x^2)$

Δmax. $\left(\text{at guided end}\right)$ . . . . $= \dfrac{wl^4}{24EI}$

Δ_x . . . . $= \dfrac{w(l^2 - x^2)^2}{24EI}$

BEAM DIAGRAMS AND FORMULAS
FOR VARIOUS STATIC LOADING CONDITIONS

---

21. CANTILEVER BEAM—CONCENTRATED LOAD AT ANY POINT

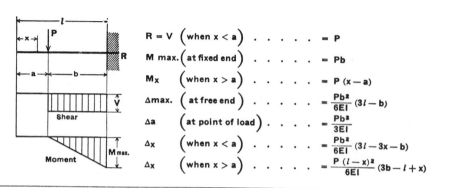

$R = V \left(\text{when } x < a \right)$ . . . . . $= P$

$M \text{ max.} \left(\text{at fixed end} \right)$ . . . . . $= Pb$

$M_x \left(\text{when } x > a \right)$ . . . . . $= P(x - a)$

$\Delta \text{max.} \left(\text{at free end} \right)$ . . . . . $= \dfrac{Pb^2}{6EI} (3l - b)$

$\Delta a \left(\text{at point of load} \right)$ . . . . . $= \dfrac{Pb^3}{3EI}$

$\Delta x \left(\text{when } x < a \right)$ . . . . . $= \dfrac{Pb^2}{6EI} (3l - 3x - b)$

$\Delta x \left(\text{when } x > a \right)$ . . . . . $= \dfrac{P(l - x)^2}{6EI} (3b - l + x)$

---

22. CANTILEVER BEAM—CONCENTRATED LOAD AT FREE END

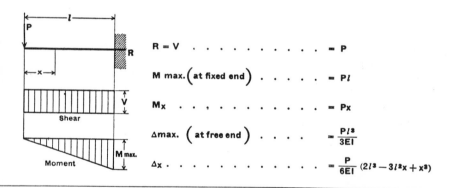

$R = V$ . . . . $= P$

$M \text{ max.} \left(\text{at fixed end} \right)$ . . . . . $= Pl$

M_x . . , ... $= Px$

$\Delta \text{max.} \left(\text{at free end} \right)$ . . . . $= \dfrac{Pl^3}{3EI}$

Δx . . . . $= \dfrac{P}{6EI} (2l^3 - 3l^2 x + x^3)$

---

23. BEAM FIXED AT ONE END, FREE BUT GUIDED AT OTHER—
CONCENTRATED LOAD AT GUIDED END

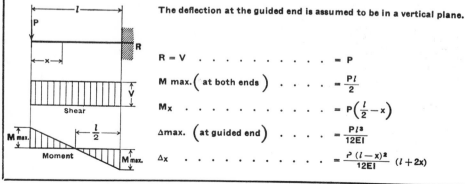

The deflection at the guided end is assumed to be in a vertical plane.

$R = V$ . . . . $= P$

$M \text{ max.} \left(\text{at both ends} \right)$ . . . . . $= \dfrac{Pl}{2}$

M_x . . . . $= P \left(\dfrac{l}{2} - x \right)$

$\Delta \text{max.} \left(\text{at guided end} \right)$ . . . . $= \dfrac{Pl^3}{12EI}$

Δx . . . . $= \dfrac{P(l - x)^2}{12EI} (l + 2x)$

BEAM DIAGRAMS AND FORMULAS
FOR VARIOUS STATIC LOADING CONDITIONS

24. BEAM OVERHANGING ONE SUPPORT—UNIFORMLY DISTRIBUTED LOAD

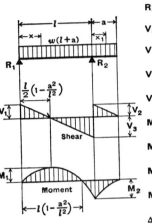

$R_1 = V_1$ . . . . $= \dfrac{w}{2l}(l^2 - a^2)$

$R_2 = V_2 + V_3$ . . . . $= \dfrac{w}{2l}(l + a)^2$

V_2 . . . . $= wa$

V_3 . . . . $= \dfrac{w}{2l}(l^2 + a^2)$

V_x $\left(\text{between supports}\right)$ . . $= R_1 - wx$

V_{x_1} $\left(\text{for overhang}\right)$ . . . . $= w(a - x_1)$

M_1 $\left(\text{at } x = \dfrac{l}{2}\left[1 - \dfrac{a^2}{l^2}\right]\right)$ . . $= \dfrac{w}{8l^2}(l + a)^2(l - a)^2$

M_2 $\left(\text{at } R_2\right)$ . . . . . $= \dfrac{wa^2}{2}$

M_x $\left(\text{between supports}\right)$ . . $= \dfrac{wx}{2l}(l^2 - a^2 - xl)$

M_{x_1} $\left(\text{for overhang}\right)$ . . . . $= \dfrac{w}{2}(a - x_1)^2$

Δ_x $\left(\text{between supports}\right)$ . . $= \dfrac{wx}{24EIl}(l^4 - 2l^2x^2 + lx^3 - 2a^2l^2 + 2a^2x^2)$

Δ_{x_1} $\left(\text{for overhang}\right)$ . . . . $= \dfrac{wx_1}{24EI}(4a^2l - l^3 + 6a^2x_1 - 4ax_1^2 + x_1^3)$

25. BEAM OVERHANGING ONE SUPPORT—UNIFORMLY DISTRIBUTED LOAD ON OVERHANG

$R_1 = V_1$ . . . . $= \dfrac{wa^2}{2l}$

$R_2 = V_1 + V_2$ . . . . $= \dfrac{wa}{2l}(2l + a)$

V_2 . . . . $= wa$

V_{x_1} $\left(\text{for overhang}\right)$ . . . . $= w(a - x_1)$

$M \text{ max.}\left(\text{at } R_2\right)$ . . . . . . $= \dfrac{wa^2}{2}$

M_x $\left(\text{between supports}\right)$ . . $= \dfrac{wa^2x}{2l}$

M_{x_1} $\left(\text{for overhang}\right)$ . . . . $= \dfrac{w}{2}(a - x_1)^2$

$\Delta \text{max.}$ $\left(\text{between supports at } x = \dfrac{l}{\sqrt{3}}\right) = \dfrac{wa^2l^2}{18\sqrt{3}EI} = .03208\dfrac{wa^2l^2}{EI}$

$\Delta \text{max.}$ $\left(\text{for overhang at } x_1 = a\right)$. $= \dfrac{wa^3}{24EI}(4l + 3a)$

Δ_x $\left(\text{between supports}\right)$ . . $= \dfrac{wa^2x}{12EIl}(l^2 - x^2)$

Δ_{x_1} $\left(\text{for overhang}\right)$ . . . . $= \dfrac{wx_1}{24EI}(4a^2l + 6a^2x_1 - 4ax_1^2 + x_1^3)$

BEAM DIAGRAMS AND FORMULAS
FOR VARIOUS STATIC LOADING CONDITIONS

26.   BEAM OVERHANGING ONE SUPPORT—CONCENTRATED LOAD AT END OF OVERHANG

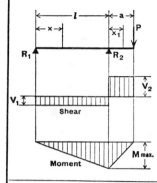

$$R_1 = V_1 \;\ldots\ldots\ldots\ldots = \frac{Pa}{l}$$

$$R_2 = V_1 + V_2 \;\ldots\ldots\ldots = \frac{P}{l}(l+a)$$

$$V_2 \;\ldots\ldots\ldots\ldots\ldots = P$$

$$M \text{ max.}\left(\text{at } R_2\right) \;\ldots\ldots = Pa$$

$$M_x \quad \left(\text{between supports}\right) \;\ldots = \frac{Pax}{l}$$

$$M_{x_1} \quad \left(\text{for overhang}\right) \;\ldots\ldots = P(a - x_1)$$

$$\Delta\text{max.}\left(\text{between supports at } x = \frac{l}{\sqrt{3}}\right) = \frac{Pal^2}{9\sqrt{3}\,EI} = .06415\,\frac{Pal^2}{EI}$$

$$\Delta\text{max.}\left(\text{for overhang at } x_1 = a\right) \;. = \frac{Pa^2}{3EI}(l+a)$$

$$\Delta_x \quad \left(\text{between supports}\right) \;\ldots = \frac{Pax}{6EIl}(l^2 - x^2)$$

$$\Delta_{x_1} \quad \left(\text{for overhang}\right) \;\ldots\ldots = \frac{Px_1}{6EI}(2al + 3ax_1 - x_1{}^2)$$

Shear

Moment

M max.

27.   BEAM OVERHANGING ONE SUPPORT—UNIFORMLY DISTRIBUTED LOAD BETWEEN SUPPORTS

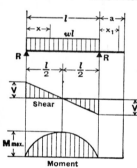

$$R = V \;\ldots\ldots\ldots\ldots\ldots = \frac{wl}{2}$$

$$V_x \;\ldots\ldots\ldots\ldots\ldots\ldots = w\left(\frac{l}{2} - x\right)$$

$$M \text{ max.}\left(\text{at center}\right) \;\ldots\ldots = \frac{wl^2}{8}$$

$$M_x \;\ldots\ldots\ldots\ldots\ldots\ldots = \frac{wx}{2}(l - x)$$

$$\Delta\text{max.}\left(\text{at center}\right) \;\ldots\ldots = \frac{5wl^4}{384EI}$$

$$\Delta_x \;\ldots\ldots\ldots\ldots\ldots\ldots = \frac{wx}{24EI}(l^3 - 2lx^2 + x^3)$$

$$\Delta_{x_1} \;\ldots\ldots\ldots\ldots\ldots\ldots = \frac{wl^3 x_1}{24EI}$$

Shear

Moment

M max.

28.   BEAM OVERHANGING ONE SUPPORT—CONCENTRATED LOAD AT ANY POINT BETWEEN SUPPORTS

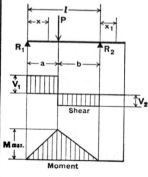

$$R_1 = V_1\left(\text{max. when } a < b\right) \;\ldots = \frac{Pb}{l}$$

$$R_2 = V_2\left(\text{max. when } a > b\right) \;\ldots = \frac{Pa}{l}$$

$$M \text{ max.}\left(\text{at point of load}\right) \;\ldots = \frac{Pab}{l}$$

$$M_x \quad \left(\text{when } x < a\right) \;\ldots\ldots = \frac{Pbx}{l}$$

$$\Delta\text{max.}\left(\text{at } x = \sqrt{\frac{a(a+2b)}{3}} \text{ when } a > b\right) = \frac{Pab\,(a+2b)\,\sqrt{3a\,(a+2b)}}{27EIl}$$

$$\Delta a \quad \left(\text{at point of load}\right) \;\ldots\ldots = \frac{Pa^2b^2}{3EIl}$$

$$\Delta_x \quad \left(\text{when } x < a\right) \;\ldots\ldots = \frac{Pbx}{6EIl}(l^2 - b^2 - x^2)$$

$$\Delta_x \quad \left(\text{when } x > a\right) \;\ldots\ldots = \frac{Pa\,(l-x)}{6EIl}(2lx - x^2 - a^2)$$

$$\Delta_{x_1} \;\ldots\ldots\ldots\ldots\ldots\ldots = \frac{Pabx_1}{6EIl}(l+a)$$

Shear

Moment

M max.

BEAM DIAGRAMS AND FORMULAS
FOR VARIOUS STATIC LOADING CONDITIONS

29. CONTINUOUS BEAM—TWO EQUAL SPANS—UNIFORM LOAD ON ONE SPAN

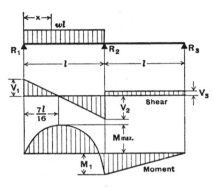

Equivalent Tabular Load . $= \dfrac{49}{64}\,wl$

$R_1 = V_1$ . . . . $= \dfrac{7}{16}\,wl$

$R_2 = V_2 + V_3$ . . . . . . $= \dfrac{5}{8}\,wl$

$R_3 = V_3$ . . . . $= -\dfrac{1}{16}\,wl$

V_2 . . . . $= \dfrac{9}{16}\,wl$

M Max. $\left(\text{at } x = \dfrac{7}{16}\,l\right)$ . . $= \dfrac{49}{512}\,wl^2$

M_1 $\left(\text{at support } R_2\right)$. $= \dfrac{1}{16}\,wl^2$

M_x $\left(\text{when } x < l\right)$ . . . $= \dfrac{wx}{16}\,(7l - 8x)$

30. CONTINUOUS BEAM—TWO EQUAL SPANS—CONCENTRATED LOAD AT CENTER OF ONE SPAN

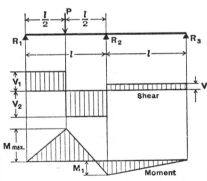

$R_1 = V_1$ . . . . $= \dfrac{13}{32}\,P$

$R_2 = V_2 + V_3$ . . . . . $= \dfrac{11}{16}\,P$

$R_3 = V_3$ . . . . $= -\dfrac{3}{32}\,P$

V_2 . . . . $= \dfrac{19}{32}\,P$

M Max. $\left(\text{at point of load}\right)$. $= \dfrac{13}{64}\,Pl$

M_1 $\left(\text{at support } R_2\right)$. $= \dfrac{3}{32}\,Pl$

31. CONTINUOUS BEAM—TWO EQUAL SPANS—CONCENTRATED LOAD AT ANY POINT

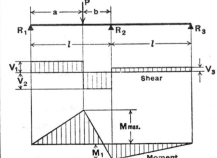

$R_1 = V_1$ . . . . $= \dfrac{Pb}{4l^3}\left(4l^2 - a(l+a)\right)$

$R_2 = V_2 + V_3$ . . . . . $= \dfrac{Pa}{2l^3}\left(2l^2 + b(l+a)\right)$

$R_3 = V_3$ . . . . $= -\dfrac{Pab}{4l^3}\,(l+a)$

V_2 . . . . $= \dfrac{Pa}{4l^3}\left(4l^2 + b(l+a)\right)$

M max. $\left(\text{at point of load}\right)$. $= \dfrac{Pab}{4l^3}\left(4l^2 - a(l+a)\right)$

M_1 $\left(\text{at support } R_2\right)$. $= \dfrac{Pab}{4l^2}\,(l+a)$

BEAM DIAGRAMS AND FORMULAS
For various static loading conditions

32. BEAM—UNIFORMLY DISTRIBUTED LOAD AND VARIABLE END MOMENTS

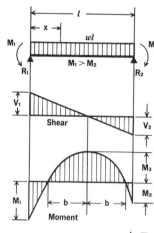

$$R_1 = V_1 = \frac{wl}{2} + \frac{M_1 - M_2}{l}$$

$$R_2 = V_2 = \frac{wl}{2} - \frac{M_1 - M_2}{l}$$

$$V_x = w\left(\frac{l}{2} - x\right) + \frac{M_1 - M_2}{l}$$

$$M_3 \left(\text{at } x = \frac{l}{2} + \frac{M_1 - M_2}{wl}\right)$$

$$= \frac{wl^2}{8} - \frac{M_1 + M_2}{2} + \frac{(M_1 - M_2)^2}{2wl^2}$$

$$M_x = \frac{wx}{2}(l - x) + \left(\frac{M_1 - M_2}{l}\right)x - M_1$$

$$b\left(\begin{array}{l}\text{To locate}\\ \text{inflection points}\end{array}\right) = \sqrt{\frac{l^2}{4} - \left(\frac{M_1 + M_2}{w}\right)} + \left(\frac{M_1 - M_2}{wl}\right)^2$$

$$\Delta_x = \frac{wx}{24EI}\left[x^3 - \left(2l - \frac{4M_1}{wl} + \frac{4M_2}{wl}\right)x^2 + \frac{12M_1}{w}x + l^3 - \frac{8M_1 l}{w} - \frac{4M_2 l}{w}\right]$$

33. BEAM—CONCENTRATED LOAD AT CENTER AND VARIABLE END MOMENTS

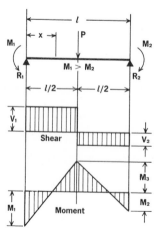

$$R_1 = V_1 = \frac{P}{2} + \frac{M_1 - M_2}{l}$$

$$R_2 = V_2 = \frac{P}{2} - \frac{M_1 - M_2}{l}$$

$$M_3 \text{ (At center)} = \frac{Pl}{4} - \frac{M_1 + M_2}{2}$$

$$M_x \left(\text{When } x < \frac{l}{2}\right) = \left(\frac{P}{2} + \frac{M_1 - M_2}{l}\right)x - M_1$$

$$M_x \left(\text{When } x > \frac{l}{2}\right) = \frac{P}{2}(l - x) + \frac{(M_1 - M_2)x}{l} - M_1$$

$$\Delta_x \left(\text{When } x < \frac{l}{2}\right) = \frac{Px}{48EI}\left(3l^2 - 4x^2 - \frac{8(l - x)}{Pl}[M_1(2l - x) + M_2(l + x)]\right)$$

BEAM DIAGRAMS AND DEFLECTIONS
For various static loading conditions

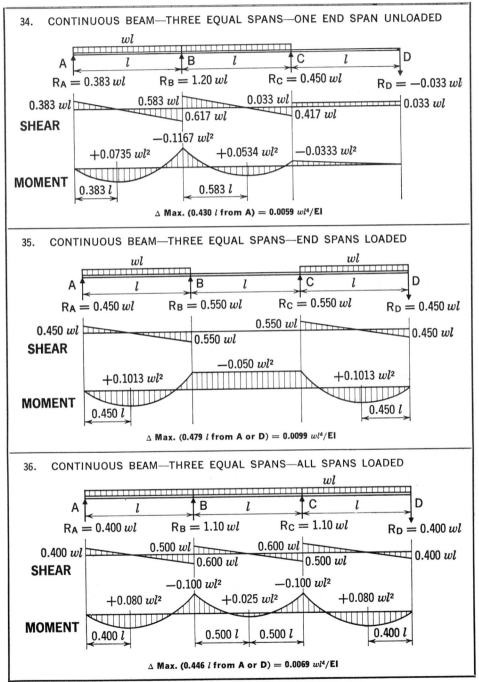

34. CONTINUOUS BEAM—THREE EQUAL SPANS—ONE END SPAN UNLOADED

wl

A l B l C l D

$R_A = 0.383\,wl$ $R_B = 1.20\,wl$ $R_C = 0.450\,wl$ $R_D = -0.033\,wl$

SHEAR

$0.383\,wl$ $0.583\,wl$ $0.033\,wl$ $0.033\,wl$
$0.617\,wl$ $0.417\,wl$

MOMENT

$-0.1167\,wl^2$
$+0.0735\,wl^2$ $+0.0534\,wl^2$ $-0.0333\,wl^2$
$0.383\,l$ $0.583\,l$

$\triangle$ **Max. (0.430 l from A) = 0.0059 wl^4/EI**

35. CONTINUOUS BEAM—THREE EQUAL SPANS—END SPANS LOADED

wl wl

A l B l C l D

$R_A = 0.450\,wl$ $R_B = 0.550\,wl$ $R_C = 0.550\,wl$ $R_D = 0.450\,wl$

SHEAR

$0.450\,wl$ $0.550\,wl$ $0.450\,wl$
$0.550\,wl$

MOMENT

$-0.050\,wl^2$
$+0.1013\,wl^2$ $+0.1013\,wl^2$
$0.450\,l$ $0.450\,l$

$\triangle$ **Max. (0.479 l from A or D) = 0.0099 wl^4/EI**

36. CONTINUOUS BEAM—THREE EQUAL SPANS—ALL SPANS LOADED

wl

A l B l C l D

$R_A = 0.400\,wl$ $R_B = 1.10\,wl$ $R_C = 1.10\,wl$ $R_D = 0.400\,wl$

SHEAR

$0.400\,wl$ $0.500\,wl$ $0.600\,wl$ $0.400\,wl$
$0.600\,wl$ $0.500\,wl$

MOMENT

$-0.100\,wl^2$ $-0.100\,wl^2$
$+0.080\,wl^2$ $+0.025\,wl^2$ $+0.080\,wl^2$
$0.400\,l$ $0.500\,l$ $0.500\,l$ $0.400\,l$

$\triangle$ **Max. (0.446 l from A or D) = 0.0069 wl^4/EI**

BEAM DIAGRAMS AND DEFLECTIONS
For various static loading conditions

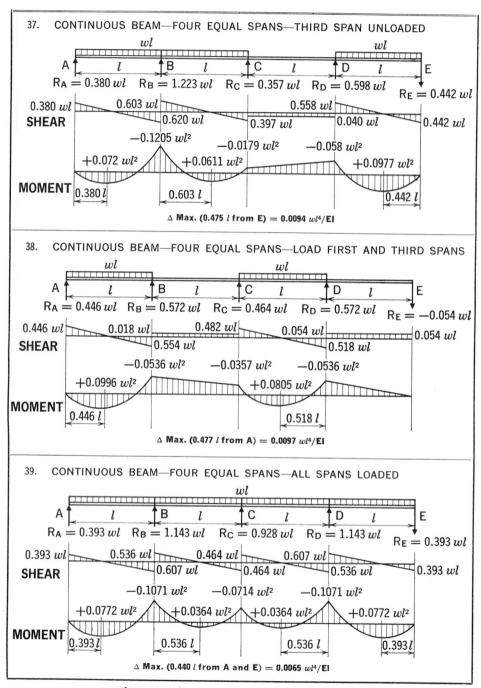

37. CONTINUOUS BEAM—FOUR EQUAL SPANS—THIRD SPAN UNLOADED

wl wl

A l B l C l D l E

$R_A = 0.380\ wl$ $R_B = 1.223\ wl$ $R_C = 0.357\ wl$ $R_D = 0.598\ wl$
$R_E = 0.442\ wl$

SHEAR

$0.380\ wl$ $0.603\ wl$ $0.558\ wl$
$0.620\ wl$ $0.397\ wl$ $0.040\ wl$ $0.442\ wl$

$-0.1205\ wl^2$ $-0.0179\ wl^2$ $-0.058\ wl^2$

$+0.072\ wl^2$ $+0.0611\ wl^2$ $+0.0977\ wl^2$

MOMENT $0.380\ l$ $0.603\ l$ $0.442\ l$

$\triangle$ Max. (0.475 l from E) = 0.0094 wl^4/EI

38. CONTINUOUS BEAM—FOUR EQUAL SPANS—LOAD FIRST AND THIRD SPANS

wl wl

A l B l C l D l E

$R_A = 0.446\ wl$ $R_B = 0.572\ wl$ $R_C = 0.464\ wl$ $R_D = 0.572\ wl$
$R_E = -0.054\ wl$

$0.446\ wl$ $0.018\ wl$ $0.482\ wl$ $0.054\ wl$ $0.054\ wl$

SHEAR

$0.554\ wl$ $0.518\ wl$

$-0.0536\ wl^2$ $-0.0357\ wl^2$ $-0.0536\ wl^2$

$+0.0996\ wl^2$ $+0.0805\ wl^2$

MOMENT $0.446\ l$ $0.518\ l$

$\triangle$ Max. (0.477 l from A) = 0.0097 wl^4/EI

39. CONTINUOUS BEAM—FOUR EQUAL SPANS—ALL SPANS LOADED

wl

A l B l C l D l E

$R_A = 0.393\ wl$ $R_B = 1.143\ wl$ $R_C = 0.928\ wl$ $R_D = 1.143\ wl$
$R_E = 0.393\ wl$

$0.393\ wl$ $0.536\ wl$ $0.464\ wl$ $0.607\ wl$

SHEAR

$0.607\ wl$ $0.464\ wl$ $0.536\ wl$ $0.393\ wl$

$-0.1071\ wl^2$ $-0.0714\ wl^2$ $-0.1071\ wl^2$

$+0.0772\ wl^2$ $+0.0364\ wl^2$ $+0.0364\ wl^2$ $+0.0772\ wl^2$

MOMENT $0.393\ l$ $0.536\ l$ $0.536\ l$ $0.393\ l$

$\triangle$ Max. (0.440 l from A and E) = 0.0065 wl^4/EI

BEAM DIAGRAMS AND FORMULAS
For various concentrated moving loads

The values given in these formulas do not include impact which varies according to the requirements

---

40. SIMPLE BEAM—ONE CONCENTRATED MOVING LOAD

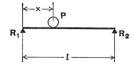

R_1 max. $= V_1$ max. $\left(\text{at } x = 0\right)$ . . . . $= P$

M max. $\left(\text{at point of load, when } x = \dfrac{l}{2}\right)$. $= \dfrac{Pl}{4}$

---

41. SIMPLE BEAM—TWO EQUAL CONCENTRATED MOVING LOADS

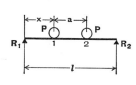

R_1 max. $= V_1$ max. $\left(\text{at } x = 0\right)$ . . . . $= P\left(2 - \dfrac{a}{l}\right)$

M max. $\begin{cases}\left[\begin{array}{l}\text{when } a < (2-\sqrt{2})\ l = .586l \\ \text{under load 1 at } x = \dfrac{1}{2}\left(l - \dfrac{a}{2}\right)\end{array}\right] = \dfrac{P}{2l}\left(l - \dfrac{a}{2}\right)^2 \\[3em] \left[\begin{array}{l}\text{when } a > (2-\sqrt{2})\ l = .586l \\ \text{with one load at center of span} \\ \text{(case 32)}\end{array}\right] = \dfrac{Pl}{4}\end{cases}$

---

42. SIMPLE BEAM—TWO UNEQUAL CONCENTRATED MOVING LOADS

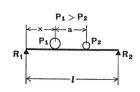

R_1 max. $= V_1$ max. $\left(\text{at } x = 0\right)$ . . . . $= P_1 + P_2\dfrac{l-a}{l}$

M max. $\begin{cases}\left[\text{under } P_1, \text{at } x = \dfrac{1}{2}\left(l - \dfrac{P_2 a}{P_1 + P_2}\right)\right] = \left(P_1 + P_2\right)\dfrac{x^2}{l} \\[2em] \left[\begin{array}{l}\text{M max. may occur with larger} \\ \text{load at center of span and other} \\ \text{load off span (case 32)}\end{array}\right] = \dfrac{P_1 l}{4}\end{cases}$

GENERAL RULES FOR SIMPLE BEAMS CARRYING MOVING CONCENTRATED LOADS

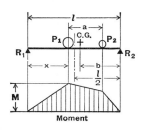

Moment

The maximum shear due to moving concentrated loads occurs at one support when one of the loads is at that support. With several moving loads, the location that will produce maximum shear must be determined by trial.

The maximum bending moment produced by moving concentrated loads occurs under one of the loads when that load is as far from one support as the center of gravity of all the moving loads on the beam is from the other support.

In the accompanying diagram, the maximum bending moment occurs under load P_1 when $x = b$. It should also be noted that this condition occurs when the center line of the span is midway between the center of gravity of loads and the nearest concentrated load.

AMERICAN INSTITUTE OF STEEL CONSTRUCTION

TABLES AND CHARTS

TABLE 1

Bar sizes, No.	Weights, lb/ft	Nominal dimensions—round sections		
		Diameters, in.	Cross-sectional area, in^2	Perimeters, in.
STANDARD A305 REINFORCING BARS				
2	.167	.250	.05	.786
3	.376	.375	.11	1.178
4	.668	.500	.20	1.571
5	1.043	.625	.31	1.963
6	1.502	.750	.44	2.356
7	2.044	.875	.60	2.749
8	2.670	1.000	.79	3.142
9	3.400	1.128	1.00	3.544
10	4.303	1.270	1.27	3.990
11	5.313	1.410	1.56	4.430

SPECIAL DEFORMED ROUND STEEL BARS
(ASTM Designation A408)

14S	7.65	1.693	2.25	5.32
18S	13.60	2.257	4.00	7.09

TABLE 2.   Areas, Perimeters, and Weights of Deformed Bars

Number of bars		Size of deformed bars, No.				
		2	3	4	5	6
1	A	0.05	0.11	0.20	0.31	0.44
	Σo Perimeter	0.786	1.178	1.571	1.963	2.356
	W	0.167	0.376	0.668	1.043	1.502
2	A	0.10	0.22	0.40	0.62	0.88
	Σo	1.57	2.36	3.14	3.93	4.71
	W	0.33	0.75	1.34	2.09	3.00
3	A	0.15	0.33	0.60	0.93	1.32
	Σo	2.36	3.53	4.71	5.89	7.07
	W	0.50	1.12	2.00	3.13	4.51
4	A	0.20	0.44	0.80	1.24	1.75
	Σo	3.14	4.71	6.28	7.85	9.42
	W	0.67	1.50	2.67	4.17	6.01
5	A	0.25	0.55	1.00	1.55	2.20
	Σo	3.90	5.90	7.85	9.80	11.8
	W	0.84	1.88	3.34	5.21	7.51
6	A	0.30	0.66	1.20	1.86	2.64
	Σo	4.68	7.08	9.42	11.8	14.2
	W	1.00	2.25	4.01	6.26	9.01
7	A	0.35	0.77	1.40	2.17	3.08
	Σo	5.46	8.26	11.0	13.7	16.5
	W	1.17	2.63	4.68	7.3	10.51
8	A	0.40	0.88	1.60	2.48	3.52
	Σo	6.24	9.44	12.6	15.7	18.9
	W	1.34	3.01	5.34	8.34	12.02
9	A	0.45	0.99	1.80	2.79	3.96
	Σo	7.02	10.6	14.1	17.6	21.2
	W	1.50	3.38	6.01	9.39	13.52
10	A	0.50	1.10	2.00	3.10	4.40
	Σo	7.80	11.8	15.7	19.6	23.6
	W	1.67	3.76	6.68	10.43	15.02
11	A	0.55	1.21	2.20	3.41	4.84
	Σo	8.58	13.0	17.3	21.6	26.0
	W	1.84	4.14	7.35	11.47	16.52
12	A	0.60	1.32	2.40	3.72	5.28
	Σo	9.36	14.2	18.8	23.5	28.3
	W	2.00	4.51	8.02	12.52	18.02

Number of bars		Size of deformed bars, No.				
		7	8	9	10	11
1	A	0.60	0.79	1.00	1.27	1.56
	$\sum_0$	2.749	3.142	3.544	3.990	4.430
	W	2.044	2.670	3.40	4.303	5.313
2	A	1.20	1.58	2.00	2.54	3.12
	$\sum_0$	5.50	6.28	7.09	7.98	8.86
	W	4.09	5.34	6.80	8.61	10.63
3	A	1.80	2.37	3.00	3.81	4.68
	$\sum_0$	8.25	9.43	10.63	11.97	13.29
	W	6.13	8.01	10.20	12.91	15.94
4	A	2.41	3.16	4.00	5.08	6.24
	$\sum_0$	11.00	12.57	14.18	15.96	17.72
	W	8.18	10.68	13.60	17.21	21.25
5	A	3.00	3.95	5.00	6.35	7.80
	$\sum_0$	13.8	15.7	17.7	20.0	22.2
	W	10.22	13.35	17.00	21.51	26.6
6	A	3.60	4.74	6.00	7.62	9.36
	$\sum_0$	16.5	18.8	21.3	23.9	26.6
	W	12.26	16.02	20.40	25.8	31.9
7	A	4.20	5.53	7.00	8.89	10.9
	$\sum_0$	19.2	22.0	24.8	27.9	31.0
	W	14.31	18.69	23.80	30.12	37.2
8	A	4.80	6.32	8.00	10.2	12.5
	$\sum_0$	22.00	25.1	28.4	31.9	35.4
	W	16.35	21.36	27.20	34.4	42.5
9	A	5.40	7.11	9.00	11.4	14.0
	$\sum_0$	24.8	28.3	31.9	35.9	39.9
	W	18.40	24.03	30.6	38.7	47.8
10	A	6.00	7.90	10.00	12.7	15.6
	$\sum_0$	27.5	31.4	35.4	39.9	44.3
	W	20.44	26.70	34.0	43.0	53.1
11	A	6.60	8.69	11.0	14.0	17.2
	$\sum_0$	30.2	34.5	39.0	43.9	48.7
	W	22.48	29.37	37.4	47.3	58.4
12	A	7.20	9.48	12.0	15.2	18.7
	$\sum_0$	33.0	37.7	42.5	47.9	53.2
	W	24.53	32.04	40.8	51.6	63.8

TABLE 3. Values of k, j, p, K for Various Combinations of Steel and Concrete Stresses for Rectangular Beams and Slabs, Working or Elastic Stresses

$$M = Kbd^2$$

$$k = \frac{1}{1 + (f_s/nf_c)}, \text{design} \qquad p = (f_c k)/2 f_s, \qquad j = 1 - (k/3).$$

$$K = \tfrac{1}{2} f_c k j = p f_s j,$$

$$f_c = 0.45 f'_c,$$

f'_c and n	f_c	$f_s = 16{,}000$ psi $k = 0.458$ $j = 0.847$		$f_s = 18{,}000$ psi $k = 0.429$ $j = 0.857$		$f_s = 20{,}000$ psi $k = 0.403$ $j = 0.866$		$f_s = 24{,}000$ psi $k = 0.360$ $j = 0.880$		$f_s = 30{,}000$ psi $k = 0.310$ $j = 0.897$	
		p	K	p	K	p	K	p	K	p	K
2000 15	900	0.0129	174.6	0.1071	165.2	0.0091	157.0	0.0068	142.6	0.0047	125.1
2500 12	1125	0.0161	218.1	0.0134	206.4	0.0113	196.0	0.0084	178.0	0.0058	156.5
3000 10	1350	0.0193	261.6	0.0161	247.8	0.0136	235.4	0.0101	213.9	0.0070	187.7
3750 8	1687	0.0241	326.8	0.0201	309.2	0.0170	294.2	0.0126	266.9	0.0087	234.5
5000 6	2250	0.0322	436.0	0.0268	412.8	0.0227	392.6	0.0169	356.1	0.0116	312.9

$f_c = .45 f'_c$

TABLE 4 (ACI Code)

MINIMUM BEAM WIDTHS, IN.								
Size of bars, No.	Number of bars in single layer of reinforcing							Add for each added bar
	2	3	4	5	6	7	8	
4	$5\frac{3}{4}$	$7\frac{1}{4}$	$8\frac{3}{4}$	$10\frac{1}{4}$	$11\frac{3}{4}$	$13\frac{1}{4}$	$14\frac{3}{4}$	$1\frac{1}{2}$
5	6	$7\frac{3}{4}$	$9\frac{1}{4}$	11	$12\frac{1}{2}$	$14\frac{1}{4}$	$15\frac{3}{4}$	$1\frac{5}{8}$
6	$6\frac{1}{4}$	8	$9\frac{3}{4}$	$11\frac{1}{2}$	$13\frac{1}{4}$	15	$16\frac{3}{4}$	$1\frac{3}{4}$
7	$6\frac{1}{2}$	$8\frac{1}{2}$	$10\frac{1}{4}$	$12\frac{1}{4}$	14	16	$17\frac{3}{4}$	$1\frac{7}{8}$
8	$6\frac{3}{4}$	$8\frac{3}{4}$	$10\frac{3}{4}$	$12\frac{3}{4}$	$14\frac{3}{4}$	$16\frac{3}{4}$	$18\frac{3}{4}$	2
9	$7\frac{1}{4}$	$9\frac{1}{2}$	$11\frac{3}{4}$	14	$16\frac{1}{4}$	$18\frac{1}{2}$	$20\frac{3}{4}$	$2\frac{1}{4}$
10	$7\frac{3}{4}$	$10\frac{1}{4}$	$12\frac{3}{4}$	$15\frac{1}{4}$	$17\frac{3}{4}$	$20\frac{1}{4}$	23	$2\frac{5}{8}$
11	8	11	$13\frac{3}{4}$	$16\frac{1}{2}$	$19\frac{1}{2}$	$22\frac{1}{4}$	25	$2\frac{7}{8}$

Table shows minimum beam widths when No. 3 stirrups are used; if no stirrups are required, deduct $\frac{3}{4}$ in. from figures shown.

For additional bars, add dimension in last column for each added bar.

For bars of different sizes, determine from table the beam width which would be required for the given number of smaller size bars, and then add last column figure for each larger bar used.

Clear space between bars should be at last $1\frac{1}{3}$ times the maximum size of coarse aggregate, which often requires increased beam width when aggregate exceeds $\frac{3}{4}$ in.

TABLE 5. AASHO Specifications

MINIMUM BEAM WIDTHS, IN.								
Size of bars, No.	Number of bars in single layer of reinforcing							Add for each added bar
	2	3	4	5	6	7	8	
4	7	$8\frac{1}{2}$	10					$1\frac{1}{2}$
5	7	9	$10\frac{1}{2}$	12	$13\frac{1}{2}$			$1\frac{5}{8}$
6	$7\frac{1}{2}$	$9\frac{1}{2}$	$11\frac{1}{2}$	13	15	17		$1\frac{7}{8}$
7	8	10	$12\frac{1}{2}$	$14\frac{1}{2}$	17	19	21	$2\frac{3}{16}$
8	$8\frac{1}{2}$	11	$13\frac{1}{2}$	16	$18\frac{1}{2}$	21	$23\frac{1}{2}$	$2\frac{1}{2}$
9	9	12	$14\frac{1}{2}$	$17\frac{1}{2}$	20	23	26	$2\frac{13}{16}$
10	$9\frac{1}{2}$	$12\frac{1}{2}$	16	19	22	$25\frac{1}{2}$	$28\frac{1}{2}$	$3\frac{3}{16}$
11	10	$13\frac{1}{2}$	17	$20\frac{1}{2}$	24	$27\frac{1}{2}$	31	$3\frac{1}{2}$

Table shows minimum beam widths when No. 3 or No. 4 stirrups are used; if no stirrups are required, deduct one inch from figures shown.

If larger stirrups are used, add twice the increment of stirrup size over $\frac{1}{2}$ in.

For additional bars, add dimension in last column for each added bar.

For bars of different sizes, determine from table the beam width which would be required for the given number of smaller size bars, and then add last column figure for each larger bar used.

TABLE 6

		Spacing of Bars, In.																		
Size of bar, No.		3	3½	4	4½	5	5½	6	6½	7	7½	8	8½	9	9½	10	10½	11	11½	12
		Area of steel, in.^{2}																		
2	A_s	0.20	0.17	0.15	0.13	0.12	0.11	0.10	0.09	0.08	0.08	0.07	0.07	0.07	0.06	0.06	0.06	0.05	0.05	0.05
	Σ_0	3.12	2.67	2.34	2.08	1.87	1.70	1.56	1.44	1.34	1.25	1.17	1.10	1.04	0.99	0.94	0.89	0.85	0.81	0.78
3	A_s	0.44	0.38	0.33	0.29	0.26	0.24	0.22	0.20	0.19	0.18	0.17	0.16	0.15	0.14	0.13	0.13	0.12	0.11	0.11
	Σ_0	4.72	4.05	3.54	3.15	2.83	2.57	2.36	2.18	2.02	1.89	1.77	1.67	1.57	1.49	1.42	1.35	1.29	1.23	1.18
4	A_s	0.80	0.69	0.60	0.53	0.48	0.44	0.40	0.37	0.34	0.32	0.30	0.28	0.27	0.25	0.24	0.23	0.22	0.21	0.20
	Σ_0	6.28	5.39	4.71	4.19	3.77	3.43	3.14	2.90	2.69	2.51	2.36	2.22	2.09	1.98	1.88	1.79	1.71	1.64	1.57
5	A_s	1.24	1.06	0.93	0.82	0.74	0.67	0.62	0.57	0.53	0.49	0.46	0.43	0.41	0.39	0.37	0.35	0.33	0.32	0.31
	Σ_0	7.84	6.72	5.88	5.23	4.70	4.28	3.92	3.62	3.36	3.14	2.94	2.77	2.61	2.48	2.35	2.24	2.14	2.05	1.96
6	A_s	1.76	1.51	1.32	1.17	1.05	0.96	0.88	0.81	0.75	0.70	0.66	0.62	0.58	0.55	0.52	0.50	0.48	0.46	0.44
	Σ_0	9.44	8.09	7.08	6.29	5.66	5.15	4.72	4.36	4.05	3.78	3.54	3.34	3.15	2.99	2.83	2.70	2.57	2.46	2.36
7	A_s	2.40	2.06	1.80	1.60	1.44	1.31	1.20	1.11	1.03	0.96	0.90	0.85	0.80	0.76	0.72	0.69	0.66	0.63	0.60
	Σ_0	11.00	9.43	8.25	7.33	6.60	6.00	5.50	5.08	4.71	4.40	4.12	3.89	3.67	3.48	3.30	3.15	3.00	2.87	2.75
8	A_s	3.16	2.71	2.37	2.10	1.89	1.72	1.58	1.45	1.35	1.26	1.18	1.11	1.05	0.99	0.94	0.90	0.86	0.82	0.79
	Σ_0	12.56	10.77	9.42	8.37	7.54	6.85	6.28	5.80	5.38	5.02	4.71	4.45	4.19	3.98	3.77	3.60	3.43	3.28	3.14
9	A_s	4.00	3.43	3.00	2.67	2.40	2.18	2.00	1.85	1.72	1.60	1.50	1.41	1.33	1.26	1.20	1.14	1.09	1.04	1.00
	Σ_0	14.18	12.15	10.63	9.45	8.51	7.73	7.09	6.54	6.08	5.67	5.32	5.02	4.72	4.48	4.25	4.06	3.87	3.70	3.54
10	A_s		4.35	3.81	3.38	3.04	2.77	2.54	2.34	2.17	2.03	1.90	1.79	1.69	1.60	1.52	1.45	1.38	1.32	1.27
	Σ_0		13.68	11.97	10.64	9.58	8.70	7.98	7.37	6.84	6.38	5.98	5.65	5.32	5.06	4.79	4.57	4.35	4.17	3.99
11	A_s			4.68	4.16	3.74	3.40	3.12	2.88	2.67	2.50	2.34	2.20	2.08	1.97	1.87	1.78	1.70	1.63	1.56
	Σ_0			13.29	11.81	10.63	9.66	8.86	8.18	7.59	7.09	6.64	6.27	5.91	5.62	5.32	5.08	4.83	4.63	4.43

SYMBOLS

SYMBOLS

Symbol	Definition
A	Length of clear span in short direction for two-way slabs
a_b	Depth of equivalent rectangular stress block for balanced conditions $(k_1 c_b)$
a	Depth of equivalent rectangular stress block $(k_1 c)$
A_c	Area of core of spirally reinforced column measured to the outside diameter of the spiral Area of concrete within the core of a composite column Area of concrete within a pipe column
A_g	Gross area defined by the outside dimensions of spirally reinforced or tied columns Total area of the concrete of composite columns Total area of the concrete encasement of combination column
A_r	Area of steel or cast-iron core of a composite, combination, or pipe column
A_s	Area of tensile reinforcement
A_s'	Area of compression reinforcement
A_{sf}	Steel area to develop compressive strength of overhanging flanges in T-sections
A_{st}	Total area of longitudinal reinforcement
A_v	Total area of web reinforcement in tension within a distance, s, measured in a direction parallel to the longitudinal reinforcement
B	Length of clear span in long direction for two-way slabs
b	Width of rectangular flexural member (and eccentrically loaded columns) or width of flange for T- and I-sections Least width of the compression face of laterally unsupported beams
b'	Width of webs in T- and I-sections
b_0	Periphery of critical section for slabs and footings
C	Compression force Moment coefficient for two-way slabs
C'	Factor modifying bending moments prescribed for one-way constructions for use in proportioning the slabs and beams in the direction of L of slabs supported on four sides
c	Distance from extreme compression fiber to neutral axis at ultimate strength
c_b	Distance from extreme compression fiber to neutral axis [balanced conditions $= d(87{,}000)/(87{,}000 + f_y)$]
D	Nominal diameter of bar, inches Overall depth of beam

Symbol	Definition
D_s	Diameter of circle through centers of the longitudinal reinforcement in spiral columns
d	Distance from extreme compression fiber to centroid of tension reinforcement
d'	Distance from extreme compression fiber to centroid of compression reinforcement
d''	Distance from plastic centroid to centroid of tension reinforcement
d_p	Effective depth of the tension reinforcement in precast component
E_c	Flexural modulus of elasticity of concrete
E_s	Modulus of elasticity of steel
e	Eccentricity of the resultant load on a column, measured from the gravity axis
e_b	Maximum permissible eccentricity of N_b
e'	Eccentricity of axial load at end of member measured from the centroid of tension reinforcement, calculated by conventional methods of frame analysis
F_b	Allowable bending stress that would be permitted for bending alone
F_{sp}	Ratio of split-cylinder tensile strength to the square root of the cylinder strength in compression
f_c	Compressive stress in concrete
f_c'	Compression strength of concrete
f_{sp}'	Split-cylinder tensile strength of concrete
f_{xc}, f_{by}	Bending moment about the x- or y-axis divided by the section modulus of the transformed section, using $2n$ times the total area of longitudinal bars
f_r	Allowable stress in the metal core of a composite column
f_r'	Allowable stress on unencased metal columns and pipe columns
f_s	$\begin{cases} \text{Stress in steel reinforcement} \\ \text{Nominal allowable stress in vertical column reinforcement} \end{cases}$
f_a	Axial load divided by area of member, A_g
f_{ci}'	Compressive strength of concrete at time of initial prestress
f_{ct}'	Compressive strength of concrete at time considered
f_{cp}	Permissible compressive concrete stress on bearing area under anchor plate of post-tensioning steel
$\sqrt{f_c'}$	Relationship expressed in psi; for example, for $f_c' = 3600$ psi, $\sqrt{f_c'} = 60$ psi.
f_v	Tensile stress in web reinforcement
f_y	$\begin{cases} \text{Specified yield point of reinforcement} \\ \text{Reinforcement yield point to be used in design computations} \end{cases}$
f_{su}	Calculated stress in prestressing steel at ultimate load
f_{sy}	Nominal yield strength of prestressing steel
f_y'	Yield point stress of nonprestressed reinforcing steel
H	Story height (in feet) of the column or support of a flat slab center-to-center of slabs

SYMBOL	DEFINITION
h	$\begin{cases}\text{Actual unsupported length of column}\\\text{Total depth of beam or girder}\end{cases}$
h'	Effective length of column
I	Moment of inertia of the transformed section
j	Ratio of distance between centroid of compression and centroid of tension to the depth d
K	A constant $= f_c k j$
K'	Stiffness factor $= EI/l$
k	Ratio of distance from extreme compression fiber to neutral axis to the effective depth of section
k_1	A constant
L	Specified live load plus impact
l	Span length of slab or beam
l'	Clear span for positive moment and shear and the average of the two adjacent clear spans for negative moment
M	Bending moment
M'	Modified bending moment
M_b	Moment capacity at simultaneous crushing of concrete and yielding of tension steel (balanced conditions) $= (P_b e_b)$
M_0	Numerical sum of assumed positive and average negative moments at the critical design sections of a flat slab panel
M_D	Moment due to dead load, produced prior to the time at which the cast-in-place concrete attains 75% of its specified 28-day strength
M_L	Moment due to live load and superimposed dead load
m	$f_y/0.85 f_c'$
m'	$m - 1$
m_r	Ratio of short span to long span for two-way slabs
μ	$\begin{cases}\text{Poisson ratio}\\\text{Coefficient of friction}\end{cases}$
N	Number of stirrups
N_e	Load normal to the cross section to be taken as positive for compression, and negative for tension, including the effects of tension due to shrinkage
N_b	The value of P below which the allowable eccentricity is controlled by tension and above which by compression
n	Ratio of modulus of elasticity of steel to that of concrete
P	Concentrated load or force
P_b	Axial load capacity at simultaneous crushing of concrete and yielding of tension steel (balanced conditions)
P_c	Axial load capacity of actual member under concentric load
P_u	Axial load capacity under combined axial load and bending
p	Ratio of longitudinal tensile reinforcement to effective area of concrete
p_s	Ratio of volume of spiral reinforcement to total volume of core (out-to-out of spirals) of a spirally reinforced concrete or composite column

Symbol	Definition
Q	Statical moment of the transformed area outside the contact surface about the neutral axis of the composite section
R	Reduction factor for long columns
r'	The ratio of $\sum K'$ of columns to $\sum K'$ of floor members in a plane at one end of a column
S	Length of short span for two-way slabs. The span shall be considered as the center-to-center distance between supports or the clear span plus twice the thickness of slab, whichever value is the smaller
s	Spacing of stirrups or bent bars in a direction parallel to the longitudinal reinforcement
T	Tension force
t	$\begin{cases} \text{Minimum thickness of flexural member} \\ \text{Slab thickness} \\ \text{Overall diameter of a column section} \end{cases}$
t_1	Thickness (in inches) of slabs without drop panels, or through drop panel, if any
t_2	Thickness (in inches) of slabs with drop panels, at points beyond the drop panel
u	Bond stress per unit of surface area of bar
u_u	Nominal ultimate bond stress
V	Total shear
V'	Shear to be carried by web reinforcement
V_u	Total ultimate shear
V_u'	Ultimate shear carried by web reinforcement
v	Nominal shear stress as a measure of diagonal tension
v_c	$\begin{cases} \text{Shear stress permitted on the concrete} \\ \text{Shear stress assumed carried by concrete} \end{cases}$
v_{uc}	Nominal ultimate shear stress as a measure of diagonal tension
W	Total dead and live load on panel
W_D	Total dead load on panel
W_L	Total live load on panel, uniformly distributed
w	Total uniform load per square foot
w'	Uniformly distributed unit dead and live load
z	Distance from extreme compressive fiber to neutral axis of a T-section
θ,ϕ,α	Angles; ϕ is also a coefficient.
Δ,δ	Deflections or deformations
$\sum_0$	Sum of perimeters of all effective bars crossing the section on the tension side if of uniform size; for mixed sizes, substitute $4A_s/D$, where A_s is the total steel area and D is the largest bar diameter. For bundled bars, use the sum of the exposed portions of the perimeters.
x,y,z	Rectangular coordinates

INDEX

INDEX

ACI BUILDING CODE

 PUBLICATION

ACI Standard

Building Code Requirements
for
Reinforced Concrete

(ACI 318-63)

JUNE 1963

ACI Standard

Building Code Requirements

for

Reinforced Concrete*

(ACI 318-63)

Reported by ACI Committee 318

RAYMOND C. REESE
Chairman

JOHN P. THOMPSON
Secretary

W. C. E. BECKER
FRANK H. BEINHAUER
DELMAR L. BLOEM
FRANK B. BROWN
ROSS H. BRYAN
EDWARD COHEN
THEODORE F. COLLIER
JAMES N. DE SERIO
MALCOLM S. DOUGLAS
WILLIAM EIPEL
PHIL M. FERGUSON
E. I. FIESENHEISER
A. H. GUSTAFERRO
EIVIND HOGNESTAD

HARRY F. IRWIN
ROBERT O. JAMESON
ROBERT C. JOHNSON
OLIVER G. JULIAN
FRANK KEREKES
WALTER E. KUNZE
GEORGE E. LARGE
T. Y. LIN
NOLAN D. MITCHELL
NATHAN M. NEWMARK
DOUGLAS E. PARSONS
JEROME L. PETERSON
ORLEY O. PHILLIPS
W. GORDON PLEWES
M. V. PREGNOFF

THEODORE O. REYHNER
PAUL F. RICE
PAUL ROGERS
EMILIO ROSENBLUETH
ROBERT SAILER
MORRIS SCHUPACK
CHESTER P. SIESS
HOWARD SIMPSON
IRWIN J. SPEYER
M. P. VAN BUREN
A. CARL WEBER
WALTER H. WHEELER
C. A. WILLSON
GEORGE WINTER
H. B. ZACKRISON, SR.

SYNOPSIS

This code provides minimum requirements for the design and construction of reinforced concrete, or composite structural elements of any structure erected under the requirements of the general building code of which this code forms a part. For special structures, such as arches, tanks, reservoirs, grain elevators, shells, domes, blast-resistant structures, and chimneys, the provisions of this code shall govern so far as they are applicable.

This code is written in such a form that it may be incorporated verbatim or adopted by reference in a general building code, and earlier editions of it have been widely used in this manner.

*Adopted as a standard of the American Concrete Institute at its 59th Annual Convention, Mar. 6, 1963, as amended; ratified by latter ballot May 27, 1963. ACI 318-63 supersedes ACI 318-56 published May 1956. Copyright ©, 1963, American Concrete Institute, P. O. Box 4754, Redford Station, Detroit 19, Mich. Printed in the United States of America. Price: $3.00 ($1.50 to ACI members) in paper covers; $4.00 ($2.50 to ACI members) in hard covers.

CONTENTS

APPENDIX

While not part of this standard, metric equivalents of all the dimensional values in this
code and metric conversions of nonhomoge-
neous equations are given on pp. 137-141.

PART I – GENERAL

CHAPTER 1 — GENERAL REQUIREMENTS

101—Scope

(a) This code provides minimum requirements for the design and construction of reinforced concrete or composite structural elements of any structure erected under the requirements of the general building code of which this code forms a part.

(b) This code supplements the general building code and shall govern in all matters pertaining to design and construction wherever it is in conflict with the requirements in the general building code.

(c) For special structures, such as arches, tanks, reservoirs, grain elevators, shells, domes, blast-resistant structures, and chimneys, the provisions of this code shall govern so far as they are applicable.

102—Permits and drawings

(a) Copies of structural drawings, typical details, and specifications for all reinforced concrete construction shall bear the seal of a licensed engineer or architect and shall be filed with the building department as a permanent record before a permit to construct such work will be issued. These drawings, details, and specifications shall show the size and position of all structural elements and reinforcing steel; provision for dimensional changes resulting from creep, shrinkage, and temperature; the specified strength of the concrete at stated ages; the specified strength of the reinforcing steel; the magnitude and location of prestressing forces; and the live load used in the design.

(b) Calculations pertaining to the design shall be filed with the drawings when required by the Building Official.

(c) Building Official means the officer or other designated authority charged with the administration and enforcement of this code, or his duly authorized representative.

103—Inspection*

(a) Concrete work on the site shall be inspected by a competent engineer or architect, preferably the one responsible for its design, or by a competent representative responsible to him, who shall keep a record which shall cover the quality and quantity of concrete materials; the mixing, placing, and curing of concrete; the placing of reinforcing steel; the sequence of erection and connection of precast members; and the general progress of the work.

(b) When the temperature falls below 40 F or rises above 100 F, a

---

*Detailed recommendations for concrete inspection are given in *ACI Manual of Concrete Inspection*, ACI 611.

complete record of the temperatures and of the protection given to the concrete while curing shall be kept.

(c) The records of inspection required in (a) and (b) shall be kept available to the Building Official during the progress of the work and for 2 years thereafter and shall be preserved by the engineer or architect for that purpose.

104—Approval of special systems of design or construction

(a) The sponsors of any system of design or construction within the scope of this code and which has been in successful use, or the adequacy of which has been shown by analysis or test, and the design of which is either not consistent with, or not covered by this code shall have the right to present the data on which their design is based to a "Board of Examiners for Special Construction"* appointed by the Building Official. This Board shall be composed of competent engineers and shall have the authority to investigate the data so submitted, to require tests, and to formulate rules governing the design and construction of such systems to meet the intent of this code. These rules when approved by the Building Official and promulgated shall be of the same force and effect as the provisions of this code.

---

*The exact name of this board and its selection should be adapted to the local legal conditions.

CHAPTER 2 — LOAD TESTS OF STRUCTURES*

200—Notation

$D =$ service dead load

$L =$ service live load

$\Delta =$ maximum deflection, produced by a test load, of a member relative to the ends of the span, or of the free end of a cantilever relative to its support

$l =$ span of member under load test (the shorter span of flat slabs and of slabs supported on four sides). The span, except as provided in Section 202(a)3, is the distance between the centers of the supports or the clear distance between supports plus the depth of the member, whichever is smaller (in in.)

$t =$ total thickness or depth of member under load test (in in.)

201—Static load tests of structures

(a) The Building Official shall have the right to order the test under load of any portion of a structure when conditions are such as to cause doubt about the safety of the structure.

(b) When such load tests of a structure are required, a qualified engineer acceptable to the Building Official shall conduct the tests.

(c) A load test of a structure shall not be made until the portion subjected to load is at least 56 days old, unless the owner of the structure agrees to the test being made at an earlier age.

(d) When the whole structure is not to be tested, the portion of the structure thought to provide the least margin of safety shall be selected for loading. Prior to the application of the test load, a load which simulates the effect of that portion of the service dead load which is not already present shall be applied and shall remain in place until after a decision has been made regarding the acceptability of the structure. The test load shall not be applied until the structural members to be tested have borne the full service dead load for at least 48 hr.

(e) Immediately prior to the application of the test load to flexural members (including beams, slabs, and floor and roof constructions), the necessary initial readings shall be made for the measurements of deflections (and strains, if these are considered necessary) caused by the application of the test load.

(f) The members selected for loading shall be subjected to a superimposed test load equivalent to 0.3 times the service dead load plus 1.7 times the service live load (test load $= 0.3D + 1.7L$). The test load shall be applied without shock to the structure and in a manner to avoid arching of the loading materials.

---

*For approval of special systems of design or construction, see Section 104.

(g) The test load shall be left in position for 24 hr whereupon readings of the deflections shall be taken. The test load shall be removed and additional readings of deflections shall be taken 24 hr after the removal of the test load.

202—Criteria for evaluation of load tests

(a) If the structure shows evident failure or fails to meet the following criteria, the changes needed to make the structure adequate for the rated capacity shall be made or a lower rating may be established.

1. If the maximum deflection, Δ, of a reinforced concrete beam, floor or roof exceeds $l^2/20,000t$, the recovery of deflection within 24 hr after the removal of the test load shall be at least 75 percent of the maximum deflection.

2. If the maximum deflection, Δ, is less than $l^2/20,000t$, the requirement on recovery of deflection in 1 may be waived.

3. In determining the limiting deflection for a cantilever, l shall be taken as twice the distance from the support to the end, and the deflection shall be adjusted for movement of the support.

4. Construction failing to show 75 percent recovery of the deflection may be retested. The second test loading shall not be made until at least 72 hr after removal of the test load for the first test. The structure shall show no evidence of failure in the retest, and the recovery of deflection caused by the second test load shall be at least 75 percent.

CHAPTER 3 — DEFINITIONS

301—General definitions

(a) The following terms are defined for general use in this code; specialized definitions appear in individual chapters:

Admixture—A material other than portland cement, aggregate, or water added to concrete to modify its properties.

Aggregate—Inert material which is mixed with portland cement and water to produce concrete.

Aggregate, lightweight—Aggregate having a dry, loose weight of 70 lb per cu ft or less.

Building official—See Section 102(c).

Column—An upright compression member the length of which exceeds three times its least lateral dimension.

Combination column—A column in which a structural steel member, designed to carry the principal part of the load, is encased in concrete of such quality and in such manner that the remaining load may be allowed thereon.

Composite column—A column in which a steel or cast-iron structural member is completely encased in concrete containing spiral and longitudinal reinforcement.

Composite concrete flexural construction—A precast concrete member and cast-in-place reinforced concrete so interconnected that the component elements act together as a flexural unit.

Compressive strength of concrete (f_c') * — Specified compressive strength of concrete in pounds per square inch (psi). Compressive strength shall be determined by tests of standard 6 x 12-in. cylinders made and tested in accordance with ASTM specifications at 28 days or such earlier age as concrete is to receive its full service load or maximum stress.

Concrete—A mixture of portland cement, fine aggregate, coarse aggregate, and water.

Concrete, structural lightweight — A concrete containing lightweight aggregate conforming to Section 403.

Deformed bar—A reinforcing bar conforming to "Specifications for Minimum Requirements for the Deformations of Deformed Steel Bars for Concrete Reinforcement" (ASTM A 305) or "Specifications for Special Large Size Deformed Billet-Steel Bars for Concrete Reinforcement" (ASTM A 408). Welded wire fabric with welded intersections not farther apart than 12 in. in the direction of the principal reinforcement and with cross wires not more than six gage numbers smaller in

---

*Wherever this quantity appears under a radical sign, the root of only the numerical value is intended; all values are in pounds per square inch (psi).

size than the principal reinforcement may be considered equivalent to a deformed bar when used in slabs.

Effective area of concrete—The area of a section which lies between the centroid of the tension reinforcement and the compression face of the **flexural member.**

Effective area of reinforcement—The area obtained by multiplying the right cross-sectional area of the reinforcement by the cosine of the angle between its direction and the direction for which the **effectiveness** is to be determined.

Pedestal—An upright compression member whose height does not exceed three times its average least lateral dimension.

Plain bar—Reinforcement that does not conform to the definition of deformed bar.

Plain concrete—Concrete that does not conform to the definition for reinforced concrete.

Precast concrete—A plain or reinforced concrete element cast in other than its final position in the structure.

Prestressed concrete—Reinforced concrete in which there have been introduced internal stresses of such magnitude and distribution that the stresses resulting from service loads are counteracted to a desired degree.

Reinforced concrete—Concrete containing reinforcement and designed on the assumption that the two materials act together in resisting forces.

Reinforcement—Material that conforms to Section 405, excluding prestressing steel unless specifically included.

Service dead load—The calculated dead weight supported by a member.

Service live load—The live load specified by the general building code of which this code forms a part.

Splitting tensile strength—(see Section 505)

Stress—Intensity of force per unit area.

Surface water—Water carried by an aggregate except that held by absorption within the aggregate particles themselves.

Yield strength or yield point (f_y)—Specified minimum yield strength or yield point of reinforcement in pounds per square inch. Yield strength or yield point shall be determined in tension according to applicable ASTM specifications.

PART II – SPECIFICATIONS AND TESTS FOR MATERIALS

CHAPTER 4 — MATERIALS

401—Tests of materials

(a) The Building Official shall have the right to order from time to time the test of any material entering into the concrete or reinforced concrete to determine whether the materials and methods in use are such as to produce the specified quality.

(b) Tests of materials and of concrete shall be made in accordance with the standards of the American Society for Testing and Materials, as noted elsewhere in this code. The complete records of such tests shall be available for inspection during the progress of the work and for two years thereafter, and shall be preserved by the engineer or architect for that purpose.

402—Portland cement

(a) Portland cement shall conform to "Specifications for Portland Cement" (ASTM C 150) or "Specifications for Air-Entraining Portland Cement" (ASTM C 175).

(b) If provisions are made for sufficient damp curing of the concrete in the structure to develop a compressive strength at least equal to that of concrete containing cement conforming to (a), portland type cements which conform to the following standards may be used: "Specifications for Portland Blast-Furnace Slag Cement" (ASTM C 205) and "Specifications for Portland-Pozzolan Cement" (ASTM C 340).

403—Concrete aggregates

(a) Concrete aggregates shall conform to "Specifications for Concrete Aggregates" (ASTM C 33) or to "Specifications for Lightweight Aggregates for Structural Concrete" (ASTM C 330), except that aggregates failing to meet these specifications but which have been shown by special test or actual service to produce concrete of adequate strength and durability may be used under Section 502 (a), Method 2, where authorized by the Building Official.

(b) Except as permitted elsewhere in this code, the maximum size of the aggregate shall be not larger than one-fifth of the narrowest dimension between sides of the forms of the member for which the concrete is to be used nor larger than three-fourths of the minimum clear spacing between individual reinforcing bars or bundles of bars.

404—Water

(a) Water used in mixing concrete shall be clean and free from injurious amounts of oils, acids, alkalis, salts, organic materials, or other substances that may be deleterious to concrete or steel. Mortar cubes made with nonpotable mixing water shall have 7-day and 28-day strengths equal to at least 90 percent of the strengths of similar specimens made with potable water.

405—Metal reinforcement

(a) Reinforcing bars shall conform to "Specifications for Billet-Steel Bars for Concrete Reinforcement" (ASTM A 15), "Specifications for Rail-Steel Bars for Concrete Reinforcement" (ASTM A 16), "Specifications for Deformed Rail-Steel Bars for Concrete Reinforcement with 60,000 psi Minimum Yield Strength" (ASTM A 61), "Specifications for Axle-Steel Bars for Concrete Reinforcement" (ASTM A 160), "Specifications for Special Large Size Deformed Billet-Steel Bars for Concrete Reinforcement" (ASTM A 408), "Specifications for High Strength Deformed Billet-Steel Bars for Concrete Reinforcement with 75,000 psi Minimum Yield Strength" (ASTM A 431), or "Specifications for Deformed Billet-Steel Bars for Concrete Reinforcement with 60,000 psi Minimum Yield Strength" (ASTM A 432). Deformations on deformed bars shall conform to "Specifications for Deformations of Deformed Steel Bars for Concrete Reinforcement" (ASTM A 305) or "Specifications for Special Large Size Deformed Billet-Steel Bars for Concrete Reinforcement" (ASTM A 408).

If reinforcing bars are to be welded, these ASTM specifications shall be supplemented by requirements assuring satisfactory weldability in conformity with AWS D12.1, "Recommended Practices for Welding Reinforcing Steel, Metal Inserts and Connections in Reinforced Concrete Construction."

(b) Bar and rod mats for concrete reinforcement shall conform to "Specifications for Fabricated Steel Bar or Rod Mats for Concrete Reinforcement" (ASTM A 184).

(c) Wire for concrete reinforcement shall conform to "Specifications for Cold-Drawn Steel Wire for Concrete Reinforcement" (ASTM A 82).

(d) Welded wire fabric for concrete reinforcement shall conform to "Specifications for Welded Steel Wire Fabric for Concrete Reinforcement" (ASTM A 185) except that the weld shear strength requirement of Sec. 5b of those specifications shall be extended to include a wire size differential up to and including six gages.

(e) Wire and strands for prestressed concrete shall conform to "Specifications for Uncoated Seven-Wire Stress-Relieved Strand for Prestressed Concrete" (ASTM A 416) or "Specifications for Wire, Uncoated Stress-Relieved for Prestressed Concrete" (ASTM A 421). Wires used in making strands for post-tensioning shall be cold-drawn and either stress-relieved in the case of uncoated strands, or hot-dip galvanized in the case of galvanized strands.

(f) High strength alloy steel bars for post-tensioning shall be proof-stressed to 90 percent of the guaranteed tensile strength. After proof-stressing, the bars shall conform to the following minimum properties:

Tensile strength f_s' .... 145,000 psi
Yield strength (0.2 percent offset) .... 0.90 f_s'
Elongation at rupture in 20 diameters .... 4 percent
Reduction of area at rupture .... 25 percent

(g) Structural steel shall conform to "Specifications for Steel for Bridges and Buildings" (ASTM A 7), or "Specifications for Structural Steel" (ASTM A 36), or "Specifications for Structural Steel for Welding" (ASTM A 373).

(h) Steel pipe for concrete-filled pipe columns shall conform to Grade B of "Specifications for Welded and Seamless Steel Pipe" (ASTM A 53).

(i) Cast-iron pipe for composite columns shall conform to "Specifications for Cast Iron Pressure Pipe" (ASTM A 377).

406—Air-entraining admixtures

(a) Air-entraining admixtures, if used, shall conform to "Specifications for Air-Entraining Admixtures for Concrete" (ASTM C 260).

407—Accelerating, retarding, and water-reducing admixtures

(a) Water-reducing admixtures, retarding admixtures, accelerating admixtures, water-reducing and retarding admixtures, and water-reducing and accelerating admixtures, if used, shall conform to "Specifications for Chemical Admixtures for Concrete" (ASTM C 494).

408—Pozzolanic admixtures

(a) Fly ash, when used as an admixture, shall conform to "Specifications for Fly Ash for Use as an Admixture in Portland Cement Concrete" (ASTM C 350).

(b) Other pozzolans used as admixtures shall conform to "Specifications for Raw or Calcined Natural Pozzolans for Use as Admixtures in Portland Cement Concrete" (ASTM C 402).

409—Storage of materials

(a) Cement and aggregates shall be stored in such a manner as to prevent their deterioration or the intrusion of foreign matter. Any material which has deteriorated or which has been damaged shall not be used for concrete.

410—Specifications cited in this code*

(a) The specifications of the American Society for Testing and Materials referred to in this code are listed below with their serial designation including the year of adoption or revision and are declared to be a part of this code the same as if fully set forth elsewhere herein:

---

*The specifications listed were the latest editions at the time this code was prepared. Since these specifications are revised frequently, generally in minor details only, the user of this code should check directly with the sponsoring society if it is desired to refer to the latest edition.

A 7-61T   Specifications for Steel for Bridges and Buildings

A 15-62T   Specifications for Billet-Steel Bars for Concrete Reinforcement

A 16-63T   Specifications for Rail-Steel Bars for Concrete Reinforcement

A 36-62T   Specifications for Structural Steel

A 61-63T   Specifications for Deformed Rail-Steel Bars for Concrete Reinforcement with 60,000 psi Minimum Yield Strength

A 53-62T   Specifications for Welded and Seamless Steel Pipe

A 82-62T   Specifications for Cold-Drawn Steel Wire for Concrete Reinforcement

A 160-62T Specifications for Axle-Steel Bars for Concrete Reinforcement

A 184-37   Specifications for Fabricated Steel Bar or Rod Mats for Concrete Reinforcement

A 185-61T Specifications for Welded Steel Wire Fabric for Concrete Reinforcement

A 305-56T Specifications for Minimum Requirements for the Deformations of Deformed Steel Bars for Concrete Reinforcement

A 370-61T Methods and Definitions for Mechanical Testing of Steel Products

A 373-58T Specifications for Structural Steel for Welding

A 377-57   Specifications for Cast Iron Pressure Pipe

A 408-62T Specifications for Special Large Size Deformed Billet-Steel Bars for Concrete Reinforcement

A 416-59T Specifications for Uncoated Seven-Wire Stress-Relieved Strand for Prestressed Concrete

A 421-59T Specifications for Uncoated Stress-Relieved Wire for Prestressed Concrete

A 431-62T Specifications for High Strength Deformed Billet-Steel Bars for Concrete Reinforcement with 75,000 psi Minimum Yield Strength

A 432-62T Specifications for Deformed Billet-Steel Bars for Concrete Reinforcement with 60,000 psi Minimum Yield Strength

C 31-62T   Standard Method of Making and Curing Concrete Compression and Flexure Test Specimens in the Field

C 33-61T   Specifications for Concrete Aggregates

C 39-61   Standard Method of Test for Compressive Strength of Molded Concrete Cylinders

C 42-62   Standard Methods of Securing, Preparing and Testing Specimens from Hardened Concrete for Compressive and Flexural Strengths

C 94-62   Specifications for Ready-Mixed Concrete

C 144-62T Specifications for Aggregate for Masonry Mortar

C 150-62 Specifications for Portland Cement

C 172-54 Standard Method of Sampling Fresh Concrete

C 175-61 Specifications for Air-Entraining Portland Cement

C 192-62T Standard Method of Making and Curing Concrete Compression and Flexure Test Specimens in the Laboratory

C 205-62T Specifications for Portland Blast-Furnace Slag Cement

C 260-60T Specifications for Air-Entraining Admixtures for Concrete

C 330-60T Specifications for Lightweight Aggregates for Structural Concrete

C 340-62T Specifications for Portland-Pozzolan Cement

C 350-60T Specifications for Fly Ash for Use as an Admixture in Portland Cement Concrete

C 402-62T Specifications for Raw or Calcined Natural Pozzolans for Use as Admixtures in Portland Cement Concrete

C 494-62T Specifications for Chemical Admixtures for Concrete

C 496-62T Method of Test for Splitting Tensile Strength of Molded Concrete Cylinders

E 6-62 Definitions of Terms relating to Methods of Mechanical Testing

(b) The specifications of the American Welding Society "Recommended Practices for Welding Reinforcing Steel, Metal Inserts and Connections in Reinforced Concrete Construction" AWS D12.1-61 is declared to be a part of this code the same as if fully set forth herein.

ACI standards and recommendations

"Building Code Requirements for Reinforced Concrete" are minimum standards of performance in legally enforceable phraseology. These results may be achieved through many equally satisfactory methods. Many detailed recommendations for acceptable practices are available in the following American Concrete Institute Standards and Recommendations:

Institute Standards

ACI 214-57 Recommended Practice for Evaluation of Compression Test Results of Field Concrete

ACI 315-57 Manual of Standard Practice for Detailing Reinforced Concrete Structures

ACI 347-63 Recommended Practice for Concrete Formwork

ACI 505-54 Specification for the Design and Construction of Reinforced Concrete Chimneys

ACI 525-63 Minimum Requirements for Thin-Section Precast Concrete Construction

ACI 604-56 Recommended Practice for Winter Concreting

ACI 605-59 Recommended Practice for Hot Weather Concreting

ACI 613-54 Recommended Practice for Selecting Proportions for Concrete

ACI 613A-59 Recommended Practice for Selecting Proportions for Structural Lightweight Concrete

ACI 614-59 Recommended Practice for Measuring, Mixing, and Placing Concrete

ACI 711-58 Minimum Standard Requirements for Precast Concrete Floor Units

ACI 805-51 Recommended Practice for the Applications of Mortars by Pneumatic Pressure

Committee reports

Tentative Recommendations for Prestressed Concrete (Report of ACI Committee 323, 1958)

Tentative Recommendations for Design of Composite Beams and Girders for Buildings (Report of ACI Committee 333, 1960)

Consolidation of Concrete (Report of ACI Committee 609, 1960)

Special publications

ACI Manual of Concrete Inspection, SP-2, (Reported by Committee 611, 4th Edition revised 1961)

Reinforced Concrete Design Handbook, SP-3, (Reported by Committee 317, 2nd Edition, 1955)

Formwork for Concrete, SP-4, (By M. K. Hurd under direction of Committee 347, 1963)

PART III – CONSTRUCTION REQUIREMENTS

CHAPTER 5 — CONCRETE QUALITY

500—Notation

f_c' = compressive strength of concrete (see Section 301)

F_{sp} = ratio of splitting tensile strength to the square root of compressive strength

501—Concrete quality

(a) For the design of reinforced concrete structures, the value f_c' shall be used in determining stresses in Part IV-A and strengths in Part IV-B.

(b) All plans submitted for approval or used for any project shall clearly show the specified strength, f_c', of concrete at the specified age for which each part of the structure was designed.

(c) Concrete that is to be subject to freezing temperatures while wet shall have a water-cement ratio not exceeding 6 gal. per bag and it shall contain entrained air.*

(d) Concrete that will be exposed to sulfate-containing or other chemically aggressive solutions shall be proportioned in accordance with "Recommended Practice for Selecting Proportions for Concrete (ACI 613)" and "Recommended Practice for Selecting Proportions for Structural Lightweight Concrete (ACI 613A)."

502—Methods of determining the proportions of concrete

(a) The determination of the proportions of cement, aggregate, and water to attain the required strengths shall be made by one of the following methods, but lower water-cement ratios may be required for conformance with Sections 501(c) and (d).

Method 1 — Without preliminary tests

Where preliminary test data on the materials to be used in the con-

TABLE 502(a)—MAXIMUM PERMISSIBLE WATER-CEMENT RATIOS FOR CONCRETE (METHOD NO. I)

Specified compressive strength at 28 days, psi f_c'	Maximum permissible water-cement ratio†			
	Non-air-entrained concrete		Air-entrained concrete	
	U.S. gal. per 94-lb bag of cement	Absolute ratio by weight	U.S. gal. per 94-lb bag of cement	Absolute ratio by weight
2500	7¼	0.642	6¼	0.554
3000	6½	0.576	5¼	0.465
3500	5¾	0.510	4½	0.399
4000	5	0.443	4	0.354

†Including free surface moisture on aggregates.

*Detailed recommendations for quality of concrete and requirements for air content for various exposures are given in "Recommended Practice for Selecting Proportions for Concrete" (ACI 613).

crete have not been obtained, the water-cement ratio for a given strength of concrete shall not exceed the values shown in Table 502(a).* When strengths in excess of 4000 psi are required or when lightweight aggregates or admixtures (other than those exclusively for the purpose of entraining air) are used, the required water-cement ratio shall be determined in accordance with Method 2.

Method 2 — For combinations of materials previously evaluated or to be established by trial mixtures

Water-cement ratios or strengths greater than shown in Table 502(a) may be used provided that the relationship between strength and water-cement ratio for the materials to be used has been previously established by reliable test data and the resulting concrete satisfies the requirements of Section 504.

Where previous data are not available, concrete trial mixtures having proportions and consistency suitable for the work shall be made using at least three different water-cement ratios (or cement content in the case of lightweight aggregates) which will produce a range of strengths encompassing those required for the work. These tests shall be made in accordance with the procedure given in the appendix to "Recommended Practice for Selecting Proportions for Concrete" (ACI 613) or "Recommended Practice for Selecting Proportions for Structural Lightweight Concrete" (ACI 613A). For each water-cement ratio (or cement content), at least three specimens for each age to be tested shall be made and cured in accordance with "Method of Making and Curing Concrete Compression and Flexure Test Specimens in the Laboratory" (ASTM C 192) and tested for strength in accordance with "Method of Test for Compressive Strength of Molded Concrete Cylinders" (ASTM C 39).

The strength tests shall be made at 28 days or the earlier age at which the concrete is to receive load, as indicated on the plans. A curve shall be established showing the relationship between water-cement ratio (or cement content) and compressive strength. The maximum permissible water-cement ratio for the concrete to be used in the structure shall be that shown by the curve to produce an average strength to satisfy the requirements of Section 504 provided that the water-cement ratio shall be no greater than that required by Section 501(c).

Where different materials are to be used for different portions of the work, each combination shall be evaluated separately.

503—Concrete proportions and consistency†

(a) The proportions of aggregate to cement for any concrete shall be such as to produce a mixture which will work readily into the corners and angles of the forms and around reinforcement with the method of

---

*The tabulated water-cement ratios are more conservative than those given in ACI 613 and will generally produce appreciably higher strengths than indicated.

†Detailed recommendations for proportioning concrete are given in "Recommended Practice for Selecting Proportions for Concrete" (ACI 613) and "Recommended Practice for Selecting Proportions for Structural Lightweight Concrete" (ACI 613A).

placing employed on the work, but without permitting the materials to segregate or excess free water to collect on the surface.

(b) The methods of measuring concrete materials shall be such that the proportions can be accurately controlled and easily checked at any time during the work.

504—Strength tests of concrete

(a) When strength is a basis for acceptance, each class of concrete shall be represented by at least five tests (10 specimens). Two specimens shall be made for each test at a given age, and not less than one test shall be made for each 150 cu yd of structural concrete, but there shall be at least one test for each day's concreting. The Building Official may require a reasonable number of additional tests during the progress of the work. Samples from which compression test specimens are molded shall be secured in accordance with "Method of Sampling Fresh Concrete" (ASTM C 172). Specimens made to check the adequacy of the proportions for strength of concrete or as a basis for acceptance of concrete shall be made and laboratory-cured in accordance with "Method of Making and Curing Concrete Compression and Flexure Test Specimens in the Field" (ASTM C 31). Additional test specimens cured entirely under field conditions may be required by the Building Official to check the adequacy of curing and protection of the concrete. Strength tests shall be made in accordance with "Method of Test for Compressive Strength of Molded Concrete Cylinders" (ASTM C 39).

(b) The age for strength tests shall be 28 days or, where specified, the earlier age at which the concrete is to receive its full load or maximum stress. Additional tests may be made at earlier ages to obtain advance information on the adequacy of strength development where age-strength relationships have been established for the materials and proportions used.

(c) To conform to the requirements of this code.*

1. For structures designed in accordance with Part IV-A of this code, the average of any five consecutive strength tests of the laboratory-cured specimens representing each class of concrete shall be equal to or greater than the specified strength, f_c', and not more than 20 percent of the strength tests shall have values less than the specified strength.

2. For structures designed in accordance with Part IV-B of this code, and for prestressed structures the average of any three consecutive strength tests of the laboratory-cured specimens repre-

---

*For ordinary conditions of control, the requirements of (c)1 will usually be met if the average strength of the concrete exceeds the specified strength by 15 percent. For a similar degree of control, the requirements of (c)2 will be met by an average strength 25 percent greater than the specified strength. If the number of tests is small, there may be more than the indicated permissive percentage below the specified strength even though the average strength and the uniformity of the concrete are satisfactory. If that occurs, the procedures of ACI 214 should be employed to determine if the average strength being supplied is adequately in excess of the specified strength.

senting each class of concrete shall be equal to or greater than the specified strength, f_c', and not more than 10 percent of the strength tests shall have values less than the specified strength.

(d) When it appears that the laboratory-cured specimens will fail to conform to the requirements for strength, the Building Official shall have the right to order changes in the concrete sufficient to increase the strength to meet these requirements. The strengths of any specimens cured on the job are intended to indicate the adequacy of protection and curing of the concrete and may be used to determine when the forms may be stripped, shoring removed, or the structure placed in service. When, in the opinion of the Building Official, the strengths of the job-cured specimens are excessively below those of the laboratory-cured specimens, the contractor may be required to improve the procedures for protecting and curing the concrete.

(e) In addition, when concrete fails to conform to the requirements of (c) or when tests of field-cured cylinders indicate deficiencies in protection and curing, the Building Official may require tests in accordance with "Methods of Securing, Preparing and Testing Specimens from Hardened Concrete for Compressive and Flexural Strength" (ASTM C 42) or order load tests as outlined in Chapter 2 for that portion of the structure where the questionable concrete has been placed.

505—Splitting tensile tests of concrete

(a) To determine the splitting ratio, F_{sp}, for a particular aggregate, tests of concrete shall be made as follows:

1. Twenty-four 6 x 12-in. cylinders shall be made in accordance with "Method of Making and Curing Concrete Compression and Flexure Test Specimens in the Laboratory" (ASTM C 192), twelve at a compressive strength level of approximately 3000 psi and twelve at approximately 4000 or 5000 psi. After 7 days moist curing followed by 21 days drying at 73 F and 50 percent relative humidity, eight of the test cylinders at each of the two strength levels shall be tested for splitting strength and four for compressive strength.

2. The splitting tensile strength shall be determined in accordance with "Method of Test for Splitting Tensile Strength of Molded Concrete Cylinders" (ASTM C 496), and the compressive strength in accordance with "Method of Test for Compressive Strength of Molded Concrete Cylinders" (ASTM C 39).

(b) The ratio, F_{sp}, of splitting tensile strength to the square root of compressive strength shall be obtained by using the average of all 16 splitting tensile tests and all eight compressive tests.

CHAPTER 6 — MIXING AND PLACING CONCRETE

601—Preparation of equipment and place of deposit

(a) Before concrete is placed, all equipment for mixing and transporting the concrete shall be clean, all debris and ice shall be removed from the spaces to be occupied by the concrete, forms shall be thoroughly wetted or oiled, masonry filler units that will be in contact with concrete shall be well drenched, and the reinforcement shall be thoroughly clean of ice or other deleterious coatings.

(b) Water shall be removed from the place of deposit before concrete is placed unless a tremie is to be used or unless otherwise permitted by the Building Official.

(c) All laitance and other unsound material shall be removed from hardened concrete before additional concrete is added.

602—Mixing of concrete*

(a) All concrete shall be mixed until there is a uniform distribution of the materials and shall be discharged completely before the mixer is recharged.

(b) For job-mixed concrete, mixing shall be done in a batch mixer of approved type. The mixer shall be rotated at a speed recommended by the manufacturer and mixing shall be continued for at least 1½ min after all materials are in the drum.

(c) Ready-mixed concrete shall be mixed and delivered in accordance with the requirements set forth in "Specifications for Ready-Mixed Concrete" (ASTM C 94), and shall conform to Chapter 5.

603—Conveying*

(a) Concrete shall be conveyed from the mixer to the place of final deposit by methods which will prevent the separation or loss of materials.

(b) Equipment for chuting, pumping, and pneumatically conveying concrete shall be of such size and design as to insure a practically continuous flow of concrete at the delivery end without separation of materials.

604—Depositing*

(a) Concrete shall be deposited as nearly as practicable in its final position to avoid segregation due to rehandling or flowing. The concreting shall be carried on at such a rate that the concrete is at all times plastic and flows readily into the spaces between the bars. No concrete

---

*Detailed recommendations are given in "Recommended Practice for Measuring, Mixing, and Placing Concrete" (ACI 614).

that has partially hardened or been contaminated by foreign materials shall be deposited in the structure, nor shall retempered concrete be used unless approved by the engineer.

(b) When concreting is once started, it shall be carried on as a continuous operation until the placing of the panel or section is completed. The top surface shall be generally level. When construction joints are necessary, they shall be made in accordance with Section 704.

(c) All concrete shall be thoroughly consolidated by suitable means during placement, and shall be thoroughly worked around the reinforcement and embedded fixtures and into the corners of the forms. Effective vibration is commonly the most suitable means.

(d) Where conditions make consolidation difficult, or where reinforcement is congested, batches of mortar containing the same proportions of cement to sand as used in the concrete, shall first be deposited in the forms to a depth of at least 1 in.

605—Curing

(a) Concrete shall be maintained above 50 F and in a moist condition for at least the first 7 days after placing, except that high-early-strength concrete shall be so maintained for at least the first 3 days. Other curing periods may be used if the specified strengths are obtained.

606—Cold weather requirements*

(a) Adequate equipment shall be provided for heating the concrete materials and protecting the concrete during freezing or near-freezing weather. All concrete materials and all reinforcement, forms, fillers, and ground with which the concrete is to come in contact shall be free from frost. No frozen materials or materials containing ice shall be used.

607—Hot weather requirements*

(a) During hot weather, steps shall be taken to reduce concrete temperature and water evaporation by proper attention to ingredients, production methods, handling, placing, protection, and curing.

---

*Details of approved procedures are available in "Recommended Practice for Winter Concreting" (ACI 604) and "Recommended Practice for Hot Weather Concreting" (ACI 605).

CHAPTER 7 — FORMWORK, EMBEDDED PIPES, AND CONSTRUCTION JOINTS

701—Design of formwork*

(a) Forms shall conform to the shape, lines, and dimensions of the members as called for on the plans, and shall be substantial and sufficiently tight to prevent leakage of mortar. They shall be properly braced or tied together so as to maintain position and shape.

(b) Design of formwork shall include consideration of the following factors:

1. Rate and method of placing concrete
2. Loads, including live, dead, lateral, and impact
3. Selection of materials and stresses
4. Deflection, camber, eccentricity, and uplift
5. Horizontal and diagonal shore bracing
6. Shore splices
7. Cross grain compression
8. Loads on ground or on previously-placed structure

702—Removal of forms

(a) No construction loads exceeding the structural design loads shall be supported upon any unshored portion of the structure under construction. No construction load shall be supported upon, nor any shoring removed from any part of the structure under construction until that portion of the structure has attained sufficient strength to support safely its weight and the loads placed thereon. This strength may be demonstrated by job-cured test specimens and by a structural analysis considering the proposed loads in relation to these test strengths. Such analyses and test data shall be furnished by the contractor to the engineer.

(b) Forms shall be removed in such manner as to insure the complete safety of the structure. Where the structure as a whole is adequately supported on shores, the removable floor forms, beam and girder sides, column and similar vertical forms may be removed after 24 hr provided the concrete is sufficiently strong not to be injured thereby.

(c) Form supports of prestressed members may be removed when sufficient prestressing has been applied to enable them to carry their dead loads and anticipated construction loads.

703—Conduits and pipes embedded in concrete

(a) Electric conduits and other pipes whose embedment is allowed shall not, with their fittings, displace more than 4 percent of the area of the cross section of a column on which stress is calculated or which is

---

*Detailed recommendations for formwork are given in "Recommended Practice for Concrete Formwork" (ACI 347).

required for fire protection. Sleeves, conduits, or other pipes passing through floors, walls, or beams shall be of such size or in such location as not to impair unduly the strength of the construction; such sleeves, conduits, or pipes may be considered as replacing structurally in compression the displaced concrete, provided they are not exposed to rusting or other deterioration, are of uncoated or galvanized iron or steel not thinner than standard steel pipe, have a nominal inside diameter not over 2 in., and are spaced not less than three diameters on centers. Except when plans of conduits and pipes are approved by the structural engineer, embedded pipes or conduits, other than those merely passing through, shall be not larger in outside diameter than one-third the thickness of the slab, wall, or beam in which they are embedded, nor shall they be spaced closer than three diameters on center, nor so located as to impair unduly the strength of the construction. Sleeves, pipes, or conduits of any material not harmful to concrete and within the limitations of this section may be embedded in the concrete with the approval of the engineer provided they are not considered to replace the displaced concrete.

(b) Pipes which will contain liquid, gas, or vapor may be embedded in structural concrete under the following additional conditions:

1. The temperature of the liquid, gas, or vapor shall not exceed 150 F.

2. The maximum pressure to which any piping or fittings shall be subjected shall be 200 psi above atmospheric pressure.

3. All piping and fittings shall be tested as a unit for leaks immediately prior to concreting. The testing pressure above atmospheric pressure shall be 50 percent in excess of the pressure to which the piping and fittings may be subjected but the minimum testing pressure shall be not less than 150 psi above atmospheric pressure. The pressure test shall be held for 4 hr with no drop in pressure except that which may be caused by air temperature.

4. Pipes carrying liquid, gas, or vapor which is explosive or injurious to health shall again be tested as specified in 3 after the concrete has hardened.

5. No liquid, gas or vapor, except water not exceeding 90 F nor 20 psi pressure, is to be placed in the pipes until the concrete has thoroughly set.

6. In solid slabs the piping, except for radiant heating and snow melting, shall be placed between the top and bottom reinforcement.

7. The concrete covering of the pipes and fittings shall be not less than 1 in.

8. Reinforcement with an area equal to at least 0.2 percent of the area of the concrete section shall be provided normal to the piping.

9. The piping and fittings shall be assembled by welding, brazing, solder-sweating, or other equally satisfactory method. Screw connections shall be prohibited. The piping shall be so fabricated and installed that it will not require any cutting, bending, or displacement of the reinforcement from its proper location.

10. No liquid, gas, or vapor which may be injurious or detrimental to the pipes shall be placed in them.

11. Drain pipes and other piping designed for pressures of not more than 1 psi above atmospheric pressure need not be tested as required in 3.

704—Construction joints

(a) Joints not indicated on the plans shall be so made and located as not to impair significantly the strength of the structure. Where a joint is to be made, the surface of the concrete shall be thoroughly cleaned and all laitance removed. In addition to the foregoing, vertical joints shall be thoroughly wetted, and slushed with a coat of neat cement grout immediately before placing of new concrete.

(b) A delay at least until the concrete is no longer plastic must occur in columns or walls before concreting beams, girders, or slabs supported thereon. Beams, girders, brackets, column capitals, and haunches shall be considered as part of the floor system and shall be placed monolithically therewith.

(c) Construction joints in floors shall be located near the middle of the spans of slabs, beams, or girders, unless a beam intersects a girder at this point, in which case the joints in the girders shall be offset a distance equal to twice the width of the beam. Provision shall be made for transfer of shear and other forces through the construction joint.

CHAPTER 8 — DETAILS OF REINFORCEMENT*

801—Hooks and bends†

(a) *Hooks* — The term "standard hook" as used herein shall mean either

    1. A semicircular turn plus an extension of at least four bar diameters but not less than 2½ in. at the free end of the bar, or

    2. A 90-deg turn plus an extension of at least 12 bar diameters at the free end of the bar, or

    3. For stirrup and tie anchorage only, either a 90-deg or a 135-deg turn plus an extension of at least six bar diameters but not less than 2½ in. at the free end of the bar.

(b) *Minimum radii* — The radii of bend measured on the inside of the bar for standard hooks shall not be less than the values of Table 801(b), except that for sizes #6 to #11, inclusive, in structural and intermediate grades of bars only, the minimum radius shall be 2½ bar diameters.

TABLE 801 (b)—MINIMUM RADII OF BEND

Bar size	Minimum radii
#3, #4, or #5	2½ bar diameters
#6, #7, or #8	3 bar diameters
#9, #10, or #11	4 bar diameters
#14S or #18S‡	5 bar diameters

(c) *Bends other than standard hooks*

    1. Bends for stirrups and ties shall have radii on the inside of the bar not less than one bar diameter.

    2. Bends for all other bars shall have radii on the inside of the bar not less than the values of Table 801(b). When such bends are made at points of high stress in the bar, an adequate radius of bend shall be provided to prevent crushing of concrete.

(d) *Bending* — All bars shall be bent cold, unless otherwise permitted by the engineer. No bars partially embedded in concrete shall be field bent except as shown on the plans or specifically permitted by the engineer.

802—Cleaning reinforcement

(a) Metal reinforcement, at the time concrete is placed, shall be free from loose flaky rust, mud, oil, or other coatings that will destroy or reduce the bond.

---

*For useful information on the detailing of reinforcing steel, see "Manual cf Standard Practice for Detailing Reinforced Concrete Structures" (ACI 315).
†See also Sections 918-919.
‡Special fabrication is required for bends exceeding 90 deg for bars of these sizes and grades having a specified yield point of 50,000 psi or more.

803—Placing reinforcement

(a) *Supports* — Reinforcement shall be accurately placed and adequately supported by concrete, metal, or other approved chairs; spacers; or ties and secured against displacement within tolerances permitted.

(b) *Tolerances* — Unless otherwise specified by the engineer, reinforcement shall be placed in specified positions within the following tolerances:

> 1. Depth, d, in flexural members, walls, and columns where d is 24 in. or less: $\pm\frac{1}{4}$ in.

> 2. Depth, d, in flexural members and columns where d is more than 24 in.: $\pm\frac{1}{2}$ in.

> 3. Longitudinal location of bends and ends of bars: ±2 in., except that specified concrete cover at ends of members shall not be reduced.

(c) *Draped fabric* — When wire or other reinforcement, not exceeding $\frac{1}{4}$ in. in diameter is used as reinforcement for slabs not exceeding 10 ft in span, the reinforcement may be curved from a point near the top of the slab over the support to a point near the bottom of the slab at midspan, provided such reinforcement is either continuous over, or securely anchored to, the support.

804—Spacing of bars

(a) The clear distance between parallel bars (except in columns and between multiple layers of bars in beams) shall be not less than the nominal diameter of the bars, $1\frac{1}{3}$ times the maximum size of the coarse aggregate, nor 1 in.

(b) Where reinforcement in beams or girders is placed in two or more layers, the clear distance between layers shall be not less than 1 in., and the bars in the upper layers shall be placed directly above those in the bottom layer.

(c) In walls and slabs other than concrete joist construction, the principal reinforcement shall be centered not farther apart than three times the wall or slab thickness nor more than 18 in.

(d) In spirally reinforced and in tied columns, the clear distance between longitudinal bars shall be not less than $1\frac{1}{2}$ times the bar diameter, $1\frac{1}{2}$ times the maximum size of the coarse aggregate, nor $1\frac{1}{2}$ in.

(e) The clear distance between bars shall also apply to the clear distance between a contact splice and adjacent splices or bars.

(f) Groups of parallel reinforcing bars bundled in contact to act as a unit must be deformed bars with not over four in any one bundle and shall be used only when stirrups or ties enclose the bundle. Bars in a bundle shall terminate at different points with at least 40 bar diameters stagger unless all of the bars end in a support. Where spacing limitations are based on bar size, a unit of bundled bars shall be treated as a single bar of equivalent area.

805—Splices in reinforcement

(a) No splices of reinforcement shall be made except as shown on the design drawings, or as specified, or as authorized by the engineer. Except as provided herein, all welding shall conform to AWS D12.1, "Recommended Practices for Welding Reinforcing Steel, Metal Inserts and Connections in Reinforced Concrete Construction."

(b) *Splices in reinforcement in which the critical design stress is tensile—*

Lapped splices in tension shall not be used for bar sizes larger than #11.

Splices at points of maximum tensile stress shall be avoided wherever possible; such splices where used shall be welded, lapped, or otherwise fully developed. In any case the splice shall transfer the entire computed stress* from bar to bar without exceeding three-fourths of the permissible bond values given in this code; however, the length of lap for deformed bars shall be not less than 24, 30, and 36 bar diameters for specified yield strengths of 40,000, 50,000, and 60,000 psi, respectively, nor less than 12 in. For plain bars the minimum length of lap shall be twice that for deformed bars.

For contact splices spaced laterally closer than 12 bar diameters or located closer than 6 in. or 6 bar diameters from an outside edge, the lap shall be increased by 20 percent, or stirrups as prescribed in Section 918 (c)2 or closely spaced spirals shall enclose the splice for its full length.

Where more than one-half of the bars are spliced within a length of 40 bar diameters or where splices are made at points of maximum stress, special precautions shall be taken, such as increased length of lap and the use of spirals or closely-spaced stirrups around and for the length of the splice.

(c) *Splices in reinforcement in which the critical design stress is compressive—*

1. Where lapped splices are used, the minimum amount of lap shall be:

With concrete having a strength of 3000 psi or more, the length of lap for deformed bars shall be 20, 24, and 30 bar diameters for specified yield strengths of 50,000 and under, 60,000, and 75,000 psi, respectively, nor less than 12 in. When the specified concrete strengths are less than 3000 psi, the amount of lap shall be one-third greater than the values given above.

For plain bars, the minimum amount of lap shall be twice that specified for deformed bars.

---

*Computed stress is based on M for design by Part IV-A and M/ϕ for design by Part IV-B.

2. Welded splices or other positive connections may be used instead of lapped splices. Where the bar size exceeds #11, welded splices or other positive connections shall preferably be used. In bars required for compression only, the compressive stress may be transmitted by bearing of square-cut ends held in concentric contact by a suitably welded sleeve or mechanical device.

3. Where longitudinal bars are offset at a splice, the slope of the inclined portion of the bar with the axis of the column shall not exceed 1 in 6, and the portions of the bar above and below the offset shall be parallel to the axis of the column. Adequate horizontal support at the offset bends shall be treated as a matter of design, and shall be provided by metal ties, spirals, or parts of the floor construction. Metal ties or spirals so designed shall be placed near (not more than eight bar diameters from) the point of bend. The horizontal thrust to be resisted shall be assumed as 1½ times the horizontal component of the nominal stress in the inclined portion of the bar.

Offset bars shall be bent before they are placed in the forms. See Section 801(d).

4. Where column faces are offset 3 in. or more, splices of vertical bars adjacent to the offset face shall be made by separate dowels overlapped as specified above.

5. In tied columns the amount of reinforcement spliced by lapping shall not exceed a steel ratio of 0.04 in any 3 ft length of column.

(d) An approved welded splice is one in which the bars are butted and welded so that it will develop in tension at least 125 percent of the specified yield strength of the reinforcing bar. Approved positive connections for bars designed to carry critical tension or compression shall be equivalent in strength to an approved welded splice.

(e) Metal cores in composite columns shall be accurately milled at splices and positive provision shall be made for alignment of one core above another. At the column base, provision shall be made to transfer the load to the footing at safe unit stresses in accordance with Section 1002(a). The base of the metal section shall be designed to transfer the load from the entire composite column to the footing, or it may be designed to transfer the load from the metal section only, provided it is so placed in the pier or pedestal as to leave ample section of concrete above the base for the transfer of load from the reinforced concrete section of the column by means of bond on the vertical reinforcement and by direct compression on the concrete.

(f) Welded wire fabric used as reinforcement in **structural** slabs shall be spliced in accordance with the following provisions:

1. Lapped splices of wires in regions of maximum stress (where they are carrying more than one-half of the permissible stress) shall be avoided wherever possible; such splices where used shall be so made that the overlap measured between outermost cross wires of each fabric sheet is not less than the spacing of the cross wires plus 2 in.

2. Splices of wires stressed at not more than one-half the permissible stress shall be so made that the overlap measured between outermost cross wires is not less than 2 in.

806—Lateral reinforcement

(a) Spiral column reinforcement shall consist of evenly spaced continuous spirals held firmly in place and true to line by vertical spacers. At least two spacers shall be used for spirals 20 in. or less in diameter, three for spirals 20 to 30 in. in diameter, and four for spirals more than 30 in. in diameter. When spiral rods are ⅝ in. or larger, three spacers shall be used for spirals 24 in. or less in diameter and four for spirals more than 24 in. in diameter. The spirals shall be of such size and so assembled as to permit handling and placing without being distorted from the designed dimensions. The material used in spirals shall have a minimum diameter of ¼ in. for rolled bars or No. 4 AS&W gage for drawn wire. Anchorage of spiral reinforcement shall be provided by 1½ extra turns of spiral rod or wire at each end of the spiral unit. Splices when necessary in spiral rods or wires shall be made by welding or by a lap of 1½ turns. The center to center spacing of the spirals shall not exceed one-sixth of the core diameter. The clear spacing between spirals shall not exceed 3 in. nor be less than 1⅜ in. or 1½ times the maximum size of coarse aggregate used. The reinforcing spiral shall extend from the floor level in any story or from the top of the footing to the level of the lowest horizontal reinforcement in the slab, drop panel, or beam above. In a column with a capital, the spiral shall extend to a plane at which the diameter or width of the capital is twice that of the column.

(b) All bars for tied columns shall be enclosed by lateral ties at least ¼ in. in diameter spaced apart not over 16 bar diameters, 48 tie diameters, or the least dimension of the column. The ties shall be so arranged that every corner and alternate longitudinal bar shall have lateral support provided by the corner of a tie having an included angle of not more than 135 deg and no bar shall be farther than 6 in. from such a laterally supported bar. Where the bars are located around the periphery of a circle, a complete circular tie may be used.

(c) Compression reinforcement in beams or girders shall be **anchored** by ties or stirrups, which shall be not less than ¼ in in diameter **spaced** not farther apart than 16 bar diameters, or 48 tie diameters. At least one tie at each spacing shall extend completely around all longitudinal bars. Such stirrups or ties shall be used throughout the distance where the compression reinforcement is required.

807—Shrinkage and temperature reinforcement

(a) Reinforcement for shrinkage and temperature stresses normal to the principal reinforcement shall be provided in structural floor and roof slabs where the principal reinforcement extends in one direction only. Such reinforcement shall provide at least the following ratios of reinforcement area to gross concrete area, but in no case shall such reinforcing bars be placed farther apart than five times the slab thickness or more than 18 in.

Slabs where plain bars are used 0.0025
Slabs where deformed bars with specified yield strengths
   less than 60,000 psi are used 0.0020

Slabs where deformed bars with 60,000 psi specified yield
   strength or welded wire fabric having welded intersections
   not farther apart in the direction of stress than 12 in.
   are used 0.0018

808—Concrete protection for reinforcement

(a) The reinforcement of footings and other principal structural members in which the concrete is deposited against the ground shall have not less than 3 in. of concrete between it and the ground contact surface. If concrete surfaces after removal of the forms are to be exposed to the weather or be in contact with the ground, the reinforcement shall be protected with not less than 2 in. of concrete for bars larger than #5 and 1½ in. for #5 bars or smaller.

(b) The concrete protective covering for any reinforcement at surfaces not exposed directly to the ground or weather shall be not less than ¾ in. for slabs and walls, and not less than 1½ in. for beams and girders. In concrete joist floors in which the clear distance between joists is not more than 30 in., the protection of reinforcement shall be at least ¾ in.

(c) Column spirals or ties shall be protected everywhere by a covering of concrete cast monolithically with the core, for which the thickness shall be not less than 1½ in. nor less than 1½ times the maximum size of the coarse aggregate.

(d) Concrete protection for reinforcement shall in all cases be at least equal to the diameter of bars, except for concrete slabs and joists as in (b).

(e) In extremely corrosive atmospheres or other severe exposures, the amount of protection shall be suitably increased.

(f) Exposed reinforcing bars, inserts, and plates intended for bonding with future extensions shall be protected from corrosion by concrete or other adequate covering.

(g) If the general code of which this code forms a part specifies, as fire-protective covering of the reinforcement, thicknesses of concrete greater than those given in this section, then such greater thicknesses shall be used.

(h) For special requirements for precast construction, see Chapter 24 and for prestressed construction, see Chapter 26.

PART IV – STRUCTURAL ANALYSIS AND PROPORTIONING OF MEMBERS

CHAPTER 9 — DESIGN — GENERAL CONSIDERATIONS

900—Notation

A_c = area of core of spirally reinforced column measured to the outside diameter of the spiral

= area of concrete within the core of a composite column

A_g = gross area of spirally reinforced or tied column

= area of the concrete of composite columns

A_s = area of tension reinforcement

A_s' = area of compression reinforcement

b = width of compression face of flexural member

d = distance from extreme compression fiber to centroid of tension reinforcement

E_c = modulus of elasticity of concrete (see Section 1102)

f_c' = compressive strength of concrete (see Section 301)

f_y = yield strength of reinforcement (see Section 301)

h = actual unsupported length of column

h' = effective length of column

I = moment of inertia of beam or column

K = stiffness factor = EI/l

l = span length of slab or beam

l' = clear span for positive moment and shear and the average of the two adjacent clear spans for negative moment (Section 904)

p = ratio of area of tension reinforcement to effective area of concrete in rectangular beam or in web of flanged member

p_s = ratio of volume of spiral reinforcement to total volume of core (out to out of spirals) of a spirally reinforced concrete or composite column

r = radius of gyration of gross concrete area of a column

r' = the ratio of ΣK of columns to ΣK of floor members in a plane at one end of a column

R = a reduction factor for long columns as defined in Section 916

t = thickness of flexural member

w = total load per unit of length of beam or per unit area of slab

901—Design methods

(a) The design of reinforced concrete members shall be made either with reference to allowable working stresses, service loads, and the accepted straight-line theory of flexure as outlined in Part IV-A (Working Stress Design) or with reference to load factors and strengths as outlined in Part IV-B (Ultimate Strength Design). The control of construction shall be consistent with the design method selected by the engineer.

902—Design loads*

(a) The provisions for design herein specified are based on the assumption that all structures shall be designed for all dead and live loads coming upon them, the live loads to be in accordance with the general requirements of the building code of which this forms a part, with such reductions for girders and lower story columns as are permitted therein.

903—Resistance to wind, earthquake, and other forces*

(a) In structures designed to resist wind and earthquake forces, only the integral structural parts shall be considered as resisting elements.

(b) The effects of wind or earthquake forces determined in accordance with recognized methods shall be combined with the effects of dead and live loads.

(c) Consideration shall be given to the effects of forces due to prestressing, crane loads, vibration, impact, shrinkage, temperature changes, creep, and unequal settlement of supports.

904—Frame analysis—General

(a) All members of frames or continuous construction shall be designed to resist at all sections the maximum effects of the prescribed loads as determined by the theory of elastic frames in which the simplifying assumptions of Section 905 may be used.

(b) Except in the case of prestressed concrete, approximate methods of frame analysis may be used for buildings of usual types of construction, spans, and story heights.

(c) Except for prestressed concrete, in the case of two or more approximately equal spans (the larger of two adjacent spans not exceeding the shorter by more than 20 percent) with loads uniformly distributed, where the unit live load does not exceed three times the unit dead load, the following moments and shears may be used in design in lieu of more accurate analyses.

---

*The provisions in this code are suitable for live, wind, and earthquake loads such as those recommended in "Building Code Requirements for Minimum Design Loads in Buildings and Other Structures," ASA A 58.1, of the American Standards Association.

Positive moment

  End spans

    If discontinuous end is unrestrained .... $\frac{1}{11} wl'^2$

    If discontinuous end is integral with the support .... $\frac{1}{14} wl'^2$

  Interior spans .... $\frac{1}{16} wl'^2$

Negative moment at exterior face of first interior support

  Two spans .... $\frac{1}{9} wl'^2$

  More than two spans .... $\frac{1}{10} wl'^2$

Negative moment at other faces of interior supports .... $\frac{1}{11} wl'^2$

Negative moment at face of all supports for, (a) slabs with
spans not exceeding 10 ft, and (b) beams and girders
where ratio of sum of column stiffnesses to beam stiffness
exceeds eight at each end of the span .... $\frac{1}{12} wl'^2$

Negative moment at interior faces of exterior supports for
members built integrally with their supports

  Where the support is a spandrel beam or girder .... $\frac{1}{24} wl'^2$

  Where the support is a column .... $\frac{1}{16} wl'^2$

Shear in end members at first interior support .... $1.15 \frac{wl'}{2}$

Shear at all other supports .... $\frac{wl'}{2}$

905—Frame analysis—Details*

(a) Arrangement of live load

    1. The live load may be considered to be applied only to the floor or roof under consideration, and the far ends of the columns may be assumed as fixed.

    2. Consideration may be limited to combinations of dead load on all spans with full live load on two adjacent spans and with full live load on alternate spans.

(b) Span length

    1. The span length, *l*, of members that are not built integrally with their supports shall be considered the clear span plus the

---

*For moments in columns see Section 914.

depth of the slab or beam but shall not exceed the distance between centers of supports.

2. In analysis of continuous frames, center to center distances shall be used in the determination of moments. Moments at faces of supports may be used for design of beams and girders.

3. Solid or ribbed slabs with clear spans of not more than 10 ft that are built integrally with their supports may be designed as continuous slabs on knife edge supports with spans equal to the clear spans of the slab and the width of beams otherwise neglected.

(c) *Stiffness*

1. Any reasonable assumptions may be adopted for computing the relative flexural stiffness of columns, of walls, and of floor and roof systems. The assumptions made shall be consistent throughout the analysis.

2. In computing the value of *I* for the relative flexural stiffness of slabs, beams, girders, and columns, the reinforcement may be neglected. In T-shaped sections allowance shall be made for the effect of flange.

3. If the total torsional stiffness in the plane of a continuous system at a joint does not exceed 20 percent of the flexural stiffness at the joint, the torsional stiffness need not be taken into account in the analysis.

(d) *Haunched members*

1. The effect of haunches shall be considered both in determining bending moments and in design of members.

906—Requirements for T-beams

(a) In T-beam construction the slab and beam shall be built integrally or otherwise effectively bonded together.

(b) The effective flange width to be used in the design of symmetrical T-beams shall not exceed one-fourth of the span length of the beam, and its overhanging width on either side of the web shall not exceed eight times the thickness of the slab nor one-half the clear distance to the next beam.

(c) Isolated beams in which the T-form is used only for the purpose of providing additional compression area, shall have a flange thickness not less than one-half the width of the web and a total flange width not more than four times the width of the web.

(d) For beams having a flange on one side only, the effective overhanging flange width shall not exceed 1/12 of the span length of the beam, nor six times the thickness of the slab, nor one-half the clear distance to the next beam.

(e) Where the principal reinforcement in a slab which is considered as the flange of a T-beam (not a joist in concrete joist floors) is parallel to the beam, transverse reinforcement shall be provided in the top of the slab. This reinforcement shall be designed to carry the load on the portion of the slab required for the flange of the T-beam. The flange shall be assumed to act as a cantilever. The spacing of the bars shall not exceed five times the thickness of the flange, nor in any case 18 in.

(f) The overhanging portion of the flange of the beam shall not be considered as effective in computing the shear and diagonal tension resistance of T-beams.

(g) Provision shall be made for the compressive stress at the support in continuous T-beam construction, care being taken that the provisions of Section 804 relating to the spacing of bars, and of Section 604 relating to the placing of concrete shall be fully met.

907—Effective depth of beam or slab

(a) The effective depth, d, of a beam or slab shall be taken as the distance from the centroid of its tensile reinforcement to its compression face.

(b) Any floor finish not placed monolithically with the floor slab shall not be included as a part of the structural member. When the top of a monolithic slab is the wearing surface and unusual wear is expected as in buildings of the warehouse or industrial class, there shall be placed an additional depth of ½ in. over that required by the design of the member.

908—Distance between lateral supports

(a) The effects of lateral eccentricity of load shall be taken into account in determining the spacing of lateral supports for a beam, which shall never exceed 50 times the least width, b, of compression flange or face.

909—Control of deflections*

(a) Reinforced concrete members subject to bending shall be designed to have adequate stiffness to prevent deflections or other deformations which may adversely affect the strength or serviceability of the structure.

(b) The minimum thicknesses, t, stipulated in Table 909(b) shall apply to flexural members of normal weight concrete, except when calculations of deflections prove that lesser thicknesses may be used without adverse effects.

---

*Deflections in reinforced concrete structures depend on the elastic and inelastic properties of concrete and steel, as well as on shrinkage and creep which, in turn, are influenced by temperature and humidity, curing conditions, age of concrete at the time of loading, and other factors. All simple methods for computation of deflections are, therefore, necessarily approximate. The methods specified in (c) and (d) of this section may be considered satisfactory for guarding against excessive deflections in structures of common types and sizes.

TABLE 909(b)—MINIMUM THICKNESS OR DEPTH OF FLEXURAL MEMBERS UNLESS DEFLECTIONS ARE COMPUTED

Member	Minimum ~~thickness~~ or depth t			
	Simply supported	One end continuous	Both ends continuous	Cantilever
One-way slabs	$l/25$	$l/30$	$l/35$	$l/12$
Beams	$l/20$	$l/23$	$l/26$	$l/10$

(c) Where deflections are to be computed, those which occur immediately upon application of service load shall be computed by the usual methods and formulas for elastic deflections, using the modulus of elasticity for concrete specified in Section 1102. The moment of inertia shall be based on the gross section when pf_y is equal to or less than 500 psi and on the transformed cracked section when pf_y is greater. In continuous spans, the moment of inertia may be taken as the average of the values obtained for the positive and negative moment regions.

(d) The additional long-time deflections may be obtained by multiplying the immediate deflection caused by the sustained part of the load by 2.0 when $A_s' = 0$; 1.2 when $A_s' = 0.5A_s$; and 0.8 when $A_s' = A_s$.

(e) Maximum limits for immediate deflection due to live load computed as above are:

    1. For roofs which do not support plastered ceilings .... $l/180$

    2. For roofs which support plastered ceilings or for floors which do not support partitions .... $l/360$

(f) For a floor or roof construction intended to support or to be attached to partitions or other construction likely to be damaged by large deflections of the floor, the allowable limit for the sum of the immediate deflection due to live load and the additional deflection due to shrinkage and creep under all sustained loads computed as above shall not exceed $l/360$.

910—Deep beams

(a) Beams with depth/span ratios greater than 2/5 for continuous spans, or 4/5 for simple spans shall be designed as deep beams taking account of nonlinear distribution of stress, lateral buckling, and other pertinent effects. The minimum horizontal and vertical reinforcement in the faces shall be as in Section 2202(f); the minimum tensile reinforcement as in Section 911.

911—Minimum reinforcement of flexural members

(a) Wherever at any section of a flexural member (except slabs of uniform thickness) positive reinforcement is required by analysis, the ratio, p, supplied shall not be less than $200/f_y$, unless the area of reinforcement provided at every section, positive or negative, is at least one-third greater than that required by analysis.

(b) In structural slabs of uniform thickness, the minimum amount of reinforcement in the direction of the span shall not be less than that required for shrinkage and temperature reinforcement (see Section 807).

912—Limiting dimensions of columns

(a) *Minimum size*—Columns constituting the principal supports of a floor or roof shall have a diameter of at least 10 in., or in the case of rectangular columns, a thickness of at least 8 in., and a gross area not less than 96 sq in. Auxiliary supports placed at intermediate locations and not continuous from story to story may be smaller but not less than 6 in. thick.

(b) *Isolated column with multiple spirals*—If two or more inter-locking spirals are used in a column, the outer boundary of the column shall be taken at a distance outside the extreme limits of the spiral equal to the requirements of Section 808(c).

(c) *Limits of section of column built monolithically with wall*—For a spiral column built monolithically with a concrete wall or pier, the outer boundary of the column section shall be taken either as a circle at least 1½ in. outside the column spiral or as a square or rectangle, the sides of which are at least 1½ in. outside the spiral or spirals.

(d) *Equivalent circular columns*—As an exception to the general procedure of utilizing the full gross area of the column section, it shall be permissible to design a circular column and to build it with a square, octagonal, or other shaped section of the same least lateral dimension. In such case, the allowable load, the gross area considered, and the required percentages of reinforcement shall be taken as those of the circular column.

(e) *Limits of column section*—In a tied column which has a larger cross section than required by considerations of loading, a reduced effective area, A_y, not less than one-half of the total area may be used for determining minimum steel area and load capacity.

913—Limits for reinforcement of columns

(a) The vertical reinforcement for columns shall be not less than 0.01 nor more than 0.08 times the gross cross-sectional area. The minimum size of bar shall be #5. The minimum number of bars shall be six for spiral columns and four for tied columns.

(b) The ratio of spiral reinforcement, p_s, shall be not less than the value given by

$$p_s = 0.45 \ (A_g/A_c - 1) \ f_c'/f_y \ \ldots\ldots\ldots \ (9\text{-}1)$$

wherein f_y is the yield strength of spiral reinforcement but not more than 60,000 psi.

914—Bending moments in columns

(a) Columns shall be designed to resist the axial forces from loads on all floors, plus the maximum bending due to loads on a single adjacent span of the floor under consideration. Account shall also be taken of the loading condition giving the maximum ratio of bending moment to axial load. In building frames, particular attention shall be given to the effect of unbalanced floor loads on both exterior and interior columns and of eccentric loading due to other causes. In computing moments in columns due to gravity loading, the far ends of columns which are monolithic with the structure may be considered fixed.

Resistance to bending moments at any floor level shall be provided by distributing the moment between the columns immediately above and below the given floor in proportion to their relative stiffnesses and conditions of restraint.

915—Length of columns

(a) For purposes of determining the limiting dimensions of columns, the unsupported length of reinforced concrete columns shall be taken as the clear distance between floor slabs, except that

1. In flat slab construction, it shall be the clear distance between the floor and the lower extremity of the capital, the drop panel or the slab, whichever is least.

2. In beam and slab construction, it shall be the clear distance between the floor and the underside of the deeper beam framing into the column in each direction at the next higher floor level.

3. In columns restrained laterally by struts, it shall be the clear distance between consecutive struts in each vertical plane; provided that to be an adequate support, two such struts shall meet the column at approximately the same level, and the angle between vertical planes through the struts shall not vary more than 15 deg from a right angle. Such struts shall be of adequate dimensions and anchorage to restrain the column against lateral deflection.

4. In columns restrained laterally by struts or beams, with brackets used at the junction, it shall be the clear distance between the floor and the lower edge of the bracket, provided that the bracket width equals that of the beam or strut and is at least half that of the column.

(b) For rectangular columns, that length shall be considered which produces the greatest ratio of length to radius of gyration of section.

C — Cols. furnish lateral stability $r' \leq 25$ each and
3) Sidesway + double curvature $h' = ((d)3) \downarrow$
$r'_A = \frac{1}{2}(r'_{Top} + r'_{Bot.})$ $R = (9-3)$

DESIGN — GENERAL CONSIDERATIONS 318-43

4) Sidesway & Single curvature $h' = ((d)2)$ $R = (9-3)$
$r' \leq 25$

(c) The effective length, h', of columns in structures where lateral stability or resistance to lateral forces is provided by shear walls or rigid bracing, by fastening to an adjoining structure of sufficient lateral stability, or by any other means that affords adequate lateral support, shall be taken as the unbraced length, h.

(d) Larger effective lengths, h', shall be used for all columns in structures which depend upon the column stiffness for lateral stability:

1. The end of a column shall be considered hinged in a plane if in that plane r' (see Section 900) exceeds 25.

2. For columns restrained against rotation at one end and hinged at the other end the effective length shall be taken as $h' = 2h (0.78 + 0.22r') \geq 2h$, where r' is the value at the restrained end.

3. For columns restrained against rotation at both ends the effective length h' shall be taken as $h' = h(0.78 + 0.22r') \geq h$, where r' is the average of the values at the two ends of the column.

4. For cantilever columns, that is, those fixed at one end and free at the other, the effective length h' shall be taken as twice the over-all length.

916—Strength reductions for length of compression members

(a) When compression governs the design of the section, the axial load and moment computed from the analysis shall be divided by the appropriate factor R as given in 1, 2, or 3 below, and the design shall be made using the appropriate formulas for short members in Chapters 14 and 19.

1. If relative lateral displacement of the ends of the member is prevented and the ends of the member are fixed or definitely restrained such that a point of contraflexure occurs between the ends, no correction for length shall be made unless h/r exceeds 60. For h/r between 60 and 100, the design shall be based on an analysis according to (d) or the following factor shall be used

$$R = [1.32 - 0.006h/r] \leq 1.0 \qquad (9\text{-}2)$$

If h/r exceeds 100, an analysis according to (d) shall be made.

2. If relative lateral displacement of the ends of the members is prevented and the member is bent in single curvature, the following factor shall be used

$$R = [1.07 - 0.008h/r] \leq 1.0 \qquad (9\text{-}3)$$

3. The design of restrained members for which relative lateral displacement of the ends is not prevented shall be made using the factor given in Eq. (9-4); that is, with the effective length h' from Section 915 substituted for h.

margin handwritten: $r'_B = 1.0$; $h' = 2h$; Case 5) Cantilever column $h' = (9\text{-}3)$ $R = (9\text{-}3)$

handwritten at bottom:

A — short cols. $e/h < 60$ $\boxed{P' = P/R}$

B — Long cols. $R = (9\text{-}2)$ at $60-100$

1) No sidesway double curvature

2) Single curvature, no sidesway $(9\text{-}3)$

$$R = 1.07 - 0.008h'/r \leq 1.0 \dots\dots\dots\dots \text{(9-4)}$$

When the design is governed by lateral loads of short duration, such as wind or earthquake loading, the factor R may be increased by 10 percent, which is equivalent to using

$$R = 1.18 - 0.009h'/r \leq 1.0 \dots\dots\dots\dots \text{(9-5)}$$

4. The radius of gyration, r, may be taken equal to 0.30 times the over-all depth in the direction of bending for a rectangular column and 0.25 times the diameter of circular columns. For other shapes r may be computed for the gross concrete section.

(b) When tension governs the design of the section, the axial load and moment computed from the analysis shall be increased as required in (a) except that the factor R shall be considered to vary linearly with axial load from the values given by Eq. (9-2) and (9-3) at the balanced condition [as defined in Section 1407 or 1900(b)] to a value of 1.0 when the axial load is zero.

(c) When a column design is governed by the minimum eccentricities specified for ultimate strength design in Section 1901(a) the effect of length on column strength shall be determined in one of the following ways:

1. Where the actual computed eccentricities at both ends are less than the specified minimum eccentricity, the strength reduction for length shall correspond to the actual conditions of curvature and end restraint.

2. If column moments have not been considered in the design of the column or if computations show that there is no eccentricity at one or both ends of the column, the factor in (a)2 shall be used.

(d) In lieu of other requirements of this section, an analysis may be made taking into account the effect of additional deflections on moments in columns.

In such an analysis a reduced modulus of elasticity, not greater than one-third the value specified in Section 1102, shall be used in calculations of deflections caused by sustained loads.

917—Transmission of column load through floor system

(a) When the specified strength of concrete in columns exceeds that specified for the floor system by more than 40 percent, proper transmission of load through the weaker concrete shall be provided by one of the following:

1. Concrete of the strength specified for the column shall be placed in the floor for an area four times A_g, about the column, well integrated into floor concrete, and placed in accordance with Section 704(b).

2. The capacity of the column through the floor system shall be computed using the weaker concrete strength and adding vertical dowels and spirals as required.

3. For columns laterally supported on four sides by beams of approximately equal depth or by slabs, the capacity may be computed by using an assumed concrete strength in the column formulas equal to 75 percent of the column concrete strength plus 35 percent of the floor concrete strength.

918—Anchorage requirements—General

(a) The calculated tension or compression in any bar at any section must be developed on each side of that section by proper embedment length, end anchorage, or hooks. A tension bar may be anchored by bending it across the web at an angle of not less than 15 deg with the longitudinal portion of the bar and making it continuous with the reinforcement on the opposite face of the member.

(b) Except at supports, every reinforcing bar shall be extended beyond the point at which it is no longer needed to resist flexural stress, for a distance equal to the effective depth of the member or 12 bar diameters, whichever is greater.

(c) No flexural bar shall be terminated in a tension zone unless *one* of the following conditions is satisfied:

1. The shear is not over half that normally permitted, including allowance for shear reinforcement, if any.

2. Stirrups in excess of those normally required are provided each way from the cut off a distance equal to three-fourths of the depth of the beam. The excess stirrups shall be at least the minimum specified in Section 1206(b) or 1706(b). The stirrup spacing shall not exceed $d/8r_b$ where r_b is the ratio of the area of bars cut off to the total area of bars at the section.

3. The continuing bars provide double the area required for flexure at that point or double the perimeter required for flexural bond.

(d) Tensile negative reinforcement in any span of a continuous, restrained or cantilever beam, or in any member of a rigid frame shall be adequately anchored by bond, hooks, or mechanical anchors in or through the supporting member.

(e) At least one-third of the total reinforcement provided for negative moment at the support shall be extended beyond the extreme position of the point of inflection a distance not less than 1/16 of the clear span, or the effective depth of the member, whichever is greater.

(f) At least one-third the positive moment reinforcement in simple beams and one-fourth the positive moment reinforcement in continuous beams shall extend along the same face of the beam into the support at least 6 in.

(g) Plain bars (as defined in Section 301) in tension, except bars for shrinkage and temperature reinforcement, shall terminate in standard hooks except that hooks shall not be required on the positive reinforcement at interior supports of continuous members.

(h) Standard hooks (Section 801) in tension may be considered as developing 10,000 psi in Part IV-A or 19,000 psi in Part IV-B in the bars or may be considered as extensions of the bars at appropriate bond stresses.

(i) Hooks shall not be considered effective in adding to the compressive resistance of bars.

(j) Any mechanical device capable of developing the strength of the bar without damage to the concrete may be used in lieu of a hook. Test results showing the adequacy of such devices must be presented.

919—Anchorage of web reinforcement

(a) The ends of bars forming simple U- or multiple U-stirrups shall be anchored by one of the following methods:

1. By a standard hook, considered as developing 50 percent of the allowable stress in the bar, plus embedment sufficient to develop by bond the remaining stress in the bar, in conformance with Chapters 13 and 18. The effective embedment of a stirrup leg shall be taken as the distance between the middepth of the member, $d/2$, and the center of radius of bend of the hook.

2. Welding to longitudinal reinforcement.

3. Bending tightly around the longitudinal reinforcement through at least 180 deg.

4. Embedment above or below the middepth, $d/2$, of the beam on the compression side, a distance sufficient to develop by bond the stress to which the bar will be subjected, at the bond stresses permitted by Sections 1301 and 1801 but, in any case, a minimum of 24 bar diameters.

(b) Between the anchored ends, each bend in the continuous portion of a simple U- or multiple U-stirrup shall be made around a longitudinal bar.

(c) Hooking or bending stirrups around the longitudinal reinforcement shall be considered effective only when these bars are perpendicular to the longitudinal reinforcement or make an angle of at least 45 deg with deformed longitudinal bars.

(d) Longitudinal bars bent to act as web reinforcement shall, in a region of tension, be continuous with the longitudinal reinforcement and in a compression zone shall be anchored as in (a)1 or (a)4.

(e) In all cases web reinforcement shall be carried as close to the compression surface of the beam as fireproofing regulations and the proximity of other steel will permit.

920—Transfer of moments and effect of openings in slabs and footings

(a) When unbalanced gravity load, wind or earthquake cause transfer of bending moment between column and slab, the additional shears on the critical section shall be investigated by a rational analysis.

(b) When openings in slabs are located at a distance less than ten times the thickness of the slab from a concentrated load or reaction or when openings in flat slabs are located within the column strips as defined in Section 2101(d), that part of the periphery of the critical section for shear which is covered by radial projections of the openings to the centroid of the loaded area shall be considered ineffective.

921—Torsion

(a) In edge or spandrel beams, the stirrups provided shall be closed and at least one longitudinal bar shall be placed in each corner of the beam section, the bar to be at least the diameter of the stirrup or ½ in., whichever is larger.

PART IV-A – STRUCTURAL ANALYSIS AND PROPORTIONING OF MEMBERS – WORKING STRESS DESIGN

CHAPTER 10 — ALLOWABLE STRESSES — WORKING STRESS DESIGN

1000—Notation

f_c = compressive stress in concrete

f_c' = compressive strength of concrete (see Section 301)

n = ratio of modulus of elasticity of steel to that of concrete

v = shear stress

v_c = shear stress carried by the concrete

w = weight of concrete, lb per cu ft

1001—General

(a) For structures to be designed with reference to allowable stresses, service loads, and the accepted straight-line theory of stress and strain in flexure, the allowable stresses of this chapter shall be used, and designs shall conform to all provisions of this code except Part IV-B.

1002—Allowable stresses in concrete

(a) The stresses for flexure and bearing on all concrete designed in accordance with Part IV-A shall not exceed the values of Table 1002(a).

(b) The stresses for shear shall not exceed those given in Table 1002(a) except as provided in Chapter 12.

(c) The allowable stresses for bond shall not exceed those given in Chapter 13.

1003—Allowable stresses in reinforcement

Unless otherwise provided in this code, steel for concrete reinforcement shall not be stressed in excess of the following limits:

(a) In tension

For billet-steel or axle-steel concrete reinforcing bars of structural grade .... 18,000 psi

For main reinforcement, $\frac{3}{8}$ in. or less in diameter, in one-way slabs of not more than 12-ft span, 50 percent of the minimum yield strength specified by the American Society for Testing and Materials for the reinforcement used, but not to exceed .... 30,000 psi

For deformed bars with a yield strength of 60,000 psi or more and in sizes #11 and smaller .... 24,000 psi

For all other reinforcement .... 20,000 psi

(b) In compression, vertical column reinforcement

Spiral columns, 40 percent of the minimum yield strength, but not to exceed .... 30,000 psi

TABLE 1002(a)—ALLOWABLE STRESSES IN CONCRETE

Description		For any strength of concrete in accordance with Section 502	For strength of concrete shown below			
			$f_c' =$ 2500 psi	$f_c' =$ 3000 psi	$f_c' =$ 4000 psi	$f_c' =$ 5000 psi
Modulus of elasticity		29,000,000				
ratio: n		$w^{1.5}\, 33\sqrt{f_c'}$				
For concrete weighing 145 lb per cu ft (see Section 1102)	n		10	9	8	7
Flexure: f_c						
Extreme fiber stress in compression	f_c	$0.45 f_c'$	1125	1350	1800	2250
Extreme fiber stress in tension in plain concrete footings and walls	f_c	$1.6\sqrt{f_c'}$	80	88	102	113
Shear: v (as a measure of diagonal tension at a distance d from the face of the support)						
Beams with no web reinforcement*	v_c	$1.1\sqrt{f_c'}$	55*	60*	70*	78*
Joists with no web reinforcement	v_c	$1.2\sqrt{f_c'}$	61	66	77	86
Members with vertical or inclined web reinforcement or properly combined bent bars and vertical stirrups	v	$5\sqrt{f_c'}$	250	274	316	354
Slabs and footings (peripheral shear, Section 1207)*	v_c	$2\sqrt{f_c'}$	100*	110*	126*	141*
Bearing: f_c						
On full area		$0.25 f_c'$	625	750	1000	1250
On one-third area or less†		$0.375 f_c'$	938	1125	1500	1875

*For shear values for lightweight aggregate concrete see Section 1208.
†This increase shall be permitted only when the least distance between the edges of the loaded and unloaded areas is a minimum of one-fourth of the parallel side dimension of the loaded area. The allowable bearing stress on a reasonably concentric area greater than one-third but less than the full area shall be interpolated between the values given.

f_c' is breaking strength of concrete

Tied columns, 85 percent of the value for spiral columns,
but not to exceed .... 25,500 psi

Composite and combination columns:
Structural steel sections
For ASTM A 36 Steel .... 18,000 psi
For ASTM A 7 Steel .... 16,000 psi
Cast iron sections .... 10,000 psi
Steel pipe .... see limitations of Section 1406

(c) In compression, flexural members
For compression reinforcement in flexural members see Section 1102

(d) Spirals [yield strength for use in Eq. (9-1)]
Hot rolled rods, intermediate grade .... 40,000 psi
Hot rolled rods, hard grade .... 50,000 psi
Hot rolled rods, ASTM A 432 grade and cold-drawn wire .. 60,000 psi

1004—Allowable stresses—Wind and earthquake forces

(a) Members subject to stresses produced by wind or earthquake forces combined with other loads may be proportioned for stresses 33-1/3 percent greater than those specified in Sections 1002 and 1003, provided that the section thus required is not less than that required for the combination of dead and live load.

CHAPTER 11 — FLEXURAL COMPUTATIONS — WORKING STRESS DESIGN

1100—Notation

E_c = modulus of elasticity of concrete (see Section 1102)
E_s = modulus of elasticity of steel = 29,000,000
f_c' = compressive strength of concrete (see Section 301)
n = ratio of modulus of elasticity of steel to that of concrete
w = weight of concrete, lb per cu ft

1101—Design assumptions

(a) In the design of reinforced concrete structures by the working stress design method, the following assumptions shall be made:

1. A section plane before bending remains plane after bending; strains vary as the distance from the neutral axis.

2. The stress-strain relation for concrete is a straight line under service loads within the allowable working stresses. Stresses vary as the distance from the neutral axis except for deep beams (Section 910).

3. The steel takes all the tension due to flexure.

4. The tension reinforcement is replaced in design computations with a concrete tension area equal to n times that of the reinforcing steel.

1102—Modulus of elasticity of concrete

(a) The modulus of elasticity, E_c, for concrete may be taken as $w^{1.5} 33\sqrt{f_c'}$, in psi, for values of w between 90 and 155 lb per cu ft. For normal weight concrete, w may be considered as 145 lb per cu ft.

(b) The modular ratio, $n = E_s/E_c$, may be taken as the nearest whole number (but not less than 6). Except in calculations for deflections, the value of n for lightweight concrete shall be assumed to be the same for normal weight concrete of the same strength.

(c) In doubly reinforced beams and slabs, an effective modular ratio of $2n$ shall be used to transform the compression reinforcement and compute its stress, which shall not be taken as greater than the allowable tensile stress.

1103—Modulus of elasticity of steel

(a) The modulus of elasticity of steel reinforcement may be taken as 29,000,000 psi.

CHAPTER 12 — SHEAR AND DIAGONAL TENSION — WORKING STRESS DESIGN*

1200—Notation

A_g = gross area of section

A_s = area of tension reinforcement

A_v = total area of web reinforcement in tension within a distance, s, measured in a direction parallel to the longitudinal reinforcement

α = angle between inclined web bars and longitudinal axis of member

b = width of compression face of flexural member

b' = width of web in I- and T-sections

b_o = periphery of critical section for slabs and footings

d = distance from extreme compression fiber to centroid of tension reinforcement

f_c' = compressive strength of concrete (see Section 301)

f_v = tensile stress in web reinforcement

F_{sp} = ratio of splitting tensile strength to the square root of compressive strength (see Section 505)

M = bending moment

M' = modified bending moment

N = load normal to the cross section, to be taken as positive for compression, negative for tension, and to include the effects of tension due to shrinkage and creep

p_w = $A_s/b'd$

s = spacing of stirrups or bent bars in a direction parallel to the longitudinal reinforcement

t = total depth of section

v = shear stress

v_c = shear stress carried by concrete

V = total shear

V' = shear carried by web reinforcement

---

*The provisions for shear are based on recommendations of ACI-ASCE Committee **326**. The term j is omitted in determination of nominal shear stress.

1201—Shear stress*†

(a) The nominal shear stress, as a measure of diagonal tension, in reinforced concrete members shall be computed by:

$$v = V/bd \dots\dots\dots\dots\dots\dots\dots (12\text{-}1)*$$

For design, the maximum shear shall be considered as that at the section a distance, d, from the face of the support.‡ Wherever applicable, effects of torsion shall be added and effects of inclined flexural compression in variable-depth members shall be included.

(b) For beams of I- or T-section, b' shall be substituted for b in Eq. (12-1).

(c) The shear stress, v_c, permitted on an unreinforced web shall not exceed $1.1\sqrt{f_c'}$ at a distance d from the face of the support unless a more detailed analysis is made in accordance with (d) or (e). The shear stresses at sections between the face of the support and the section a distance d therefrom shall not be considered critical.‡ For members with axial tension, v_c shall not exceed the value given in (e).

(d) The shear stress permitted on an unreinforced web shall not exceed that given by:

$$v_c = \sqrt{f_c'} + 1300 \; \frac{p_w V d}{M} \dots\dots\dots\dots\dots (12\text{-}2)$$

but not to exceed $1.75\sqrt{f_c'}$. The shear stresses at sections between the face of the support and the section a distance d therefrom shall not be considered critical.‡ V and M are the shear and bending moment at the section considered, but M shall be not less than Vd.

(e) For members subjected to axial load in addition to shear and flexure, Eq. (12-2) shall apply except that M' shall be substituted for M where

$$M' = M - N \frac{(4t-d)}{8} \dots\dots\dots\dots\dots (12\text{-}3)$$

and v_c shall not exceed

$$v_c = 1.75 \; \sqrt{f_c' \, (1 + 0.004 \, N/A_g)} \dots\dots\dots\dots (12\text{-}4)$$

1202—Web reinforcement

(a) Wherever the value of the shear stress, v, computed by Eq. (12-1), plus effects of torsion, exceeds the shear stress, v_c, permitted for the concrete of an unreinforced web by Sections 1201(c), (d), or (e), web reinforcement shall be provided to carry the excess. Such web rein-

---

*The provisions for shear are based on recommendations of ACI-ASCE Committee 326. The term j is omitted in determination of nominal shear stress.
†Special provisions for lightweight aggregate concretes are given in Section 1208.
‡This provision does not apply to brackets and other short cantilevers.

forcement shall also be provided for a distance equal to the depth, d, of the member beyond the point theoretically required. Web reinforcement between the face of the support and the section at a distance d therefrom shall be the same as required at that section.

(b) Web reinforcement may consist of:

    1. Stirrups perpendicular to the longitudinal reinforcement

    2. Stirrups making an angle of 45 deg or more with the longitudinal tension reinforcement

    3. Longitudinal bars bent so that the axis of the bent bar makes an angle of 30 deg or more with the axis of the longitudinal portion of the bar

    4. Combinations of 1 or 2 with 3

(c) Stirrups or other bars to be considered effective as web reinforcement shall be anchored at both ends according to the provisions of Section 919.

1203—Stirrups

(a) The area of steel required in stirrups placed perpendicular to the longitudinal reinforcement shall be computed by:

$$A_v = V's/f_v d \qquad (12\text{-}5)$$

(b) The area of inclined stirrups shall be computed by Eq. (12-7).

1204—Bent bars

(a) Only the center three-fourths of the inclined portion of any longitudinal bar that is bent up for web reinforcement shall be considered effective for that purpose.

(b) When the web reinforcement consists of a single bent bar or of a single group of parallel bars all bent up at the same distance from the support, the required area shall be computed by:

$$A_v = \frac{V'}{f_v \sin \alpha} \qquad (12\text{-}6)$$

in which V' shall not exceed $1.5 \, bd \sqrt{f_c'}$.

(c) Where there is a series of parallel bars or groups of bars bent up at different distances from the support, the required area shall be computed by:

$$A_v = \frac{V's}{f_v d \, (\sin \alpha + \cos \alpha)} \qquad (12\text{-}7)$$

(d) Bent bars used alone as web reinforcement shall be so spaced that the effective inclined portion defined in (a) meets the requirements of Section 1206 (a).

(e) Where more than one type of web reinforcement is used to reinforce the same portion of the web, the total shear resistance shall be computed as the sum of the resistances computed for the various types separately. In such computations, the resistance of the concrete, v_c, shall be included only once, and no one type of reinforcement shall be assumed to resist more than $2V'/3$.

1205—Stress restrictions

(a) The tensile stress in web reinforcement, f_v, shall not exceed the values given in Section 1003.

(b) The shear stress, v, shall not exceed $5\sqrt{f_c'}$ in sections with web reinforcement.

1206—Web reinforcement restrictions

(a) Where web reinforcement is required, it shall be so spaced that every 45-deg line, representing a potential diagonal crack and extending from middepth, $d/2$, of the member to the longitudinal tension bars, shall be crossed by at least one line of web reinforcement. When the shear stress exceeds $3\sqrt{f_c'}$, every such 45-deg line shall be crossed by at least two lines of web reinforcement.

(b) Where web reinforcement is required, its area shall not be less than 0.15 percent of the area, bs, computed as the product of the width of the web and the spacing of the web reinforcement along the longitudinal axis of the member.

1207—Shear stress in slabs and footings*

(a) The shear capacity of slabs and footings in the vicinity of concentrated loads or concentrated reactions shall be governed by the more severe of two conditions:

    1. The slab or footing acting essentially as a wide beam, with a potential diagonal crack extending in a plane across the entire width. This case shall be considered in accordance with Section 1201.

    2. Two-way action existing for the slab or footing, with potential diagonal cracking along the surface of a truncated cone or pyramid around the concentrated load or reaction. The slab or footing in this case shall be designed as required in the remainder of this section.

(b) The critical section for shear to be used as a measure of diagonal tension shall be perpendicular to the plane of the slab and located at a distance $d/2$ out from the periphery of the concentrated load or reaction area.

(c) The nominal shear stress shall be computed by:

$$v = V/b_o d \dots\dots\dots\dots\dots\dots\dots\dots\dots (12\text{-}8)$$

in which V and b_o are taken at the critical section specified in (b). The shear stress, v, so computed shall not exceed $2\sqrt{f_c'}$, unless shear rein-

---

*For transfer of moments and effects of openings see Section 920.

forcement is provided in accordance with (d), in which case v shall not exceed $3\sqrt{f_c'}$.

(d) When v exceeds $2\sqrt{f_c'}$, shear reinforcement shall be provided in accordance with Sections 1202 to 1206, except that the allowable stress in shear reinforcement shall be 50 percent of that prescribed in Section 1003. Shear reinforcement consisting of bars, rods or wire shall not be considered effective in members with a total thickness of less than 10 in.

1208—Lightweight aggregate concretes

(a) When structural lightweight aggregate concretes are used, the provisions of this chapter shall apply with the following modifications:

1. The shear stress, v_c, permitted on an unreinforced web in Section 1201 (c) shall be

$$0.17\, F_{sp}\sqrt{f_c'} \quad\dotfill\quad (12\text{-}9)$$

2. Eq. (12-2) shall be replaced by:

$$v_c = 0.15\, F_{sp}\sqrt{f_c'} + 1300\,\frac{p_w V d}{M} \quad\dotfill\quad (12\text{-}10)$$

3. The limiting value for shear stress in slabs and footings, v_c, in Section 1207 (c) and (d) shall be:

$$0.3\, F_{sp}\sqrt{f_c'} \quad\dotfill\quad (12\text{-}11)$$

(b) The value of F_{sp} shall be 4.0 unless determined in accordance with Section 505 for the particular aggregate to be used.

CHAPTER 13 — BOND AND ANCHORAGE — WORKING STRESS DESIGN

1300—Notation

d = distance from extreme compression fiber to centroid of tension reinforcement

D = nominal diameter of bar, inches

f_c' = compressive strength of concrete (see Section 301)

j = ratio of distance between centroid of compression and centroid of tension to the depth, d

Σo = sum of perimeters of all effective bars crossing the section on the tension side if of uniform size; for mixed sizes, substitute $4A_s/D$, where A_s is the total steel area and D is the largest bar diameter. For bundled bars use the sum of the exposed portions of the perimeters

u = bond stress

V = total shear

1301—Computation of bond stress in flexural members

(a) In flexural members in which the tension reinforcement is parallel to the compression face, the flexural bond stress at any cross section shall be computed by

$$u = \frac{V}{\Sigma o jd} \quad\cdots\cdots\cdots\cdots\cdots (13\text{-}1)$$

Bent-up bars that are not more than $d/3$ from the level of the main longitudinal reinforcement may be included. Critical sections occur at the face of the support, at each point where tension bars terminate within a span, and at the point of inflection.

(b) To prevent bond failure or splitting, the calculated tension or compression in any bar at any section must be developed on each side of that section by proper embedment length, end anchorage, or, for tension only, hooks. Anchorage or development bond stress, u, shall be computed as the bar forces divided by the product of Σo times the embedment length.

(c) The bond stress, u, computed as in (a) or (b) shall not exceed the limits given below, except that flexural bond stress need not be considered in compression, nor in those cases of tension where anchorage bond is less than 0.8 of the permissible.

(1) For tension bars with sizes and deformations conforming to ASTM A 305:

Top bars* $\qquad \dfrac{3.4\sqrt{f_c'}}{D}$ nor 350 psi

Bars other than top bars $\qquad \dfrac{4.8\sqrt{f_c'}}{D}$ nor 500 psi

---

*Top bars, in reference to bond, are horizontal bars so placed that more than 12 in. of concrete is cast in the member below the bar.

(2) For tension bars with sizes and deformations conforming to ASTM A 408:

Top bars* $\qquad\qquad\qquad\qquad\qquad$ $2.1\sqrt{f_c'}$

Bars other than top bars $\qquad\qquad\qquad$ $3\sqrt{f_c'}$

(3) For all deformed compression bars:

$$6.5\sqrt{f_c'} \text{ nor } 400 \text{ psi}$$

(4) For plain bars the allowable bond stresses shall be one-half of those permitted for bars conforming to ASTM A 305 but not more than 160 psi

(d) Adequate anchorage shall be provided for the tension reinforcement in all flexural members to which Eq. (13-1) does not apply, such as sloped, stepped or tapered footings, brackets, or beams in which the tension reinforcement is not parallel to the compression face.

---

*Top bars, in reference to bond, are horizontal bars so placed that more than 12 in. of concrete is cast in the member below the bar.

CHAPTER 14 — REINFORCED CONCRETE COLUMNS — WORKING STRESS DESIGN

1400—Notation

A_c = area of concrete within a pipe column

A_g = gross area of spirally reinforced or tied column

= the total area of the concrete encasement of combination column

= area of concrete of a composite column

A_r = area of steel or cast-iron core of a composite, combination, or pipe column

A_s = area of tension reinforcement

A_{st} = total area of longitudinal reinforcement

b = width of compression face of flexural member

d = distance from extreme compression fiber to centroid of tension reinforcement

d' = distance from extreme compression fiber to centroid of compression reinforcement

D_s = diameter of circle through centers of the longitudinal reinforcement in spiral columns

e = eccentricity of the resultant load on a column, measured from the gravity axis

e_b = maximum permissible eccentricity of N_b

F_b = allowable bending stress that would be permitted for bending alone $.45 f'_c$

f_a = axial load divided by area of member, A_g

f'_c = compressive strength of concrete (see Section 301)

f_r = allowable stress in the metal core of a composite column

f'_r = allowable stress on unencased metal columns and pipe columns

f_s = allowable stress in column vertical reinforcement

f_y = yield strength of reinforcement (see Section 301)

h = unsupported length of column

j = ratio of distance between centroid of compression and centroid of tension to the depth, d

K_c = radius of gyration of concrete in pipe columns

K_s = radius of gyration of metal pipe in pipe columns

m = $f_y / 0.85 f'_c$

n = ratio of modulus of elasticity of steel to that of concrete

N = eccentric load normal to the cross section of a column

N_b = the value of N below which the allowable eccentricity is controlled by tension, and above which by compression

p = ratio of area of tension reinforcement to effective area of concrete

p' = ratio of area of compression reinforcement to effective area of concrete

p_g = ratio of area of vertical reinforcement to the gross area, A_g

P = allowable axial load on a reinforced concrete column without reduction for length or eccentricity

   = allowable axial load on combination, composite, or pipe column without reduction for eccentricity

t = over-all depth of rectangular column or the diameter of a round column

1401—Limiting dimensions

(a) The loads determined by the provisions of this chapter apply only when unsupported length reductions are not required by the provision of Sections 915 and 916. (See Section 912 for minimum size)

1402—Spirally reinforced columns

(a) The maximum allowable axial load, P, on columns with closely spaced spirals (see Section 913) enclosing a circular core reinforced with vertical bars shall be that given by

$$P = A_g\ (0.25\ f_c' + f_s p_g) \quad \text{Spiral} \quad (14\text{-}1)$$

where f_s = allowable stress in vertical column reinforcement, to be taken at 40 percent of the minimum specification value of the yield strength, but not to exceed 30,000 psi.

1403—Tied columns

(a) The maximum allowable axial load on columns reinforced with longitudinal bars and separate lateral ties shall be 85 percent of that given by Eq. (14-1).

Rectangular Tied

1404—Composite columns

(a) The allowable load on a composite column, consisting of a structural steel or cast iron column thoroughly encased in concrete reinforced with both longitudinal and spiral reinforcement, shall not exceed that given by

$$P = 0.225\ A_g f_c' + f_s A_{st} + f_r A_r \quad (14\text{-}2)$$

where f_r = allowable unit stress in metal core, not to exceed 18,000 psi for steel conforming to ASTM A 36, 16,000 psi for steel conforming to ASTM A 7, or 10,000 psi for a cast-iron core.

The column as a whole shall satisfy the requirements of Eq. (14-2) at any point. The reinforced concrete portion shall be designed to carry all loads imposed between metal core brackets or connections at a stress of not more than 0.35 f_c' based on an area of A_g.

(b) *Metal core and reinforcement* — The cross-sectional area of the metal core shall not exceed 20 percent of the gross area of the column. If a hollow metal core is used it shall be filled with concrete. The amounts of longitudinal reinforcement and the requirements as to spacing of bars, details of splices and thickness of protective shell outside the spiral shall conform to the limiting values specified for a spiral column of the same over-all dimensions. Spiral reinforcement shall conform to Eq. (9-1). A clearance of at least 3 in. shall be maintained between the spiral and the metal core at all points except that when the core consists of a structural steel H-column, the minimum clearance may be reduced to 2 in.

Transfer of loads to the metal core shall be provided for by the use of bearing members such as billets, brackets, or other positive connections; these shall be provided at the top of the metal core and at intermediate floor levels where required.

The metal cores shall be designed to carry safely any construction or other loads to be placed upon them prior to their encasement in concrete.

1405—Combination columns

(a) *Steel columns encased in concrete* — The allowable load on a structural steel column which is encased in concrete at least 2½ in. thick over all metal (except rivet heads), reinforced as hereinafter specified, shall be computed by

$$P = A_r f_r' \left[1 + \frac{A_g}{100 \, A_r} \right] \qquad \text{(14-3)}$$

The concrete used shall develop a compressive strength, f_c', of at least 2500 psi at 28 days. The concrete shall be reinforced by the equivalent of welded wire fabric having wires of No. 10 AS&W gage, the wires encircling the column being spaced not more than 4 in. apart and those parallel to the column axis not more than 8 in. apart. This fabric shall extend entirely around the column at a distance of 1 in. inside the outer concrete surface and shall be lap-spliced at least 40 wire diameters and wired at the splice. Special brackets shall be used to receive the entire floor load at each floor level. The steel column shall be designed to carry safely any construction or other loads to be placed upon it prior to its encasement in concrete.

1406—Concrete-filled pipe columns

(a) The allowable load on columns consisting of steel pipe filled with concrete shall be determined by

$$P = 0.25 f_c' \left(1 - 0.000025 \frac{h^2}{K_c^2} \right) A_c + f_r' A_r \quad \ldots \ldots (14\text{-}4)$$

The value of f_r' shall be given by Eq. (14-5) when the pipe has a yield strength of at least 33,000 psi, and an h/K_s ratio equal to or less than 120

$$f_r' = 17,000 - 0.485 \frac{h^2}{K_s^2} \ldots \ldots \ldots \ldots (14\text{-}5)$$

1407—Columns subjected to axial load and bending

(a) The strength of the column is controlled by compression if the load, N, has an eccentricity, e, in each principal direction, no greater than that given by Eq. (14-6), (14-7), or (14-8) and by tension if e exceeds these values in either principal direction.

For symmetrical spiral columns:

$$e_b = 0.43 \, p_g m D_s + 0.14 \, t \ldots \ldots \ldots (14\text{-}6)$$

For symmetrical tied columns:

$$e_b = (0.67 \, p_g m + 0.17) \, d \ldots \ldots \ldots (14\text{-}7)$$

For unsymmetrical tied columns:

$$e_b = \frac{p' m (d-d') + 0.1 \, d}{(p' - p) m + 0.6} \ldots \ldots \ldots (14\text{-}8)$$

(b) Columns controlled by compression shall be proportioned by Eq. (14-9) except that the allowable load N shall not exceed the load, P, permitted when the column supports axial load only.

$$f_a/F_a + f_{bx}/F_b + f_{by}/F_b \quad \text{not greater than unity} \ldots (14\text{-}9)$$

where f_{bx} and f_{by} are the bending moment components about the x and y principal axes divided by the section modulus of the respective transformed uncracked section, $2n$ being assumed as the modular ratio for all vertical reinforcement, and

$$F_a = 0.34 \, (1 + p_g m) \, f_c' \ldots \ldots \ldots (14\text{-}10)$$

(c) The allowable bending moment M on columns controlled by tension shall be considered to vary linearly with axial load, from M_o when the section is in pure flexure, to M_b when the axial load is equal to N_b; M_b and N_b shall be determined from e_b and Eq. (14-9); M_o from Eq. (14-11), (14-12), or (14-13).

For spiral columns:

$$M_o = 0.12\, A_{st}f_yD_s \dots\dots\dots\dots (14\text{-}11)$$

For symmetrical tied columns:

$$M_o = 0.40\, A_sf_y\,(d-d') \dots\dots\dots\dots (14\text{-}12)$$

For unsymmetrical tied columns:

$$M_o = 0.40\, A_sf_yjd \dots\dots\dots\dots (14\text{-}13)$$

For bending about two axes

$$\frac{M_x}{M_{ox}} + \frac{M_y}{M_{oy}} \quad \text{not greater than unity} \quad \dots\dots (14\text{-}14)$$

where M_x and M_y are bending moments about the X and Y principal axes, and M_{ox} and M_{oy} are the values of M_o for bending about these axes.

Beware length consideration   915,916

PART IV-B – STRUCTURAL ANALYSIS AND PROPORTIONING OF MEMBERS – ULTIMATE STRENGTH DESIGN

CHAPTER 15 — GENERAL STRENGTH AND SERVICEABILITY REQUIREMENTS — ULTIMATE STRENGTH DESIGN

1500—Notation

A_s = area of tension reinforcement

A_s' = area of compression reinforcement

A_{sf} = area of reinforcement to develop compressive strength of overhanging flanges in I- and T-sections

a = depth of equivalent rectangular stress block = $k_1 c$

b = width of compression face of flexural member

b' = width of web in I- and T-sections

c = distance from extreme compression fiber to neutral axis at ultimate strength

D = dead load

d = distance from extreme compression fiber to centroid of tension reinforcement

E = earthquake load

f_c' = compressive strength of concrete (see Section 301)

f_y = yield strength of reinforcement (see Section 301)

k_1 = a factor defined in Section 1503(g)

L = specified live load plus impact

p = A_s/bd

p' = A_s'/bd

p_f = $A_{sf}/b'd$

p_w = $A_s/b'd$

U = required ultimate load capacity of section

W = wind load

ϕ = capacity reduction factor (see Section 1504)

1501—Definition

Ultimate strength design is a method of proportioning reinforced concrete members based on calculations of their ultimate strength. To ensure serviceability, consideration is also given to control of deflection and cracking under service loads.

1502—General requirements

(a) All provisions of this code, except those of Part IV-A, shall apply to the design of members by ultimate strength method, unless otherwise specifically provided in this Part IV-B.

(b) Bending moments in an axially loaded member shall be taken into account in the calculation of the strength required of the member.

(c) Except as provided in (d), analysis of indeterminate structures, such as continuous beams, frames, and arches, shall be based on the assumption of elastic behavior. For buildings of usual type of construction, spans, and story heights, approximate methods as provided in Chapter 9 are acceptable for determination of moments and shears.

(d) Except where approximate values for bending moments are used, the negative moments calculated by elastic theory, for any assumed loading arrangement, at the supports of continuous flexural members may each be increased or decreased by not more than 10 percent, provided that these modified negative moments are also used for final calculations of the moments at other sections in the spans corresponding to the same loading condition. Such an adjustment shall only be made when the section at which the moment is reduced is so designed that p, $(p - p')$, or $(p_w - p_f)$, which ever is applicable, is equal to or less than 0.50 times the reinforcement ratio p_b, producing balanced conditions at ultimate strength as calculated by Eq. (16-2).

1503—Assumptions

(a) Ultimate strength design of members for bending and axial load shall be based on the assumptions given in this section, and on satisfaction of the applicable conditions of equilibrium and compatibility of strains. The simplified design equations given in Chapters 16 and 19 are satisfactory.

(b) Strain in the concrete shall be assumed directly proportional to the distance from the neutral axis. Except in anchorage regions, strain in reinforcing bars shall be assumed equal to the strain in the concrete at the same position.

(c) The maximum strain at the extreme compression fiber at ultimate strength shall be assumed equal to 0.003.

(d) Stress in reinforcing bars below the yield strength, f_y, for the grade of steel used shall be taken as 29,000,000 psi times the steel strain. For strain greater than that corresponding to the design yield strength, f_y, the reinforcement stress shall be considered independent of strain and equal to the design yield strength, f_y.

(e) Tensile strength of the concrete shall be neglected in flexural calculations.

(f) At ultimate strength, concrete stress is not proportional to strain. The diagram of compressive concrete stress distribution may be assumed to be a rectangle, trapezoid, parabola, or any other shape which results in predictions of ultimate strength in reasonable agreement with the results of comprehensive tests.

(g) The requirements of (f) may be considered satisfied by the equivalent rectangular concrete stress distribution which is defined as follows: At ultimate strength, a concrete stress intensity of 0.85 f_c' shall be assumed uniformly distributed over an equivalent compression zone bounded by the edges of the cross section and a straight line located parallel to the neutral axis at a distance $a = k_1c$ from the fiber of maximum compressive strain. The distance c from the fiber of maximum strain to the neutral axis is measured in a direction perpendicular to that axis. The fraction k_1 shall be taken as 0.85 for strengths, f_c', up to 4000 psi and shall be reduced continuously at a rate of 0.05 for each 1000 psi of strength in excess of 4000 psi.

1504—Safety provisions*

(a) Strengths shall be computed in accordance with the provisions of Part IV-B.

(b) The coefficient ϕ shall be 0.90 for flexure; 0.85 for diagonal tension, bond, and anchorage; 0.75 for spirally reinforced compression members; and 0.70 for tied compression members.

(c) The strength capacities of members so computed shall be at least equal to the total effects of the design loads required by Section 1506.

1505—Design strengths for reinforcement

(a) When reinforcement is used that has a yield strength, f_y, in excess of 60,000 psi, the yield strength to be used in design shall be reduced to 0.85 f_y or 60,000 psi, whichever is greater, unless it is shown by tension tests that at a proof stress equal to the specified yield strength, f_y, the strain does not exceed 0.003.

(b) Designs shall not be based on a yield strength, f_y, in excess of 75,000 psi. Design of tension reinforcement shall not be based on a yield strength, f_y, in excess of 60,000 psi unless tests are made in compliance with Section 1508(b).

1506—Design loads†

(a) The design loads shall be computed as follows:

    1. For structures in such locations and of such proportions that the effects of wind and earthquake may be neglected the design capacity shall be

$$.U = 1.5D + 1.8L \ \dots\dots\dots\dots\dots (15\text{-}1)$$

The loads D, L, W, and E are the loads specified in the general code of which these requirements form a part.

---

*The coefficient ϕ provides for the possibility that small adverse variations in material strengths, workmanship, dimensions, control, and degree of supervision, while individually within required tolerances and the limits of good practice, occasionally may combine to result in undercapacity.

†The provisions of Section 1506 provide for such sources of possible excess load effects as load assumptions, assumptions in structural analysis, simplifications in calculations, and effects of construction sequence and methods.

2. For structures in the design of which wind loading must be included, the design capacity shall be

$$U = 1.25 \ (D + L + W) \ \ldots\ldots\ldots\ldots (15\text{-}2)$$

or

$$U = 0.9D + 1.1W \ldots\ldots\ldots\ldots\ldots (15\text{-}3)$$

whichever is greater, provided that no member shall have a capacity less than required by Eq. (15-1).

3. For those structures in which earthquake loading must be considered, E shall be substituted for W in Eq. (15-2).

4. In considering the combination of dead, live, and wind loads, the maximum and minimum effects of live loads shall be taken into account.

5. In structures in which it is normal practice to take into account creep, elastic deformation, shrinkage, and temperature, the effects of such items shall be considered on the same basis as the effects of dead load.

1507—Control of deflections

(a) The computed deflection of members at the service load level of $D + L$ shall conform to the provisions of Section 909, and deflections shall always be checked whenever the required net reinforcement ratio p, $(p - p')$, or $(p_w - p_f)$ in any section of a flexural member exceeds $0.18f_c'/f_y$, or whenever the specified yield strength, f_y, exceeds 40,000 psi.

1508—Control of cracking

(a) Only deformed bars shall be used, except that plain bars may be used as temperature bars and column spirals and #2 plain bars may be used as stirrups and column ties. Tension reinforcement shall be well distributed in the zones of maximum concrete tension and in the flange of T-beams.

(b) The design yield strength, f_y, for tension reinforcement shall not exceed 60,000 psi, unless it is shown by full-scale tests of typical members that the average crack width at service load at the concrete surface of the extreme tension edge, does not exceed 0.015 in. for interior members and 0.010 in. for exterior members. These requirements shall not apply to compression reinforcement.

CHAPTER 16 — FLEXURAL COMPUTATIONS — ULTIMATE STRENGTH DESIGN

1600—Notation

A_s = area of tension reinforcement

A_s' = area of compression reinforcement

A_{sf} = area of reinforcement to develop compressive strength of overhanging flanges in I- and T-sections

a = depth of rectangular stress block

b = width of compression face of flexural member

b' = width of web in I- and T-sections

d = distance from extreme compression fiber to centroid of tension reinforcement

d' = distance from extreme compression fiber to centroid of compression reinforcement

f_c' = compressive strength of concrete (see Section 301)

f_y = yield strength of reinforcement (see Section 301)

k_1 = a factor defined in Section 1503 (g)

M_u = ultimate resisting moment

p = A_s/bd

p' = A_s'/bd

p_b = reinforcement ratio producing balanced conditions at ultimate strength as defined by Eq. (16-2)

p_f = $A_{sf}/b'd$

p_w = $A_s/b'd$

q = $A_s f_y/bd f_c'$

t = flange thickness in I- and T-sections

ϕ = capacity reduction factor (see Section 1504)

1601—Rectangular beams with tension reinforcement only

(a) The ultimate design resisting moment of rectangular beams with tension reinforcement only shall be calculated by:

$$M_u = \phi \, [bd^2 f_c' q \, (1 - 0.59q)] = \phi \left[A_s f_y \left(d - \frac{a}{2} \right) \right] \quad (16\text{-}1)$$

where $q = pf_y / f_c'$ and $a = A_s f_y / 0.85 f_c' b$.

(b) The reinforcement ratio, p, shall not exceed 0.75 of the ratio, p_b, which produces balanced conditions at ultimate strength given by:

$$p_b = \frac{0.85 \, k_1 \, f_c'}{f_y} \cdot \frac{87,000}{87,000 + f_y} \quad \dots\dots\dots (16\text{-}2)$$

1602—Rectangular beams with compression reinforcement

(a) The ultimate design resisting moment in rectangular beams with compression reinforcement shall be calculated by:

$$M_u = \phi \left[(A_s - A_s') f_y \left(d - \frac{a}{2} \right) + A_s' f_y (d - d') \right] \quad (16\text{-}3)$$

where $a = (A_s - A_s') f_y / 0.85 f_c'b$.

(b) Eq. (16-3) is only valid when the compression steel reaches the yield strength, f_y, at ultimate strength. This is satisfied when:

$$p - p' \geq 0.85 \, k_1 \, \frac{f_c'd'}{f_yd} \, \frac{87{,}000}{87{,}000 - f_y} \quad \ldots \ldots \ldots (16\text{-}4)$$

(c) When $(p - p')$ is less than the value given by Eq. (16-4), so that the compression steel stress is less than the yield strength, f_y, or when effects of compression steel are neglected, the calculated ultimate moment shall not exceed that given by Eq. (16-1), except when a general analysis is made on the basis of the assumptions given in Section 1503.

(d) The quantity $(p - p')$ shall not exceed 0.75 of the value p_b given by Eq. (16-2). When the compression steel does not yield at ultimate strength, or when effects of compression steel are neglected, p shall not exceed 0.75 p_b, except when it is shown by a general analysis that the tension steel ratio, p, does not exceed 75 percent of that corresponding to balanced conditions.

(e) Balanced conditions exist when, at ultimate strength of a member, the tension reinforcement reaches its yield strength, f_y, just as the concrete in compression reaches its assumed ultimate strain of 0.003.

1603—I- and T-sections

(a) When the flange thickness equals or exceeds the depth to the neutral axis, $1.18 \, qd / k_1$, the section may be designed by Eq. (16-1), with q computed as for a rectangular beam with a width equal to the over-all flange width given by Section 906.

(b) When the flange thickness is less than $1.18 \, qd / k_1$, the ultimate moment shall not exceed that given by:

$$M_u = \phi \left[(A_s - A_{sf}) f_y \left(d - \frac{a}{2} \right) + A_{sf} f_y \ (d - 0.5t) \right] (16\text{-}5)$$

in which A_{sf}, the steel area necessary to develop the compressive strength of overhanging flanges is:

$$A_{sf} = 0.85 \ (b - b') \ t f_c' / f_y \quad \ldots \ldots \ldots \ldots (16\text{-}6)$$

and

$$a = (A_s - A_{sf}) \ f_y / 0.85f_c'b'$$

(c) The quantity $(p_w - p_f)$ shall not exceed 0.75 of the value p_b given by Eq. (16-2).

1604—Other cross sections

(a) For other cross sections and for cases of nonsymmetrical bending, the ultimate moment shall be computed by a general analysis based on the assumptions given in Section 1503.

(b) The amount of tension reinforcement shall be so limited that the steel ratio, p, does not exceed 75 percent of that corresponding to balanced conditions as defined by Section 1602.

CHAPTER 17 — SHEAR AND DIAGONAL TENSION — ULTIMATE STRENGTH DESIGN*

1700—Notation

A_g = gross area of section

A_s = area of tension reinforcement

A_v = total area of web reinforcement in tension within a distance, s, measured in a direction parallel to the longitudinal reinforcement

α = angle between inclined web bars and longitudinal axis of member

b = width of compression face of flexural member

b' = width of web in I- and T-sections

b_o = periphery of critical section for slabs and footings

d = distance from extreme compression fiber to centroid of tension reinforcement

f_c' = compressive strength of concrete (see Section 301)

f_y = yield strength of reinforcement, (see Section 301)

F_{sp} = ratio of splitting tensile strength to the square root of the compressive strength (see Section 505)

M = bending moment

M' = modified bending moment

N = load normal to the cross section, to be taken as positive for compression, negative for tension, and to include the effects of tension due to shrinkage and creep

p_w = $A_s/b'd$

s = spacing of stirrups or bent bars in a direction parallel to the longitudinal reinforcement

t = total depth of section

v_c = shear stress carried by concrete

v_u = nominal ultimate shear stress as a measure of diagonal tension

V = total shear at section

V_u = total ultimate shear

V_u' = ultimate shear carried by web reinforcement

ϕ = capacity reduction factor (see Section 1504)

---

*The provisions for shear are based upon recommendations of ACI-ASCE Committee 326. The term j is omitted in the determination of nominal shear stress.

1701—Ultimate shear strength*†

(a) The nominal ultimate shear stress, as a measure of diagonal tension, in reinforced concrete members shall be computed by:

$$v_u = V_u / bd \qquad\qquad (17\text{-}1)$$

For design, the maximum shear shall be considered as that at the section a distance, d, from the face of the support.‡ Wherever applicable, effects of torsion shall be added and effects of inclined flexural compression in variable-depth members shall be included.

(b) For beams of I- or T-section, b' shall be substituted for b in Eq. (17-1).

(c) The shear stress, v_c, carried by an unreinforced web shall not exceed $2\phi\sqrt{f_c'}$ at a distance, d, from the face of the support unless a more detailed analysis is made in accordance with (d) or (e). The shear at sections between the face of the support and the section a distance, d, therefrom shall not be considered critical.‡ For members with axial tension, v_c shall not exceed the value given in 1701(e).

(d) The shear stress permitted on an unreinforced web shall not exceed that given by:

$$v_c = \phi \left(1.9\sqrt{f_c'} + 2500 \, \frac{p_w V d}{M} \right) \qquad\qquad (17\text{-}2)$$

except that v_c shall not exceed $3.5\phi\sqrt{f_c'}$. The shear at sections between the face of the support and the section a distance, d, therefrom shall, not be considered critical.‡ V and M are the shear and bending moment at the section considered, but M shall be not less than Vd.

(e) For members subjected to axial load in addition to shear and flexure Eq. (17-2) shall apply except that M' shall be substituted for M, where

$$M' = M - N \left(\frac{4t - d}{8} \right) \qquad\qquad (17\text{-}3)$$

and v_c shall not exceed

$$3.5\phi\sqrt{f_c'} \, (1 + 0.002 \, N/A_g)$$

1702—Web reinforcement

(a) Wherever the value of the ultimate shear stress, v_u, computed by Eq. (17-1) plus effects of torsion, exceeds the shear stress, v_c, permitted for the concrete of an unreinforced web by Section 1701(c), (d) or (e),

---

*The provisions for shear are based upon recommendations of ACI-ASCE Committee 326. The term j is omitted in the determination of nominal shear stress.
†Special provisions for lightweight aggregate concretes are given in Section 1708.
‡This provision does not apply to brackets and other short cantilevers.

web reinforcement shall be provided to carry the excess. Such web reinforcement shall also be provided for a distance equal to the depth, d, of the member beyond the point theoretically required. Web reinforcement between the face of the support and the section at a distance d therefrom shall be the same as required at that section.*

(b) Web reinforcement may consist of:
    1. Stirrups perpendicular to the longitudinal reinforcement
    2. Stirrups making an angle of 45 deg or more with the longitudinal tension reinforcement
    3. Longitudinal bars bent so that the axis of the bent bar makes an angle of 30 deg or more with the axis of the longitudinal portion of the bar
    4. Combinations of 1 or 2 with 3

(c) Stirrups or other bars to be considered effective as web reinforcement shall be anchored at both ends according to the provisions of Section 919.

1703—Stirrups

(a) The area of steel required in stirrups placed perpendicular to the longitudinal reinforcement shall be computed by:

$$A_v = V_u's \,/\, \phi f_y d \quad\ldots\ldots\ldots\ldots\ldots\ldots \text{(17-4)}$$

(b) The area of inclined stirrups shall be computed by Eq. (17-6).

1704—Bent bars

(a) Only the center three-fourths of the inclined portion of any longitudinal bar that is bent up for web reinforcement shall be considered effective for that purpose.

(b) When the web reinforcement consists of a single bent bar or a single group of parallel bars all bent up at the same distance from the support, the required area shall be computed by:

$$A_v = \frac{V_u'}{\phi f_y \sin \alpha} \quad\ldots\ldots\ldots\ldots\ldots \text{(17-5)}$$

where V_u' shall not exceed $3\phi b d \sqrt{f_c'}$.

(c) Where there is a series of parallel bars or groups of bars bent up at different distances from the support, the required area shall be computed by:

$$A_v = \frac{V_u's}{\phi f_y d\,(\sin \alpha + \cos \alpha)} \ldots\ldots\ldots\ldots \text{(17-6)}$$

(d) Bent bars used alone as web reinforcement shall be so spaced that the effective inclined portion defined in (a) meets the requirements of Section 1706(a).

---

*This provision does not apply to brackets and other short cantilevers.

(e) Where more than one type of web reinforcement is used to reinforce the same portion of the web, the total shear resistance shall be computed as the sum of the resistances computed for the various types separately. In such computations, the resistance of the concrete, v_c, shall be included only once, and no one type of reinforcement shall be assumed to resist more than $2V_u'/3$.

1705—Stress restrictions

(a) The specified yield point for stirrup reinforcement shall not exceed 60,000 psi.

(b) The shear stress, v_u, shall not exceed $10\phi\sqrt{f_c'}$ in sections with web reinforcement.

1706—Web reinforcement restrictions

(a) Where web reinforcement is required, it shall be so spaced that every 45-deg line, representing a potential diagonal crack and extending from middepth, $d/2$, of the member to the longitudinal tension bars, shall be crossed by at least one line of web reinforcement. When the shear stress, v_u, exceeds $6\phi\sqrt{f_c'}$, every such line shall be crossed by at least two lines of web reinforcement.

(b) Where web reinforcement is required, its area shall not be less than 0.15 percent of the area, bs, computed as the product of the width of the web and the spacing of the web reinforcement along the longitudinal axis of the member.

1707—Shear stress in slabs and footings*

(a) The shear strength of slabs and footings in the vicinity of concentrated loads or concentrated reactions is governed by the more severe of two conditions:

1. The slab or footing acting essentially as a wide beam, with a potential diagonal crack extending in a plane across the entire width. This case shall be considered in accordance with Section 1701.

2. Two-way action existing for the slab or footing, with potential diagonal cracking along the surface of a truncated cone or pyramid around the concentrated load or reaction. The slab or footing in this case shall be designed as specified in the remainder of this section.

(b) The critical section for shear to be used as a measure of diagonal tension shall be perpendicular to the plane of the slab and located at a distance $d/2$ out from the periphery of the concentrated load or reaction area.

---

*For transfer of moments and effect of openings see Section 920.

(c) The nominal ultimate shear stress shall be computed by:

$$v_u = V_u / b_o d \quad \dots\dots\dots\dots\dots\dots \text{(17-7)}$$

in which V_u and b_o are taken at the critical section specified in (b). The ultimate shear stress, v_u, so computed shall not exceed $v_c = 4\phi\sqrt{f_c'}$, unless shear reinforcement is provided in accordance with (d), in which case v_u shall not exceed $6\phi\sqrt{f_c'}$.

(d) When v_u exceeds $4\phi\sqrt{f_c'}$, shear reinforcement shall be provided in accordance with Sections 1702 to 1706, except that the design yield strength, f_y, for the shear reinforcement shall be 50 percent of that prescribed in Section 1505(b). Shear reinforcement consisting of bars, rods or wires shall not be considered effective in members with a total thickness of less than 10 in.

1708—Lightweight aggregate concretes

(a) When structural lightweight aggregate concretes are used, the provisions of this chapter shall apply with the following modifications:

1. The limiting value for v_c in Section 1701(c) shall be:

$$0.3\phi F_{sp}\sqrt{f_c'} \quad \dots\dots\dots\dots\dots\dots \text{(17-8)}$$

2. Eq. (17-2) shall be replaced by:

$$v_c = \phi \left(0.28 F_{sp}\sqrt{f_c'} + \left| 2500 \, \frac{p_w V d}{M} \right. \right) \dots\dots\dots \text{(17-9)}$$

3. The limiting value for shearing stress in slabs and footings, v_u, in Sections 1707(c) and (d) shall be:

$$0.6\phi F_{sp}\sqrt{f_c'} \quad \dots\dots\dots\dots\dots\dots \text{(17-10)}$$

(b) The value of F_{sp} shall be 4.0 unless determined for the particular aggregate in accordance with Section 505.

CHAPTER 18 — BOND AND ANCHORAGE — ULTIMATE STRENGTH DESIGN

1800—Notation

d = distance from extreme compression fiber to centroid of tension reinforcement

D = nominal diameter of bar, inches

f_c' = compressive strength of concrete (see Section 301)

Σo = sum of perimeters of all effective bars crossing the section on the tension side, if of uniform size; for mixed sizes, substitute $4A_s/D$, where A_s is the total steel area and D is the largest bar diameter. For bundled bars, use the sum of the exposed portions of the perimeters

j = ratio of distance between centroid of compression and centroid of tension to the depth, d

u_u = ultimate bond stress

V_u = total ultimate shear

1801—Ultimate bond stress

(a) In flexural members in which the tension reinforcement is parallel to the compression face, the ultimate flexural bond stress at any cross section shall be computed by:

$$u_u = \frac{V_u}{\phi \Sigma o j d} \quad \ldots \ldots \ldots \ldots \ldots \ldots \ldots (18\text{-}1)$$

Bent-up bars that are not more than $d/3$ from the level of the main longitudinal reinforcement may be included. Critical sections occur at the face of the support, at each point where tension bars terminate within a span, and at the point of inflection.

(b) To prevent bond failure or splitting, the calculated tension or compression in any bar at any section must be developed on each side of that section by proper embedment length, end anchorage, or, for tension only, hooks. Anchorage or development bond stress, u_u, shall be computed as the bar force, computed from M/ϕ, divided by the product of Σo times the embedment length.

(c) The bond stress u_u, computed as in (a) or (b) shall not exceed the limits given below, except that flexural bond stress need not be considered in compression, nor in those cases of tension where anchorage bond is less than 0.8 of the permissible.

(1) For tension bars with sizes and deformations conforming to ASTM A 305:

Top bars*	$\dfrac{6.7\sqrt{f_c'}}{D}$	nor 560 psi
Bars other than top bars	$\dfrac{9.5\sqrt{f_c'}}{D}$	nor 800 psi

*Top bars, in reference to bond, are horizontal bars so placed that more than 12 in. of concrete is cast in the member below the bar.

(2) For tension bars with sizes and deformations conforming to ASTM A 408:

Top bars* $4.2\sqrt{f_c'}$

Bars other than top bars $6\sqrt{f_c'}$

(3) For all deformed compression bars:

$$13\sqrt{f_c'} \text{ nor } 800 \text{ psi}$$

(4) For plain bars, the allowable bond stresses shall be one-half those permitted for bars conforming to ASTM A 305 but not more than 250 psi.

(d) Adequate anchorage shall be provided for the tension reinforcement in all flexural members to which Eq. (18-1) does not apply, such as sloped, stepped or tapered footings, brackets or beams in which the tension reinforcement is not parallel to the compression face.

---

*Top bars, in reference to bond, are horizontal bars so placed that more than 12 in. of concrete is cast in the member below the bar.

CHAPTER 19 — COMBINED AXIAL COMPRESSION AND BENDING — ULTIMATE STRENGTH DESIGN

1900—Notation and definitions

(a) *Notation*

a = depth of equivalent rectangular stress block, defined by Section 1503 (g) $= k_1 c$

a_b = depth of equivalent rectangular stress block for balanced conditions $= k_1 c_b$

A_g = gross area of section

A_s = area of tension reinforcement

A_s' = area of compression reinforcement

A_{st} = total area of longitudinal reinforcement

b = width of compression face of flexural member

c = distance from extreme compression fiber to neutral axis

c_b = distance from extreme compression fiber to neutral axis for balanced conditions $= d (87,000) / (87,000 + f_y)$

d = distance from extreme compression fiber to centroid of tension reinforcement

d' = distance from extreme compression fiber to centroid of compression reinforcement

d'' = distance from plastic centroid to centroid of tension reinforcement

D = over-all diameter of circular section

D_s = diameter of the circle through centers of reinforcement arranged in a circular pattern

e = eccentricity of axial load at end of member measured from plastic centroid of the section, calculated by conventional methods of frame analysis

e' = eccentricity of axial load at end of member measured from the centroid of the tension reinforcement, calculated by conventional methods of frame analysis

e_b = eccentricity of load P_b measured from plastic centroid of section

f_c' = compressive strength of concrete (see Section 301)

f_s = calculated stress in reinforcement when less than the yield strength, f_y

f_y = yield strength of reinforcement (see Section 301)

k_1 = a factor defined in Section 1503 (g)

m = $f_y / 0.85 f_c'$

m' = $m - 1$

M_b = moment capacity at simultaneous crushing of concrete and yielding of tension steel (balanced conditions) = $P_b e_b$

M_u = moment capacity under combined axial load and bending

p = A_s / bd

p' = A_s' / bd

p_t = A_{st} / A_g

P_b = axial load capacity at simultaneous crushing of concrete and yielding of tension steel (balanced conditions)

P_o = axial load capacity of actual member when concentrically loaded

P_u = axial load capacity under combined axial load and bending

t = over-all depth of a rectangular section or diameter of a circular section

ϕ = capacity reduction factor (see Section 1504)

(b) *Definitions*

The plastic centroid of a section is the centroid of the resistance to load computed for the assumptions that the concrete is stressed uniformly to $0.85 f_c'$, and the steel is stressed uniformly to f_y. For symmetrically reinforced members, the plastic centroid will correspond to the centroid of the cross section.

Balanced conditions exist when, at ultimate strength of a member, the tension reinforcement reaches its yield stress just as the concrete in compression reaches its assumed ultimate strain of 0.003.

1901—General requirements

(a) All members subjected to a compression load shall be designed for the eccentricity, e, corresponding to the maximum moment which can accompany this loading condition, but not less than $0.05t$ for spirally reinforced columns or $0.10t$ for tied columns about either principal axis.

(b) The maximum load capacities for members subject to axial load as determined by the requirements of this chapter apply only to short members and shall be reduced for the effects of length according to the requirements of Section 916.

(c) Members subjected to small compressive loads may be designed for the maximum moment, $P_u e$, in accordance with the provisions of Chapter 16, and disregarding the axial load, but the resulting section shall have a capacity, P_b, greater than the applied compressive load.

1902—Bending and axial load capacity of short members— Rectangular sections with bars in one or two faces

(a) The ultimate strength of short members subject to combined bending and axial load shall be computed from the equations of equilibrium, which may be expressed as follows when a is not more than t

and the reinforcement is in one or two faces, each parallel to the axis of bending and all the reinforcement in any one face is located at approximately the same distance from the axis of bending.

$$P_u = \phi[0.85 f_c' ba + A_s' f_y - A_s f_s] \ldots\ldots\ldots(19\text{-}1)$$

$$P_u e' = \phi \left[0.85 f_c' ba \left(d - \frac{a}{2} \right) + A_s' f_y (d - d') \right] \ldots (19\text{-}2)$$

Strain compatibility calculations shall be used to insure that the compression steel will actually yield at ultimate strength of a member as assumed in Eq. (19-1), (19-2), (19-3), (19-4), (19-5), (19-6), and (19-10).

(b) The balanced load, P_b, shall be computed using Eq. (19-1) with $a = a_b = k_1 c_b$, and $f_s = f_y$. The balanced moment, M_b, shall be computed by

$$M_b = P_b e_b = \phi \left[0.85 f_c' b a_b \left(d - d'' - \frac{a_b}{2} \right) \right.$$
$$\left. + A_s' f_y (d - d' - d'') + A_s f_y d'' \right] \ldots\ldots\ldots (19\text{-}3)$$

(c) The ultimate capacity of a member is controlled by tension in (c)1, when P_u is less than P_b (or e is greater than e_b). The capacity is controlled by compression in (c)2, when P_u is greater than P_b (or e is less than e_b).

1. When a section is controlled by tension, and has reinforcement in one or two faces, each parallel to the axis of bending, and all the reinforcement in any one face is located at approximately the same distance from the axis of bending, the ultimate strength shall not exceed that computed by:

$$P_u = \phi \left[0.85 f_c' bd \left. \right\} p'm' - pm + (1 - e'/d) \right.$$
$$\left. + \sqrt{(1 - e'/d)^2 + 2[(e'/d)(pm - p'm') + p'm'(1 - d'/d)]} \right\} \right] \quad (19\text{-}4)$$

For symmetrical reinforcement in two faces, this reduces to:

$$P_u = \phi \left[0.85 f_c' bd \left. \right\} -p + 1 - e'/d \right.$$
$$\left. + \sqrt{(1 - e'/d)^2 + 2p [m'(1 - d'/d) + e'/d]} \right\} \right] \ldots\ldots\ldots (19\text{-}5)$$

With no compression reinforcement, Eq. (19-4) reduces to:

$$P_u = \phi \left\{ 0.85 f_c' bd \left[-pm + 1 - e'/d \right. \right.$$
$$\left. \left. + \sqrt{(1 - e'/d)^2 + 2 \frac{e'pm}{d}} \right] \right\} \ldots\ldots\ldots (19\text{-}6)$$

2. When a section is controlled by compression, the ultimate load shall be assumed to decrease linearly from P_o to P_b as the moment is increased from zero to M_b, where

$$P_o = \phi[0.85 \, f_c' \, (A_g - A_{st}) + A_{st}f_y] \dotfill (19\text{-}7)$$

For this assumption the ultimate strength is given by either Eq. (19-8) or (19-9):

$$P_u = \frac{P_o}{1 + [\, (P_o/P_b) - 1] \, e/e_b} \dotfill (19\text{-}8)$$

$$P_u = P_o - (P_o - P_b) \, M_u/M_b \dotfill (19\text{-}9)$$

For symmetrical reinforcement in single layers parallel to the axis of bending, the approximate value of P_u given by Eq. (19-10) may be used:

$$P_u = \phi \left[\frac{A_s'f_y}{\dfrac{e}{d-d'} + 0.5} + \frac{b \, t \, f_c'}{(3 \, te/d^2) + 1.18} \right] \dotfill (19\text{-}10)$$

1903—Bending and axial load of short members—Circular sections with bars circularly arranged

(a) The ultimate strength of short circular members subject to combined bending and axial load shall be computed on the basis of the equations of equilibrium taking into account inelastic deformations, or by the empirical expressions given by:

When tension controls:

$$P_u = \phi \left\{ 0.85f_c' \, D^2 \left[\sqrt{\left(\frac{0.85e}{D} - 0.38\right)^2 + \frac{p_t m D_s}{2.5D}} \right.\right.$$

$$\left.\left. - \left(\frac{0.85e}{D} - 0.38\right) \right] \right\} \dotfill (19\text{-}11)$$

When compression controls:

$$P_u = \phi \left[\frac{A_{st}f_y}{\dfrac{3e}{D_s} + 1} + \frac{A_g f_c'}{\dfrac{9.6 \, De}{(0.8D + 0.67D_s)^2} + 1.18} \right] \dotfill (19\text{-}12)$$

1904—Bending and axial load of short members—Square sections with bars circularly arranged

(a) The ultimate strength of short square members with bars circularly arranged subject to combined bending and axial load shall be computed on the basis of the equations of equilibrium taking into account inelastic deformations, or by the empirical expressions:

When tension controls:

$$P_u = \phi \left\{ 0.85 \, bt \, f_c' \left[\sqrt{\left(\frac{e}{t} - 0.5 \right)^2 + 0.67 \frac{D_s}{t} \, p_t m} - \left(\frac{e}{t} - 0.5 \right) \right] \right\} \qquad \cdots \cdots (19\text{-}13)$$

When compression controls:

$$P_u = \phi \left[\frac{A_{st} f_y}{\dfrac{3e}{D_s} + 1} + \frac{A_g f_c'}{\dfrac{12te}{(t + 0.67D_s)^2} + 1.18} \right] \quad \cdots \cdots (19\text{-}14)$$

1905—Bending and axial load of short members—General case

(a) When the reinforcement is placed in all four faces, or in faces which are not parallel to the axis of bending, the design shall be based on computations considering stress and strain compatibility and using the assumptions in Section 1503.

PART V – STRUCTURAL SYSTEMS OR ELEMENTS

CHAPTER 20 — JOISTS AND TWO-WAY SLABS

2001—Concrete joist floor construction

(a) In concrete joist floor construction consisting of concrete joists and slabs placed monolithically with or without burned clay or concrete tile fillers, the joists shall not be farther apart than 30 in. face to face. The ribs shall be straight, not less than 4 in. wide, and of a depth not more than three times the width.

(b) When burned clay or concrete tile fillers of material having a unit compressive strength at least equal to that of the specified strength of the concrete in the joists are used, the vertical shells of the fillers in contact with the joists may be included in the calculations involving shear or negative bending moment. No other portion of the fillers may be included in the design calculations.

(c) The concrete slab over the fillers shall be not less than 1½ in. in thickness, nor less in thickness than 1/12 of the clear distance between joists. Shrinkage reinforcement shall be provided in the slab at right angles to the joists equal to that required in Section 807.

(d) Where removable forms or fillers not complying with (b) are used, the thickness of the concrete shall not be less than 1/12 of the clear distance between joists and in no case less than 2 in. Such slab shall be reinforced at right angles to the joists with at least the amount of reinforcement required for flexure, giving due consideration to concentrations, if any, but in no case shall the reinforcement be less than that required by Section 807.

(e) When the finish used as a wearing surface is placed monolithically with the structural slab in buildings of the warehouse or industrial class, the thickness of the concrete over the fillers shall be ½ in. greater than the thickness used for design purposes.

(f) Where the slab contains conduits or pipes as allowed in Section 703, the thickness shall not be less than 1 in. plus the total over-all depth of such conduits or pipes at any point. Such conduits or pipes shall be so located as not to impair the strength of the construction.

(g) Shrinkage reinforcement is not required in the slab parallel to the joists.

(h) The shear stress, v_c, may be increased 10 percent over those prescribed in sections 1201 or 1701.

2002—Two-way floor systems with supports on four sides

(a) This construction, reinforced in two directions, includes solid reinforced concrete slabs; concrete joists with fillers of hollow concrete units or clay tile, with or without concrete top slabs; and concrete joists with top slabs placed monolithically with the joists. The slab shall be supported by walls or beams on all sides and if not securely attached to supports, shall be reinforced in each direction as specified in (b).

(b) Special reinforcement shall be provided at exterior corners in both the bottom and top of the slab. This reinforcement shall be provided for a distance in each direction from the corner equal to one-fifth the longest span. The reinforcement in the top of the slab shall be parallel to the diagonal from the corner. The reinforcement in the bottom of the slab shall be at right angles to the diagonal or may be of bars in two directions parallel to the sides of the slab. The reinforcement in each band shall be of equivalent size and spacing to that required for the maximum positive moment in the slab.

(c) The slab shall be designed by approved methods which shall take into account the effect of continuity and fixity at supports, the ratio of length to width of slab and the effect of two-way action.*

(d) The supports of two-way slabs shall be designed by accepted methods taking into account the effect of continuity. The loading on the supports may be computed from the coefficients of the approved methods.

(e) In no case shall the slab thickness be less than 3½ in. nor less than the perimeter of the slab divided by 180. The center to center spacing of reinforcement shall be not more than three times the slab thickness and the ratio of reinforcement in each direction shall be not less than required by Section 807.

---

*The requirements of this section are satisfied by any of the methods of design shown in Appendix A.

CHAPTER 21 — FLAT SLABS WITH SQUARE OR RECTANGULAR PANELS

2100—Notation

A = distance in the direction of span from center of support to the intersection of the center line of the slab thickness with the extreme 45-deg diagonal line lying wholly within the concrete section of slab and column or other support, including drop panel, capital and bracket

b_o = periphery of critical section for shear

c = effective support size [see Section 2104(c)]

d = distance from extreme compression fiber to centroid of tension reinforcement

f_c' = compressive strength of concrete (see Section 301)

h = distance from top of slab to bottom of capital

H = story height in feet of the column or support of a flat slab center to center of slabs

K = ratio of moment of inertia of column provided to I_c required by Eq. (21-1)

L = span length of a flat slab panel center to center of supports

M_o = numerical sum of assumed positive and average negative moments at the critical design sections of a flat slab panel [see Section 2104(f)1]

R_n = factor for increasing negative moment [Section 2104, Eq. (21-2)]

R_p = factor for increasing positive moment [Section 2104, Eq. (21-3)]

t = thickness in inches of slab at center of panel

t_1 = thickness in inches of slab without drop panels, or through drop panel, if any

t_2 = thickness in inches of slab with drop panels at points beyond the drop panel

w' = uniformly distributed unit dead and live load

W = total dead and live load on panel

W_D = total dead load on panel

W_L = total live load on panel, uniformly distributed

2101—Definitions and scope

(a) *Flat slab* — A concrete slab reinforced in two or more directions, generally without beams or girders to transfer the loads to supporting members. Slabs with recesses or pockets made by permanent or removable fillers between reinforcing bars may be considered flat slabs. Slabs with paneled ceilings may be considered as flat slabs provided the panel of reduced thickness lies entirely within the area of intersecting middle strips, and is at least two-thirds the thickness of the remainder of the slab, exclusive of the drop panel, and is not less than 4 in. thick.

(b) *Column capital* — An enlargement of the end of a column designed and built to act as an integral unit with the column and flat slab. No portion of the column capital shall be considered for structural purposes which lies outside of the largest right circular cone with 90-deg vertex angle that can be included within the outlines of the column capital. Where no capital is used, the face of the column shall be considered as the edge of the capital.

(c) *Drop panel* — The structural portion of a flat slab which is thickened throughout an area surrounding the column, column capital, or bracket.

(d) *Panel strips* — A flat slab shall be considered as consisting of strips in each direction as follows:

A middle strip one-half panel in width, symmetrical about panel center line.

A column strip consisting of the two adjacent quarter-panels, one each side of the column center line.

(e) *Ultimate strength design* — Flat slabs shall be proportioned by Part IV-A only, except that Part IV-B may be used if the following modifications are made in the design:

1. For either empirical or elastic analysis the numerical sum of the positive and negative bending moments in the direction of either side of a rectangular panel shall be assumed as not less than

$$M_0 = 0.10 \; WLF \left(1 - \frac{2c}{3L}\right)^2$$

in which $F = 1.15 - c/L$ but not less than 1.

2. The thickness of slab shall not be less than shown in Table 2101(e).

TABLE 2101(e)—MINIMUM SLAB THICKNESS

f_y	With drop panels*	Without drop panels
40,000	L/40 or 4 in.	L/36 or 5 in.
50,000	L/36 or 4 in.	L/33 or 5 in.
60,000	L/33 or 4 in.	L/30 or 5 in.

*To be considered effective, the drop panel shall have a length of at least one-third the parallel span length and a projection below the slab of at least one-fourth the slab thickness.

2102—Design procedures

(a) *Methods of analysis* — All flat slab structures shall be designed in accordance with a recognized elastic analysis subject to the limitations of Sections 2102 and 2103, except that the empirical method of design given in Section 2104 may be used for the design of flat slabs conforming with the limitations given therein. Flat slabs within the limitations of Section 2104, when designed by elastic analysis, may have resulting analytical moments reduced in such proportion that the numerical sum of the positive and average negative bending moments used in design procedure need not exceed the sum of the corresponding values as determined from Table 2104(f).

(b) *Critical sections* — The slab shall be proportioned for the bending moments prevailing at every section except that the slab need not be proportioned for a greater negative moment than that prevailing at a distance A from the support center line.

(c) *Size and thickness of slabs and drop panels*

1. Subject to limitations of Section 2102(c)4, the thickness of a flat slab and the size and thickness of the drop panel, where used, shall be such that the compression due to bending at any section, and the shear about the column, column capital, and drop panel shall not exceed those permitted in Part IV-A or Part IV-B. When designed under Section 2104, three-fourths of the width of the strip shall be used as the width of the section in computing compression due to bending, except that on a section through a drop panel, three-fourths of the width of the drop panel shall be used. Account shall be taken of any recesses which reduce the compressive area.

2. The shear on vertical sections which follow a periphery, b_o, at distance, $d/2$, beyond the edges of the column, column capital, or drop panel, and concentric with them, shall be computed as required and limited in Chapters 12 or 17.

3. If shear reinforcement is used, the first line shall be not further than $d/2$ from the face of the support.

4. Slabs with drop panels whose length is at least one-third the parallel span length and whose projection below the slab is at least one-fourth the slab thickness shall be not less than $L/40$ nor 4 in. in thickness.

Slabs without drop panels as described above shall be not less than $L/36$ nor 5 in. in thickness.

5. For determining reinforcement, the thickness of the drop panel below the slab shall not be assumed to be more than one-fourth of the distance from the edge of the drop panel to the edge of the column capital.

(d) *Arrangement of slab reinforcement*

1. The spacing of the bars at critical sections shall not exceed two times the slab thickness, except for those portions of the slab

area which may be of cellular or ribbed construction. In the slab over the cellular spaces, reinforcement shall be provided as required by Section 807.

2. In exterior panels, except for bottom bars adequately anchored in the drop panel, all positive reinforcement perpendicular to the discontinuous edge shall extend to the edge of the slab and have embedment, straight or hooked, of at least 6 in. in spandrel beams, walls, or columns where provided. All negative reinforcement perpendicular to the discontinuous edge shall be bent, hooked, or otherwise anchored in spandrel beams, walls, or columns.

3. The area of reinforcement shall be determined from the bending moments at the critical sections but shall be not less than required by Section 807.

4. Required splices in bars may be made wherever convenient, but preferably away from points of maximum stress. The length of any such splice shall conform to Section 805.

5. Bars shall be spaced approximately uniformly across each panel strip, except:

a. At least 25 percent of required negative reinforcement in the column strip shall cross the periphery located at a distance of d from the column or column capital.

b. At least 50 percent of the required negative reinforcement in the column strip shall cross the drop panel, if any.

c. The spacing for the remainder of the column strip may vary uniformly from that required for a or b to that required for the middle strip.

(e) *Openings in flat slabs*

1. Openings of any size may be provided in flat slabs if provision is made for the total positive and negative moments and for shear without exceeding the allowable stresses except that when design is based on Section 2104, the limitations given therein shall not be exceeded.

2. When openings are provided within the area common to two column strips, that part of the critical section shall be considered ineffective which either passes through an opening, or is covered by a radial projection of any opening to the centroid of the support.

(f) *Design of columns*

1. All columns supporting flat slabs shall be designed as provided in Chapter 14 or 19 with the additional requirements of this chapter.

(g) *Transfer of bending moment between column and slab* — When unbalanced gravity load, wind or earthquake cause transfer of bending moment between column and slab, the stresses on the critical section shall be investigated by a rational analysis, and the section proportioned accordingly by the requirements of Part IV-A or IV-B. Concentration of reinforcement over the column head by additional reinforcement or closer spacing may be used to resist the moment of the section. A slab width between lines that are 1.5t each side of the column may be considered effective.

2103—Design by elastic analysis

(a) *Assumptions* — In design by elastic analysis the following assumptions may be used and all sections shall be proportioned for the moments and shears thus obtained.

1. The structure may be considered divided into a number of bents, each consisting of a row of columns or supports and strips of supported slabs, each strip bounded laterally by the center line of the panel on either side of the center line of columns or supports. The bents shall be taken longitudinally and transversely of the building.

2. Each such bent may be analyzed in its entirety or each floor thereof and the roof may be analyzed separately with its adjacent columns as they occur above and below, the columns being assumed fixed at their remote ends. Where slabs are thus analyzed separately, it may be assumed in determining the bending at a given support that the slab is fixed at any support two panels distant therefrom provided the slab continues beyond that point.

3. The joints between columns and slabs may be considered rigid, and this rigidity (infinite moment of inertia) may be assumed to extend in the slabs from the center of the column to the edge of the capital, and in the column from the top of slab to the bottom of the capital. The change in length of columns and slabs due to direct stress, and deflections due to shear, may be neglected.

4. Where metal column capitals are used, account may be taken of their contributions to stiffness and resistance to bending and shear.

5. The moment of inertia of the slab or column at any cross section may be assumed to be that of the cross section of the concrete. Variation in the moments of inertia of the slabs and columns along their axes shall be taken into account.

6. Where the load to be supported is definitely known, the structure shall be analyzed for that load. Where the live load is variable but does not exceed three-quarters of the dead load, or the nature of the live load is such that all panels will be loaded simultaneously, the maximum bending may be assumed to occur at all sections under full live load. For other conditions, maximum positive bending near midspan of a panel may be assumed to occur under three-quarters of the full live load in the panel and in alter-

nate panels; and maximum negative bending in the slab at a support may be assumed to occur under three-quarters of the full live load in the adjacent panels only. In no case, shall the design moments be taken as less than those occurring with full live load on all panels.

(b) *Critical sections* — The critical section for negative bending, in both the column strip and middle strip, may be assumed as not more than the distance *A* from the center of the column or support and the critical negative moment shall be considered as extending over this distance.

(c) *Distribution of panel moments* — Bending at critical sections across the slabs of each bent may be apportioned between the column strip and middle strip, as given in Table 2103(c). For design purposes, any of these percentages may be varied by not more than 10 percent of its value, but their sum for the full panel width shall not be reduced.

2104—Empirical method

(a) *General limitations* — Flat slab construction may be designed by the empirical provisions of this section when they conform to all of the limitations on continuity and dimensions given herein.

1. The construction shall consist of at least three continuous panels in each direction.

2. The ratio of length to width of panels shall not exceed 1.33.

3. The grid pattern shall consist of approximately rectangular panels. The successive span lengths in each direction shall differ by not more than 20 percent of the longer span. Within these limitations, columns may be offset a maximum of 10 percent of the span, in direction of the offset, from either axis between center lines of successive columns.

4. The calculated lateral force moments from wind or earthquake may be combined with the critical moments as determined by the empirical method, and the lateral force moments shall be distributed between the column and middle strips in the same proportions as specified for the negative moments in the strips for structures not exceeding 125 ft high with maximum story height not exceeding 12 ft 6 in.

(b) *Columns*

1. The minimum dimension of any column shall be as determined by a and b below, but in no case less than 10 in.

　　a. For columns or other supports of a flat slab, the required minimum average moment of inertia, I_c, of the gross concrete section of the columns above and below the slab shall be determined from Eq. (21-1) and shall be not less than 1000 in.[4] If there is no column above the slab, the I_c of the column below shall be $(2 - 2.3h/H)$ times that given by the formula with a minimum of 1000 in.[4]

$$I_c = \frac{t^3 H}{0.5 + \dfrac{W_D}{W_L}} \dots\dots\dots\dots\dots\dots\dots\dots (21\text{-}1)$$

where t need not be taken greater than t_1 or t_2 as determined in (d), H is the average story height of the columns above and below the slab, and W_L is the greater value of any two adjacent spans under consideration.

TABLE 2103 (c)—DISTRIBUTION BETWEEN COLUMN STRIPS AND MIDDLE STRIPS IN PERCENT OF TOTAL MOMENTS AT CRITICAL SECTIONS OF A PANEL

Strip		Moment section			
		Negative moment at interior support	Positive moment	Negative moment at exterior support	
				Slab supported on columns and on beams of total depth equal to the slab thickness*	Slab supported on reinforced concrete bearing wall or columns with beams of total depth equal or greater than 3 times the slab thickness*
Column strip		76	60	80	60
Middle strip		24	40	20	40
Half column strip adjacent and parallel to marginal beam or wall	Total depth of beam equal to slab thickness*	38	30	40	30
	Total depth of beam or wall equal to or greater than 3 times slab thickness*	19	15	20	15

*Interpolate for intermediate ratios of beam depth to slab thickness.

Note: The total dead and live reaction of a panel adjacent to a marginal beam or wall may be divided between the beam or wall and the parallel half column strip in proportion to their stiffness, but the moment provided in the slab shall not be less than that given in Table 2103(c).

b. Columns smaller than required by Eq. (21-1) may be used provided the bending moment coefficients given in Table 2104 (f) are increased in the following ratios:

For negative moments

$$R_n = 1 + \frac{(1-K)^2}{2.2\ (1+1.4W_D/W_L)} \quad \dots \dots \dots (21\text{-}2)$$

For positive moments

$$R_p = 1 + \frac{(1-K)^2}{1.2\ (1+0.10W_D/W_L)} \quad \dots \dots \dots (21\text{-}3)$$

The required slab thickness shall be modified by multiplying w' by R_n in Eq. (21-4) and (21-5).

2. Columns supporting flat slabs designed by the empirical method shall be proportioned for the bending moments developed by unequally loaded panels, or uneven spacing of columns. Such bending moment shall be the maximum value derived from

$$\frac{WL_1 - W_D L_2}{f}$$

L_1 and L_2 being lengths of the adjacent spans ($L_2 = 0$ when considering an exterior column) and f is 30 for exterior and 40 for interior columns.

This moment shall be divided between the columns immediately above and below the floor or roof line under consideration in direct proportion to their stiffness and shall be applied without further reduction to the critical sections of the columns.

(c) *Determination of "c" (effective support size)*

1. Where column capitals are used, the value of c shall be taken as the diameter of the cone described in Section 2101 (b) measured at the bottom of the slab or drop panel.

2. Where a column is without a concrete capital, the dimension c shall be taken as that of the column in the direction considered.

3. Brackets capable of transmitting the negative bending and the shear in the column strips to the columns without excessive unit stress may be substituted for column capitals at exterior columns. The value of c for the span where a bracket is used shall be taken as twice the distance from the center of the column to a point where the bracket is 1½ in. thick, but not more than the thickness of the column plus twice the depth of the bracket.

4. Where a reinforced concrete beam frames into a column without capital or bracket on the same side with the beam, for computing bending for strips parallel to the beam, the value of c for the span considered may be taken as the width of the column plus twice the projection of the beam above or below the slab or drop panel.

5. The average of the values of c at the two supports at the ends of a column strip shall be used to evaluate the slab thickness t_1 or t_2 as prescribed in (d).

(d) *Slab thickness*

1. The slab thickness, span L being the longest side of the panel, shall be at least:

$L/36$ for slab without drop panels conforming with (e), or where a drop panel is omitted at any corner of the panel, but not less than 5 in. nor t_1 as given in Eq. (21-4).

$L/40$ for slabs with drop panels conforming to (e) at all supports, but not less than 4 in. nor t_2 as given in Eq. (21-5).

2. The total thickness, t_1, in inches, of slabs without drop panels, or through the drop panel if any, shall be at least

$$t_1 = 0.028L \left(1 - \frac{2c}{3L} \right) \sqrt{\frac{w'}{f_c'/2000}} + 1\frac{1}{2} \dots \dots (21\text{-}4) *$$

3. The total thickness, t_2, in inches, of slabs with drop panels, at points beyond the drop panel shall be at least

$$t_2 = 0.024L \left(1 - \frac{2c}{3L} \right) \sqrt{\frac{w'}{f_c'/2000}} + 1 \dots \dots (21\text{-}5) *$$

4. Where the exterior supports provide only negligible restraint to the slab, the values of t_1 and t_2 for the exterior panel shall be increased by at least 15 percent.

(e) *Drop panels*

1. The maximum total thickness at the drop panel used in computing the negative steel area for the column strip shall be $1.5t_2$.

2. The side or diameter of the drop panel shall be at least 0.33 times the span in the parallel direction.

3. The minimum thickness of slabs where drop panels at wall columns are omitted shall equal $(t_1 + t_2)/2$ provided the value of c used in the computations complies with (c).

(f) *Bending moment coefficients*

1. The numerical sum of the positive and negative bending moments in the direction of either side of a rectangular panel shall be assumed as not less than

$$M_o = 0.09 \ WLF \left(1 - \frac{2c}{3L} \right)^2 \dots \dots \dots (21\text{-}6)$$

in which $F = 1.15 - c/L$ but not less than 1.

2. Unless otherwise provided, the bending moments at the critical sections of the column and middle strips shall be at least those given in Table 2104(f).

3. The average of the values of c at the two supports at the ends

---

*In these formulas t_1 and t_2 are in inches, L and c are in feet, and w' is in pounds per square foot.

TABLE 2104(f)—MOMENTS IN FLAT SLAB PANELS IN PERCENTAGES OF M_0

Strip	Column head	Side support type	End support type	Exterior panel			Interior panel	
				Exterior negative moment	Positive moment	Interior negative moment	Positive moment	Negative moment
Column strip	With drop		A	44				
			B	36	24	56	20	50
			C	6	36	72		
	Without drop		A	40				
			B	32	28	50	22	46
			C	6	40	66		
Middle strip	With drop		A	10				
			B	20	20	17*	15	15*
			C	6	26	22*		
	Without drop		A	10				
			B	20	20	18*	16	16*
			C	6	28	24*		
Half column strip adjacent to marginal beam or wall	With drop	1	A	22				
			B	18	12	28	10	25
			C	3	18	36		
		2	A	17				
			B	14	9	21	8	19
			C	3	14	27		
		3	A	11				
			B	9	6	14	5	13
			C	3	9	18		
	Without drop	1	A	20				
			B	16	14	25	11	23
			C	3	20	33		
		2	A	15				
			B	12	11	19	9	18
			C	3	15	25		
		3	A	10				
			B	8	7	13	6	12
			C	3	10	17		

Percentage of panel load to be carried by marginal beam or wall in addition to loads directly superimposed thereon	Side support parallel to strip	Type of support listed in Table 2104(f)	
		Side or end edge condition of slabs of depth t	End support at right angles to strip
0	1	Columns with no beams	
20	2	Columns with beams of total depth $1\frac{1}{4}t$	A
40	3	Columns with beams of total depth $3t$ or more	B
		Reinforced concrete bearing walls integral with slab	
		Masonry or other walls providing negligible restraint	C

*Increase negative moments 30 percent of tabulated values when middle strip is continuous across support of Type B or C. No other values need be increased.

Note: For intermediate proportions of total beam depth to slab thicknesses, values for loads and moments may be obtained by interpolation. See also Fig. 2104(f)a and 2104(f)b.

PANEL	INTERIOR				EXTERIOR					
MOMENT	SUPPORT	CENTER OF SPAN	1ST INTERIOR SUPPORT	CENTER OF SPAN	EXTERIOR SUPPORT (B)	EXTERIOR SUPPORT (A)	1ST INTERIOR SUPPORT	CENTER OF SPAN	EXTERIOR SUPPORT (C)
END SUPPORT / SIDE SUPPORT									
MARGINAL HALF COLUMN STRIP — 3	−12	+6	−13	+7	−8	−10	−17	+10	−3
MARGINAL HALF COLUMN STRIP — 2	−18	+9	−19	+11	−12	−15	−25	+15	−3
MARGINAL HALF COLUMN STRIP — 1	−23	+11	−25	+14	−16	−20	−33	+20	−3
MIDDLE STRIP	−16*	+16	−18*	+20	−20	−10	−24*	+28	−6
COLUMN STRIP	−46	+22	−50	+28	−32	−40	−66	+40	−6

DIRECTION OF ALL MOMENTS

Fig. 2104(f)a—Moments in flat slab panels in percentage of M_0 — Without drops
[see Table 2104(f) for notes and classification of conditions of end supports and side supports]

*Increase negative moments 30 percent when middle strip is continuous across a support of Type B or C; no other values need be increased.

Fig. 2104(f)b—Moments in flat slab panels in percentages of M_o — With drops
[see Table 2104(f) for notes and classification of conditions of end supports and side supports]

*Increase negative moments 30 percent when middle strip is continuous across a support of Type B or C; no other values need be increased.

of a column strip shall be used to evaluate M_o in determining bending in the strip. The average of the values of M_o, as determined for the two parallel half column strips in a panel, shall be used in determining bending in the middle strip.

4. Bending in the middle strips parallel to a discontinuous edge shall be assumed the same as in an interior panel.

5. For design purposes, any of the moments determined from Table 2104(f) may be varied by not more than 10 percent, but the numerical sum of the positive and negative moments in a panel shall be not less than the amount specified.

(g) *Length of reinforcement* — In addition to the requirements of Section 2102(d), reinforcement shall have the minimum lengths given in Tables 2104(g)1 and 2104(g)2. Where adjacent spans are unequal, the extension of negative reinforcement on each side of the column center line as prescribed in Table 2104(g)1 shall be based on the requirements of the longer span.

(h) *Openings in flat slabs*

1. Openings of any size may be provided in a flat slab in the area common to two intersecting middle strips provided the total positive and negative steel areas required in (f) are maintained.

2. In the area common to two column strips, not more than one-eighth of the width of strip in any span shall be interrupted by openings. The equivalent of all bars interrupted shall be provided by extra steel on all sides of the openings. The shear stresses given in Section 2102(c)2 shall not be exceeded following the procedure of Section 920(b).

3. In any area common to one column strip and one middle strip, openings may interrupt one-quarter of the bars in either strip. The equivalent of the bars so interrupted shall be provided by extra steel on all sides of the opening.

4. Any opening larger than described above shall be analyzed by accepted engineering principles and shall be completely framed as required to carry the loads to the columns.

TABLE 2104(g)I—MINIMUM LENGTH OF NEGATIVE REINFORCEMENT

Strip	Percentage of required reinforcing steel area to be extended at least as indicated	Minimum distance beyond center line of support to end of straight bar or to bend point of bent bar*			
		Flat slabs without drop panels		Flat slabs with drop panels	
		Straight	Bend point where bars bend down and continue as positive reinforcement	Straight	Bend point where bars bend down and continue as positive reinforcement
Column strip reinforcement	Not less than 33 percent	0.30L†		0.33L‡	
	Not less than an additional 34 percent	0.27L†		0.30L‡	
	Remainder†	0.25L or 0.20L		0.25L or	To edge of drop but at least 0.20L
Middle strip reinforcement	Not less than 50 percent	0.25L		0.25L	
	Remainder§	0.25L or 0.15L		0.25L or 0.15L	

*At exterior supports where masonry walls or other construction provide only negligible restraint to the slab, the negative reinforcement need not be carried further than 0.20L beyond the center line of such support.

†Where no bent bars are used, the 0.27L bars may be omitted, provided the 0.30L bars are at least 50 percent of total required.

‡Where no bent bars are used, the 0.30L bars may be omitted provided the 0.33L bars provide at least 50 percent of the total required.

§Bars may be straight, bent, or any combination of straight and bent bars. All bars are to be considered straight bars for the end under consideration unless bent at that end and continued as positive reinforcement.

Note: See also Fig. 2104(g)a.

TABLE—2104(g)2—MINIMUM LENGTH OF POSITIVE REINFORCEMENT

Strip	Percentage of required reinforcing steel area to be extended at least as indicated	Maximum distance from center line of support to end of straight bar or bend point of bent bar			
		Flat slabs without drop panels		Flat slabs with drop panels	
		Straight	Bend point where bars bend up and continue as negative reinforcement	Straight	Bend point where bars bend up and continue as negative reinforcement
Column strip reinforcement	Not less than 33 percent	0.125L		Minimum embedment in drop panel of 16 bar diameters but at least 10 in.	
	Not less than 50 percent*	3 in. or 0.25L			
	Remainder*	0.125L or 0.25L		Minimum embedment in drop panel of 16 bar diameters but at least 10 in. or 0.25L	
Middle strip reinforcement	50 percent	0.15L		0.15L	
	50 percent*	3 in. or 0.25L		3 in. or 0.25L	

*Bars may be straight, bent, or any combination of straight and bent bars. All bars are to be considered straight bars for the end under consideration unless bent at that end and continued as negative reinforcement.

Note: See also Fig. 2104(g)a.

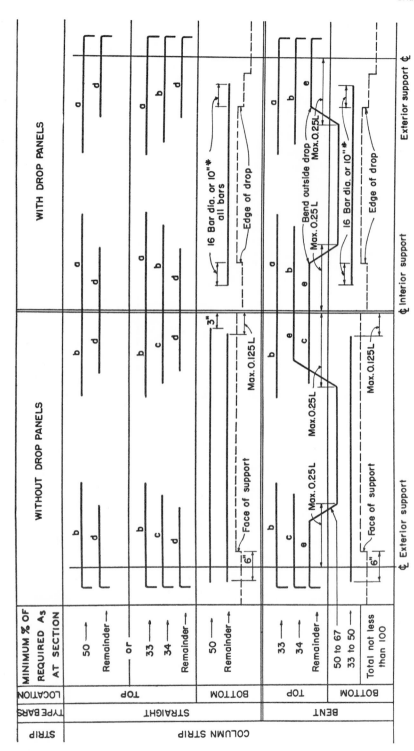

* For bars not terminating in drop panel use lengths shown for panels without drops.

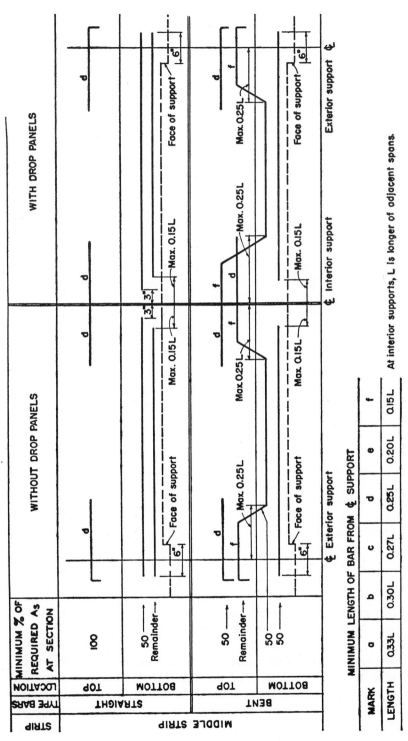

Fig. 2104(g)a—Minimum length of flat slab reinforcement

At exterior supports, where masonry walls or other construction provide only negligible restraint to the slab, the negative reinforcement need not be carried further than 0.20L beyond the center line of such support; any combination of straight and bent bars may be used provided minimum requirements are met

CHAPTER 22 — REINFORCED CONCRETE WALLS

2200—Notation

f_c　= allowable compressive stress on concrete
f_c'　= compressive strength of concrete (see Section 301)
h　= vertical distance between supports
t　= thickness of wall

2201—Structural design of walls

(a) Walls shall be designed for any lateral or other pressure to which they are subjected. Proper provisions shall be made for eccentric loads and wind stresses. Walls conforming to the provisions of Section 2202 shall be considered as meeting these requirements. The limits of thickness and quantity of reinforcement required by Section 2202 shall be waived where structural analysis shows adequate strength and stability.

2202—Empirical design of walls

(a) Reinforced concrete bearing walls carrying reasonably concentric loads may be designed by the empirical provisions of this section when they conform to all the limitations given herein.

(b) The allowable compressive stress using Part IV-A shall be

$$f_c = 0.225 f_c' \left[1 - \left(\frac{h}{40t} \right)^3 \right] \dots\dots\dots\dots (22\text{-}1)$$

When the reinforcement in bearing walls is designed, placed, and anchored in position as for tied columns, the allowable stresses shall be those for tied columns, in which the ratio of vertical reinforcement shall not exceed 0.04.

For design by Part IV-B the values from Eq. (22-1) shall be multiplied by 1.9.

(c) In the case of concentrated loads, the length of the wall to be considered as effective for each shall not exceed the center to center distance between loads, nor shall it exceed the width of the bearing plus four times the wall thickness.

(d) Reinforced concrete bearing walls shall have a thickness of at least 1/25 of the unsupported height or width, whichever is the shorter.

(e) Reinforced concrete bearing walls of buildings shall be not less than 6 in. thick for the uppermost 15 ft of their height; and for each successive 25 ft downward, or fraction thereof, the minimum thickness shall be increased 1 in. Reinforced concrete bearing walls of two-story dwellings may be 6 in. thick throughout their height.

(f) The area of the horizontal reinforcement of reinforced concrete walls shall be not less than 0.0025 and that of the vertical reinforcement not less than 0.0015 times the area of the reinforced section of the wall if of bars, and not less than three-fourths as much if of welded wire fabric. The wire of the welded fabric shall be of not less than No. 10 AS&W gage.

(g) Walls more than 10 in. thick, except for basement walls, shall have the reinforcement for each direction placed in two layers parallel with the faces of the wall. One layer consisting of not less than one-half and not more than two-thirds the total required shall be placed not less than 2 in. nor more than one-third the thickness of the wall from the exterior surface. The other layer, comprising the balance of the required reinforcement, shall be placed not less than ¾ in. and not more than one-third the thickness of the wall from the interior surface. Bars, if used, shall not be less than #3 bars, nor shall they be spaced more than 18 in. on centers. Welded wire reinforcement for walls shall be in flat sheet form.

(h) In addition to the minimum as prescribed in (f) there shall be not less than two #5 bars around all window or door openings. Such bars shall extend at least 24 in. beyond the corner of the openings.

(i) Reinforced concrete walls shall be anchored to the floors, or to the columns, pilasters, buttresses, and intersecting walls with reinforcement at least equivalent to #3 bars 12 in. on centers, for each layer of wall reinforcement.

(j) Panel and enclosure walls of reinforced concrete shall have a thickness of not less than 4 in. and not less than 1/30 the distance between the supporting or enclosing members.

(k) Exterior basement walls, foundation walls, fire walls, and party walls shall not be less than 8 in. thick.

(l) Where reinforced concrete bearing walls consist of studs or ribs tied together by reinforced concrete members at each floor level, the studs may be considered as columns, but the restrictions as to minimum diameter or thickness of columns shall not apply.

2203—Walls as grade beams

(a) Walls designed as grade beams shall have top and bottom reinforcement as required by stresses. Portions exposed above grade shall, in addition, be reinforced with not less than the amount specified in Section 2202.

CHAPTER 23 — FOOTINGS

2301—Scope

(a) The requirements prescribed in Sections 2302 through 2309 apply only to isolated footings.

(b) General procedures for the design of combined footings are given in Section 2310.

2302—Loads and reactions

(a) Footings shall be proportioned to sustain the applied loads and induced reactions without exceeding the stresses or strengths prescribed in Parts IV-A and IV-B, and as further provided in this chapter.

(b) In cases where the footing is concentrically loaded and the member being supported does not transmit any moment to the footing, computations for moments and shears shall be based on an upward reaction assumed to be uniformly distributed per unit area or per pile and a downward applied load assumed to be uniformly distributed over the area of the footing covered by the column, pedestal, wall, or metallic column base.

(c) In cases where the footing is eccentrically loaded and/or the member being supported transmits a moment to the footing, proper allowance shall be made for any variation that may exist in the intensities of reaction and applied load consistent with the magnitude of the applied load and the amount of its actual or virtual eccentricity.

(d) In the case of footings on piles, computations for moments and shears may be based on the assumption that the reaction from any pile is concentrated at the center of the pile.

2303—Sloped or stepped footings

(a) In sloped or stepped footings, the angle of slope or depth and location of steps shall be such that the allowable stresses are not exceeded at any section.

(b) In sloped or stepped footings, the effective cross section in compression shall be limited by the area above the neutral plane.

(c) Sloped or stepped footings that are designed as a unit shall be cast as a unit.

2304—Bending moment

(a) The external moment on any section shall be determined by passing through the section a vertical plane which extends completely across the footing, and computing the moment of the forces acting over the entire area of the footing on one side of said plane.

(b) The greatest bending moment to be used in the design of an isolated footing shall be the moment computed in the manner prescribed in (a) at sections located as follows:

1. At the face of the column, pedestal or wall, for footings supporting a concrete column, pedestal or wall

2. Halfway between the middle and the edge of the wall, for footings under masonry walls

3. Halfway between the face of the column or pedestal and the edge of the metallic base, for footings under metallic bases

(c) The width resisting compression at any section shall be assumed as the entire width of the top of the footing at the section under consideration.

(d) In one-way reinforced footings, the total tensile reinforcement at any section shall provide a moment of resistance at least equal to the moment computed as prescribed in (a); and the reinforcement thus determined shall be distributed uniformly across the full width of the section.

(e) In two-way reinforced footings, the total tension reinforcement at any section shall provide a moment of resistance at least equal to the moment computed as prescribed in (a); and the total reinforcement thus determined shall be distributed across the corresponding resisting section as prescribed for square footings in (f), and for rectangular footings in (g).

(f) In two-way square footings, the reinforcement extending in each direction shall be distributed uniformly across the full width of the footing.

(g) In two-way rectangular footings, the reinforcement in the long direction shall be distributed uniformly across the full width of the footing. In the case of the reinforcement in the short direction, that portion determined by Eq. (23-1) shall be uniformly distributed across a band-width (B) centered with respect to the center line of the column or pedestal and having a width equal to the length of the short side of the footing. The remainder of the reinforcement shall be uniformly distributed in the outer portions of the footing.

$$\frac{Reinforcement\ in\ band\text{-}width\ (B)}{Total\ reinforcement\ in\ short\ direction} = \frac{2}{(S+1)} \quad \text{(23-1)}$$

where S is the ratio of the long side to the short side of the footing.

2305—Shear and bond

(a) For computation of shear in footings, see Section 1207 or 1707.

(b) Critical sections for bond shall be assumed at the same planes as those prescribed for bending moment in Section 2304(b)1; also at all other vertical planes where changes of section or of reinforcement occur.

(c) Computation for shear to be used as a measure of flexural bond shall be based on a vertical section which extends completely across the footing, and the shear shall be taken as the sum of all forces acting over the entire area of the footing on one side of such section.

(d) The total tensile reinforcement at any section shall provide a bond resistance at least equal to the bond requirement as computed from the external shear at the section.

(e) In computing the external shear on any section through a footing supported on piles, the entire reaction from any pile whose center is located 6 in. or more outside the section shall be assumed as producing shear on the section; the reaction from any pile whose center is located 6 in. or more inside the section shall be assumed as producing no shear on the section. For intermediate positions of the pile center, the portion of the pile reaction to be assumed as producing shear on the section shall be based on straight-line interpolation between full value at 6 in. outside the section and zero value at 6 in. inside the section.

(f) For allowable shearing values, see Sections 1207 and 1707.

(g) For allowable bond values, see Sections 1301 (b) and 1801 (b).

2306—Transfer of stress at base of column

(a) The stress in the longitudinal reinforcement of a column or pedestal shall be transferred to its supporting pedestal or footing either by extending the longitudinal bars into the supporting member, or by dowels.

(b) In case the transfer of stress in the reinforcement is accomplished by extension of the longitudinal bars, they shall extend into the supporting member the distance required to transfer this stress to the concrete by bond.

(c) In cases where dowels are used, their total sectional area shall be not less than the sectional area of the longitudinal reinforcement in the member from which the stress is being transferred. In no case shall the number of dowels per member be less than four and the diameter of the dowels shall not exceed the diameter of the column bars by more than $\frac{1}{8}$ in.

(d) Dowels shall extend up into the column or pedestal a distance at least equal to that required for lap of longitudinal column bars [see Section 805] and down into the supporting pedestal or footing the distance required to transfer to the concrete, by allowable bond stress, the full working value of the dowel [see Section 918(i)].

(e) The compression stress in the concrete at the base of a column or pedestal shall be considered as being transferred by bearing to the top of the supporting pedestal or footing. The compression stress on the loaded area shall not exceed the bearing stress allowable for the quality of concrete in the supporting member as determined by the ratio of the loaded area to the supporting area.

(f) For allowable bearing stresses, design by Part IV-A shall conform to Table 1002(a), and for design by Part IV-B to 1.9 times those values.

(g) In sloped or stepped footings, the supporting area for bearing may be taken as the top horizontal surface of the footing, or assumed as the area of the lower base of the largest frustum of a pyramid or cone contained wholly within the footing and having for its upper base the area actually loaded, and having side slopes of one vertical to two horizontal.

2307—Pedestals and footings (plain concrete)

(a) The allowable compression stress on the gross area of a concentrically loaded pedestal under service load shall not exceed $0.25f_c'$. Where this stress is exceeded, reinforcement shall be provided and the member designed as a reinforced concrete column.

(b) The depth and width of a pedestal or footing of plain concrete shall be such that the tension in the concrete in flexure shall not exceed $1.6\sqrt{f_c'}$ for design by Part IV-A or $3.2\sqrt{f_c'}$ for design by Part IV-B. The average shear stress shall satisfy the requirements of Chapter 12 or 17.

2308—Footings supporting round columns

(a) In computing the stresses in footings which support a round or octagonal concrete column or pedestal, the "face" of the column or pedestal may be taken as the side of a square having an area equal to the area enclosed within the perimeter of the column or pedestal.

2309—Minimum edge thickness

(a) In reinforced concrete footings, the thickness above the reinforcement at the edge shall be not less than 6 in. for footings on soil, nor less than 12 in. for footings on piles.

(b) In plain concrete footings, the thickness at the edge shall be not less than 8 in. for footings on soil, nor less than 14 in. above the tops of the piles for footings on piles.

2310—Combined footings and mats

(a) The following recommendations are made for combined footings and mats — those supporting more than one column or wall:

1. Soil pressures shall be considered as acting uniformly or varying linearly, except that other assumptions may be made consistent with the properties of the soil and the structure and with established principles of soil mechanics.

2. Shear as a measure of diagonal tension shall be computed in conformance with Section 1207 or 1707.

CHAPTER 24 — PRECAST CONCRETE

2401—Scope

(a) All provisions of this code shall apply to precast concrete except for the specific variations given in this chapter and Chapter 26.

2402—Aggregates

(a) For precast concrete Section 403 (b) shall not apply; the maximum size of aggregate shall not be larger than one-third of the least dimension of the member.

2403—Concrete protection for reinforcement

(a) At surfaces not exposed to weather, all reinforcement shall be protected by concrete equal to the nominal diameter of bars but not less than 5/8 in.

2404—Details

(a) All details of jointing, inserts, anchors, and openings shall be shown on the drawings.

(b) Lifting eyes or other similar devices shall be designed for 100 percent impact. They shall be made of materials sufficiently ductile to ensure visible deformation before fracture.

2405—Curing

(a) Curing by high-pressure steam, steam vapor, or other accepted processes may be employed to accelerate the hardening of the concrete and to reduce the time of curing required by Section 605 provided that the compressive strength of the concrete at the load stage considered be at least equal to the design strength required at that load stage.

2406—Identification and marking

(a) All precast concrete members shall be plainly marked to indicate the top of the member and its location and orientation in the structure. Identification marks shall be reproduced from the placing plans.

2407—Transportation, storage, and erection

(a) Units shall be so stored, transported, and placed that they will not be overstressed or damaged.

(b) Precast concrete units shall be adequately braced and supported during erection to insure proper alignment and safety and such bracing or support shall be maintained until there are adequate permanent connections.

2408—Splicing of reinforcement

(a) Where splicing of reinforcement must be made at points of maximum stress or at closer spacing than permitted by Section 805, welding may be used when the entire procedure is suitable for the particular quality of steel used and the ambient conditions. Unless the welds develop 125 percent of the specified yield strength of the steel used, reinforcement in the form of continuous bars or fully anchored dowels shall be added to provide 25 percent excess steel area and the welds shall develop not less than the specified yield strength of the steel.

2409—Nonbearing wall panels

(a) Nonload-bearing, precast wall panels shall be exempt from the minimum thickness requirements of Section 2202.

(b) Where panels are designed to span horizontally to columns or isolated footings, the ratio of height to thickness shall not be limited, provided the effect of deep beam action and buckling are provided for in the design in accordance with Section 910(a).

2410—Minimum size of precast columns

(a) Precast columns may have a minimum thickness of 6 in. and a minimum gross area of 48 sq in. provided structural adequacy is assured by rigorous analysis.

CHAPTER 25 — COMPOSITE CONCRETE FLEXURAL CONSTRUCTION

2500—Notation

b' = width of area of contact between precast and cast-in-place concretes

d_p = effective depth of the tension reinforcement in precast component

I = moment of inertia of the transformed composite section neglecting area of concrete in tension

M_D = moment due to dead load, produced prior to the time at which the cast-in-place concrete attains 75 percent of its specified 28-day strength

M_L = moment due to live load and superimposed dead load

Q = statical moment of the transformed area outside of the contact surface about the neutral axis of the composite section

V = total shear

v_h = horizontal shear stress along contact surface

2501—Definition

(a) Composite concrete flexural construction consists of precast concrete members and cast-in-place reinforced concrete so interconnected that the component elements act together as a unit.

2502—Special design considerations

(a) In regions of negative moment, the bending moment may be assigned to either the composite section or the precast element. When the negative moments are assigned to the composite section, adequate provision for shear transfer must be made throughout the full length of the beam.

2503—Flexural design—Working stress design (Part IV-A)

(a) The design of the composite reinforced concrete member shall be based on allowable stresses, working loads, and the accepted straight-line theory of flexure as given in Part IV-A of this code. The effects of creep, shrinkage, and temperature need not be considered except in unusual cases. The effects of shoring, or lack of shoring, on deflections and stresses shall be considered.

2504—Flexural design—Ultimate strength design (Part IV-B)

(a) *Design method*

In calculating the ultimate strength of a section, no distinction is made between shored and unshored members.

(b) Limitations

1. For beams designed on the basis of ultimate strength and built without shores, the effective depth of the composite section used in the calculation of the ultimate moment shall not exceed:

$$(1.15 + 0.24 \, M_L/M_D) \, d_p$$

2. When the specified yield point of the tension reinforcement exceeds 40,000 psi, beams designed on the basis of ultimate strength should always be built with shores unless provisions are made to prevent excessive tensile cracking.

(c) Construction loads

The nonprestressed precast element shall be investigated separately to assure that the loads applied before the cast-in-place concrete has attained 75 percent of its specified 28-day strength do not cause moment in excess of 60 percent of the ultimate moment capacity of the precast section.

2505—Shear connection

(a) Shear calculation

The horizontal shear stress along the contact surface is given by:

$$v_h = \frac{VQ}{Ib'} \quad \dotfill \quad (25\text{-}1)$$

(b) Shear transfer

Shear shall be transferred along the contact surface either by bond or by shear keys. The capacity of bond at ultimate load may be taken as 1.9 times the values recommended below for service loads. Except as provided in 1, separation of the component elements in the direction normal to the surface shall be prevented by steel ties or other suitable mechanical anchorages.

1. When mechanical anchorages are not provided and the contact surface is rough and clean .... 40 psi

2. When minimum steel tie requirements of (c) are followed and the contact surface is smooth (troweled, floated, or cast against a form) .... 40 psi

3. When minimum steel tie requirements of (c) are followed and the contact surface is rough and clean........ 160 psi

4. When additional vertical ties are used the allowable bond stress on a rough surface may be increased at the rate of 75 psi for each additional area of steel ties equal to 1 percent of the contact area.

(c) *Vertical ties*

When mechanical anchorage in the form of vertical ties is provided, spacing of such ties shall not exceed four times the thickness of the slab nor 24 in. A minimum cross-sectional area of ties of 0.15 percent of the contact area shall be provided. It is preferable to provide all ties in the form of extended stirrups.

(d) *Web reinforcement*

Web reinforcement for the composite section shall be designed in the same manner as for an integral beam of the same shape. All stirrups so required shall be anchored into the cast-in-place slab, where their area may also be relied upon to provide some or all of the vertical tie steel required in (c).

CHAPTER 26 — PRESTRESSED CONCRETE

2600—Notation

a $= A_s f_{su} / 0.85 f_c' b$

A_b $=$ bearing area of anchor plate of post-tensioning steel

A_b' $=$ maximum area of the portion of the anchorage surface that is geometrically similar to and concentric with the area of the anchor plate of the post-tensioning steel

A_s $=$ area of prestressed tendons

A_{sf} $=$ area of reinforcement to develop compressive strength of overhanging flanges in flanged members

A_{sr} $=$ area of tendon required to develop the web

A_s' $=$ area of unprestressed reinforcement

A_v $=$ area of web reinforcement placed perpendicular to the axis of the member

b $=$ width of compression face of flexural member

b' $=$ minimum width of web of a flanged member

d $=$ distance from extreme compression fiber to centroid of the prestressing force

f_c' $=$ compressive strength of concrete (see Section 301)

f_{ci}' $=$ compressive strength of concrete at time of initial prestress

f_{cp} $=$ permissible compressive concrete stress on bearing area under anchor plate of post-tensioning steel

f_d $=$ stress due to dead load, at the extreme fiber of a section at which tension stresses are caused by applied loads

f_{pc} $=$ compressive stress in the concrete, after all prestress losses have occurred, at the centroid of the cross section resisting the applied loads, or at the junction of the web and flange when the centroid lies in the flange. (In a composite member f_{pc} will be the resultant compressive stress at the centroid of the composite section, or at the junction of the web and flange when the centroid lies within the flange, due to both prestress and to the bending moments resisted by the precast member acting alone.)

f_{pe} $=$ compressive stress in concrete due to prestress only, after all losses, at the extreme fiber of a section at which tension stresses are caused by applied loads

f_s' $=$ ultimate strength of prestressing steel

f_{se} $=$ effective steel prestress after losses

f_{su} $=$ calculated stress in prestressing steel at ultimate load

f_{sy} $=$ nominal yield strength of prestressing steel

f_y' $=$ strength of unprestressed reinforcement (see Section 301)

F_{sp} $=$ ratio of splitting tensile strength to the square root of compressive strength (see Section 505)

h $=$ total depth of member

I = Moment of inertia of section resisting externally applied loads*

K = wobble friction coefficient per foot of prestressing steel

L = length of prestressing steel element from jacking end to any point x

M = bending moment due to externally applied loads*

M_{cr} = net flexural cracking moment

M_u = ultimate resisting moment

p = A_s/bd; ratio of prestressing steel

p' = A_s'/bd; ratio of unprestressed steel

q = $p\,f_{su}/f_c'$

s = longitudinal spacing of web reinforcement

T_o = steel force at jacking end

T_x = steel force at any point x

t = average thickness of the compression flange of a flanged member

V = shear due to externally applied loads*

V_c = shear carried by concrete

V_{ci} = shear at diagonal cracking due to all loads, when such cracking is the result of combined shear and moment

V_{cw} = shear force at diagonal cracking due to all loads, when such cracking is the result of excessive principal tension stresses in the web

V_d = shear due to dead load

V_p = vertical component of the effective prestress force at the section considered

V_u = shear due to specified ultimate load

y = distance from the centroidal axis of the section resisting the applied loads to the extreme fiber in tension

α = total angular change of prestressing steel profile in radians from jacking end to any point x

ε = base of Naperian logarithms

μ = curvature friction coefficient

ϕ = capacity reduction factor (see Section 1504)

2601—Definitions

(a) The following terms are defined for use in this chapter:

Anchorage — The means by which the prestress force is permanently delivered to the concrete.

Bonded tendons — Tendons which are bonded to the concrete either directly or through grouting. Unbonded tendons are free to move relative to the surrounding concrete.

Effective prestress — The stress remaining in the tendons after all losses have occurred, excluding the effects of dead load and superimposed loads.

---

*The term "externally applied loads" shall be taken to mean the external ultimate loads acting on the member, excepting those applied to the member by the prestressing tendons.

Friction:

Curvature friction — Friction resulting from bends or curves in the specified cable profile.

Wobble friction — Friction caused by the unintended deviation of the prestressing steel from its specified profile.

Jacking force — The temporary force exerted by the device which introduces the tension into the tendons.

Nominal yield strength — The yield strength specified by appropriate ASTM specification or as indicated by Section 405 (f).

Post-tensioning — A method of prestressing in which the tendons are tensioned after the concrete has hardened.

Pretensioning — A method of prestressing in which the tendons are tensioned before the concrete is placed.

Tendon — A tensioned steel element used to impart prestress to the concrete.

Transfer — The operation of transferring the tendon force to the concrete.

2602—Scope

(a) Provisions in this chapter apply to flexural members prestressed with high-strength steel. Pavements, pipes, and circular tanks are not included.

(b) For prestressed concrete designs or constructions in conflict with, or not encompassed by the provisions of this chapter, see Section 104.

(c) All provisions of this code not specifically excluded and not in conflict with the provisions of this chapter are to be considered applicable to prestressed concrete.

(d) The following provisions shall not apply to prestressed concrete: Sections 906, 911, 913, Chapters 13 and 14, Section 1508, Chapter 18, Section 2001 (a), Chapter 21, and Section 2504 (b).

2603—General considerations

(a) Stresses and ultimate strength shall be investigated at service conditions and at all load stages that may be critical during the life of the structure from the time prestress is first applied.

(b) Stress concentrations due to the prestressing or other causes shall be taken into account in the design.

(c) The effects on the adjoining structure of elastic and plastic deformations, deflections, changes in length, and rotations caused by the prestressing shall be provided for. When the effect is additive to temperature and shrinkage effects, they shall be considered simultaneously.

(d) The possibility of buckling of a member between points of contact between concrete and prestressing steel and of buckling of thin webs and flanges shall be considered.

2604—Basic assumptions

(a) The following assumptions shall be made for purposes of design:

1. Strains vary linearly with depth through the entire load range.

2. At cracked sections, the ability of the concrete to resist tension is neglected.

3. In calculations of section properties prior to bonding of tendons, areas of the open ducts shall be deducted. The transformed area of bonded tendons may be included in pretensioned members and in post-tensioned members after grouting.

4. Modulus of elasticity of concrete shall be assumed as prescribed in Section 1102.

5. The modulus of elasticity of prestressing steel shall be determined by tests or supplied by the manufacturer.

2605—Allowable stresses in concrete

(a) Temporary stresses immediately after transfer, before losses due to creep and shrinkage, shall not exceed the following:

1. Compression . . . . $0.60 \, f_{ci}'$

2. Tension stresses in members without auxiliary reinforcement (unprestressed or prestressed) in the tension zone . . . . . . $3\sqrt{f_{ci}'}$

Where the calculated tension stress exceeds this value, reinforcement shall be provided to resist the total tension force in the concrete computed on the assumption of an uncracked section.

(b) Stresses at design loads, after allowance for all prestress losses, shall not exceed the following:

1. Compression . . . . $0.45 f_c'$

2. Tension in the precompressed tension zone:

Members, not exposed to freezing temperatures nor to a corrosive environment, which contain bonded prestressed or unprestressed reinforcement located so as to control cracking . . . . $6\sqrt{f_c'}$

All other members 0

These values may be exceeded when not detrimental to proper structural behavior as provided in Section 104.

(c) The bearing stress on the concrete created by the anchorage in post-tensioned concrete with adequate reinforcement in the end regions shall not exceed:

$$f_{cp} = 0.6 f_{ci}' \sqrt[3]{A_b'/A_b} \quad \dots \dots \dots \dots \dots \quad (26\text{-}1)$$

but not greater than f_{ci}'

2606—Allowable stresses in steel

(a) *Temporary stresses*

1. Due to temporary jacking force . . . . $0.80 \, f_s'$

but not greater than the maximum value recommended
by the manufacturer of the steel or of the anchorages.

2. Pretensioning tendons immediately after transfer,
or posttensioning tendons immediately after anchoring.... $0.70\ f_s'$

(b) *Effective prestress* .... $0.60\ f_s'$

or $0.80\ f_{sy}$

whichever is smaller

2607—Loss of prestress

(a) To determine the effective prestress, allowance for the following
sources of loss of prestress shall be considered.

1. Slip at anchorage
2. Elastic shortening of concrete
3. Creep of concrete
4. Shrinkage of concrete
5. Relaxation of steel stress
6. Frictional loss due to intended or unintended curvature in the
tendons

(b) Friction losses in post-tensioned steel shall be based on experimentally determined wobble and curvature coefficients,* and shall be
verified during stressing operations. The values of coefficients assumed
for design, and the acceptable ranges of jacking forces and steel elonga-
tions shall be shown on the plans. These friction losses shall be calculated:

$$T_o = T_x\ \varepsilon^{(KL+\mu a)} \dotfill (26\text{-}2)$$

When $(KL + \mu a)$ is not greater than 0.3, Eq. (26-3) may be used.

$$T_o = T_x\ (1 + KL + \mu a) \dotfill (26\text{-}3)$$

(c) When prestress in a member may be reduced through its connection with adjoining elements, such reduction shall be allowed for
in the design.

*Values of K (per lineal foot) and μ vary appreciably with duct material and method of
construction. For metal sheathing the following table may be used as a guide.

Type of steel	Usual range of observed values		Suggested design values	
	K	μ	K	μ
Wire cables	0.0005–0.0030	0.15–0.35	0.0015	0.25
High strength bars	0.0001–0.0005	0.08–0.30	0.0003	0.20
Galvanized strand	0.0005–0.0020	0.15–0.30	0.0015	0.25

2608—Ultimate flexural strength

(a) The required ultimate load on a member, determined in accordance with Part IV-B shall not exceed the ultimate flexural strength computed by:

1. Rectangular sections, or flanged sections in which the neutral axis lies within the flange: *

$$M_u = \phi \left[A_s f_{su} d \ (1 - 0.59 \ q) \right] = \phi \left[A_s f_{su} \left(d - \frac{a}{2} \right) \right] \ (26\text{-}4)$$

2. Flanged sections in which the neutral axis falls outside the flange: †

$$M_u = \phi \left[A_{sr} f_{su} d \left(1 - \frac{0.59 \ A_{sr} \ f_{su}}{b'd \ f_c'} \right) \right.$$

$$\left. + 0.85 \ f_c' \ (b - b') t \ (d - 0.5t) \right] \dots \dots (26\text{-}5)$$

where

$$A_{sr} = A_s - A_{sf}$$

and

$$A_{sf} = 0.85 \ f_c' \ (b - b') t / f_{su}$$

3. Where information for the determination of f_{su} is not available, and provided that f_{se} is not less than $0.5 \ f_s'$, the following approximate values shall be used:

Bonded members

$$f_{su} = f_s' \ (1 - 0.5 \ p f_s'/f_c') \dots \dots (26\text{-}6)$$

Unbonded members

$$f_{su} = f_{se} + 15{,}000 \text{ psi} \ \dots \dots (26\text{-}7)$$

4. Nonprestressed reinforcement, in combination with prestressed steel, may be considered to contribute to the tension force in a member at ultimate moment an amount equal to its area times its yield point, provided

$$\frac{p f_{su}}{f_c'} + \frac{p' f_y}{f_c'} \text{ does not exceed } 0.3$$

2609—Limitations on steel percentage

(a) Except as provided in (b), the ratio of prestressing steel used for calculations of M_u shall be such that

$$p f_{su} / f_c' \text{ is not more than } 0.30$$

For flanged sections, p shall be taken as the steel ratio of only that portion of the total tension steel area which is required to develop the compressive strength of the web alone.

---

*Usually where the flange thickness is *more* than 1.4 $d p f_{su}/f_c'$.
†Usually where the flange thickness is *less* than 1.4 $d p f_{su}/f_c'$.

(b) When a steel ratio in excess of that specified in (a) is used, the ultimate moment shall be taken as not greater than the following:

Rectangular sections, or flanged sections in which the neutral axis lies within the flange

$$M_u = \phi[0.25\,f_c'bd^2] \quad \ldots\ldots\ldots\ldots\ldots\ldots \text{(26-8)}$$

Flanged sections in which the neutral axis falls outside the flange

$$M_u = \phi[0.25f_c'b'd^2 + 0.85f_c'\ (b - b')t\ (d - 0.5t)\,] \ \ldots \text{(26-9)}$$

(c) The total amount of prestressed and unprestressed reinforcement shall be adequate to develop an ultimate load in flexure at least 1.2 times the cracking load calculated on the basis of a modulus of rupture of $7.5\sqrt{f_c'}$.

2610—Shear

(a) Except as provided in (c), the area of shear reinforcement placed perpendicular to the axis of a member shall be not less than:

$$A_v = \frac{(V_u - \phi V_c)\,s}{\phi\,d\,f_y} \quad\ldots\ldots\ldots\ldots\ldots\ldots \text{(26-10)}$$

nor less than

$$A_v = \frac{A_s}{80} \cdot \frac{f_s'}{f_y} \cdot \frac{s}{d} \sqrt{\frac{d}{b'}} \quad \ldots\ldots\ldots\ldots \text{(26-11)}$$

The effective depth, d, used in Eq. (26-10) and (26-11) shall be as follows:

1. In members of constant over-all depth, d, equals the effective depth at the section of maximum moment, and the length of the stirrups at the section under consideration shall be at least equal to the length of the stirrups at the section of maximum moment.

2. In members of varying depth, d equals $h(d_m/h_m)$, where d_m and h_m are the effective depth and total depth respectively at the section of maximum moment, and h is the total depth at the section under consideration. The stirrups shall extend into the member a distance d from the compression face.

(b) The shear, V_c, at diagonal cracking shall be taken as the lesser of V_{ci} and V_{cw}, determined from Eq. (26-12) and (26-13).

1. For normal weight concrete

$$V_{ci} = 0.6\ b'd\ \sqrt{f_c'} + \frac{M_{cr}}{\dfrac{M}{V} - \dfrac{d}{2}} + V_d \ \ldots\ldots \text{(26-12)}$$

but not less than $1.7\ b'd\ \sqrt{f_c'}$

where $M_{cr} = \dfrac{I}{y} \, (6\sqrt{f_c'} + f_{pe} - f_d)$

$$V_{cw} = b'd \, (3.5 \sqrt{f_c'} + 0.3 f_{pc}) + V_p \quad \ldots \ldots \ldots \text{(26-13)}$$

2. For lightweight aggregate concrete

$$V_{ci} = 0.1 \, F_{sp} \, b'd \, \sqrt{f_c'} + \frac{M_{cr}}{\dfrac{M}{V} - \dfrac{d}{2}} + V_d \quad \ldots \text{(26-12A)}$$

but not less than $0.25 \, F_{sp} \, b'd \, \sqrt{f_c'}$

where $M_{cr} = \dfrac{I}{y} \, (0.9 F_{sp} \sqrt{f_c'} + f_{pe} - f_d)$

$$V_{cw} = b'd \left[0.5 \, F_{sp} \sqrt{f_c'} + f_{pc} \left(0.2 + \frac{F_{sp}}{67} \right) \right] + V_p \quad \text{(26-13A)}$$

Alternatively V_{cw} may be taken as the live load plus dead load shear which corresponds to the occurrence of a principal tensile stress of $4\sqrt{f_c'}$ in normal weight concrete, or $0.6 F_{sp}\sqrt{f_c'}$ in lightweight concrete, at the centroidal axis of the section resisting the live load. In flanged members, if the centroidal axis is not in the web, the principal tensile stress should be determined at the intersection of the flange and the web.

When applying Eq. (26-12) and (26-12A), the effective depth, d, shall be taken as the distance from the extreme compression fiber to the centroid of the prestressing tendons.

When applying Eq. (26-13) and (26-13A), the effective depth, d, shall be taken as the distance from the extreme compression fiber to the centroid of the prestressing tendons, or as 80 percent of the over-all depth of the member, whichever is the greater.

The value of (M/V) used in Eq. (26-12) and (26-12A) shall be that resulting from the distribution of loads causing maximum moment to occur at the section.

In a pretensioned prestressed beam in which the section distant $d/2$ from the face of the support is closer to the end face of the beam than the transfer length of the wire or strand used, the reduced prestress in the concrete at sections falling within the transfer length should be considered when calculating the diagonal cracking shear, V_{cw}. The prestress at the centroid of the section may be assumed to vary linearly from zero at the end face of the beam to a maximum at a distance from the end face equal to the transfer length, assumed to be 50 diameters for strand and 100 diameters for single wire.

(c) Web reinforcement between the face of the support and the section at a distance $d/2$ therefrom shall be the same as that required at that section.

Shear reinforcement shall be provided for a distance equal to the effective depth, d, of the member beyond the point theoretically required.

Web reinforcement shall be anchored at both ends in accordance with Section 919.

Shear reinforcement not less than determined from Equation (26-11) shall be provided at all sections and shall be spaced not farther apart than three-fourths the depth of the member, nor 24 inches, whichever is the smaller, except when it is shown by tests that the required ultimate flexural and shear capacity can be developed when the web reinforcement is omitted.

A yield strength in excess of 60,000 psi shall not be considered for shear reinforcement.

2611—Bond

(a) Three or seven wire pretensioning strand shall be bonded to the concrete from the cross section under consideration for a distance in inches of not less than:

$$\left(f_{su} - \frac{2}{3}\, f_{se} \right) D$$

where D, the nominal strand diameter, is in inches and f_{su} and f_{se} are expressed in kips per square inch.

Investigation may be restricted to those cross sections nearest each end of the member that are required to develop their ultimate strength under the specified ultimate load.

2612—Repetitive loads

(a) The possibility of bond failure due to repeated loads shall be investigated in regions of high bond stress and where flexural cracking is expected at design loads.

(b) In unbonded construction subject to repetitive loads, special attention shall be given to the possibility of fatigue in the anchorages.

(c) The possibility of inclined diagonal tension cracks forming under repetitive loading at appreciably smaller stresses than under static loading shall be taken into account in the design.

2613—Composite construction

(a) General requirements for composite construction are given in Chapter 25.

2614—End regions

(a) End blocks shall be provided if necessary for end bearing or for distribution of concentrated prestressing forces safely from the anchorages to the cross section of the member.

(b) Reinforcement shall be provided in the anchorage zone to resist bursting and spalling forces induced by the concentrated loads of the prestressing steel. Points of abrupt change in section shall be adequately reinforced.

2615—Continuity

(a) For continuous girders and other statically indeterminate structures, moments, shears, and thrusts produced by external loads and prestressing shall be determined by elastic analysis. The effects of creep, shrinkage, axial deformation, restraint of attached structural elements, and foundation settlement shall be considered in the design.

(b) In the application of ultimate load factors where effects of dead and live loads are of opposite sign, the case of a dead load factor of unity shall be included in the investigation.

2616—Concrete cover

(a) The following minimum thicknesses of concrete cover shall be provided for prestressing steel, ducts and nonprestressed steel.

	Cover, in.
Concrete surfaces in contact with ground	2
Beams and girders	
Prestressing steel and main reinforcing bars	1½
Stirrups and ties	1
Slabs and joists exposed to weather	1
Slabs and joists not exposed to weather	¾

(b) In extremely corrosive atmosphere or other severe exposures, the amount of protection shall be suitably increased.

2617—Placement of prestressing steel

(a) All pretensioning steel and ducts for post-tensioning shall be accurately placed and adequately secured in position.

(b) The minimum clear spacing between pretensioning steel at each end of the member shall be four times the diameter of individual wires or three times the diameter of strands, but at least $1\frac{1}{3}$ times the maximum size of aggregate.

(c) Prestressing steel or ducts may be bundled together in the middle portion of the span, provided the requirements of (b) are satisfied.

(d) Ducts may be arranged closely together vertically when provision is made to prevent the steel, when tensioned, from breaking through the duct. Horizontal disposition of ducts shall allow proper placement of concrete.

(e) Where concentration of steel or ducts tends to create a weakened plane in the concrete cover, reinforcement shall be provided to control cracking.

(f) The inside diameter of ducts shall be at least ¼ in. larger than the diameter of the post-tensioning bar or large enough to produce an internal area at least twice the gross area of wires, strands, or cables.

2618—Concrete

(a) Suitable admixtures to obtain high early strength or to increase the workability of low-slump concrete may be used if known to have no injurious effects on the steel or the concrete. Calcium chloride or an admixture containing calcium chloride shall not be used. Sea water shall not be used.

(b) Concrete strength required at given ages shall be indicated on the plans. The strength at transfer shall be adequate for the requirements of the anchorages or of transfer through bond as well as meet camber or deflection requirements. For 7-wire strands, the minimum strength at transfer shall be 3000 psi for ⅜-in. strands and smaller, and 3500 psi for 7/16-in. and ½-in. strands.

2619—Grout

(a) Suitable admixtures, known to have no injurious effects on the steel or the concrete, may be used to increase workability and to reduce shrinkage. Calcium chloride shall not be used.

(b) Sand, if used, shall conform to "Specifications for Aggregate for Masonry Mortar" (ASTM C 144) except that gradation may be modified as necessary to obtain proper workability.

(c) Proportions of grouting materials shall be based on results of tests on fresh and hardened grout prior to beginning work. The water content shall be the minimum necessary for proper placement but in no case more than 5½ gal per sack. When permitted to stand until setting takes place, grout shall neither bleed nor segregate.

(d) Grout shall be mixed in a high-speed mechanical mixer and then passed through a strainer into pumping equipment which provides for recirculation.

(e) Just prior to grouting, the ducts shall be made free of water, dirt, and other foreign substances. The method of grouting shall be such as to ensure the complete filling of all voids between the prestressing steel and the duct and anchorage fittings.

(f) Temperature of members at the time of grouting must be above 50 F and at least this temperature shall be maintained for at least 48 hr.

2620—Steel tendons

(a) Prestressing steel shall be clean and free of excessive rust, scale, and pitting. A light oxide is permissible. Unbonded steel shall be permanently protected from corrosion.

(b) Burning and welding operations in the vicinity of prestressing steel shall be carefully performed, so that the prestressing steel shall not be subjected to excessive temperatures, welding sparks, or ground currents.

2621—Application and measurement of prestressing force

(a) Prestressing force shall be determined (1) by measuring tendon elongation and also (2) either by checking jack pressure on a recently calibrated gage or by the use of a recently calibrated dynamometer. The cause of any discrepancy which exceeds 5 percent shall be ascertained and corrected. Elongation requirements shall be taken from average load-elongation curves for the steel used.

(b) If several wires or strands are stretched simultaneously, provision must be made to induce approximately equal stress in each.

(c) Transfer of force from the bulkheads of the pretensioning bed to the concrete shall be carefully accomplished, by proper choice of cutting points and cutting sequence. Release of pretensioning may be effected by gradual means or by burning of tendons. Long lengths of exposed strands shall be cut near the member to minimize shock to the concrete.

(d) The total loss of prestress due to unreplaced broken tendons shall not exceed 2 percent of the total prestress.

(e) Where there is a considerable temperature differential between the concrete and the tendons, its effect shall be taken into account.

2622—Post-tensioning anchorages and couplers

(a) Anchorages, couplers, and splices for post-tensioned reinforcement shall develop the required ultimate capacity of the tendons without excessive slip. Couplers and splices shall be placed in areas approved by the Engineer and enclosed in housings long enough to permit the necessary movements. They shall not be used at points of sharp curvature.

(b) Anchorage and end fittings shall be permanently protected against corrosion.

2623—Formwork

(a) Forms for pretensioned members shall be constructed to permit movement of the member without damage during release of the prestressing force.

(b) Forms for post-tensioned members shall be constructed to minimize resistance to the shortening of the member. Deflection of members due to the prestressing force and deformation of falsework shall be considered in the design.

2624—Joints and bearings for precast members

(a) Design and detailing of the joints and bearings shall be based on the forces to be transmitted, and on the effects of dimensional changes due to shrinkage, elastic deformation, creep and temperature. Joints shall be detailed so as to allow sufficient tolerances \for manufacture and erection of the members.

(b) Bearings shall be detailed to provide for stress concentrations, rotations, and the possible development of horizontal forces by friction or other restraints.

APPENDIX A

DESIGN OF TWO-WAY SLABS

There are several satisfactory methods for designing two-way slabs. Although they may give somewhat different results in details, the resulting floors give reasonable over-all safety factors. Three methods which have been used extensively with satisfactory results are given in this appendix. These methods of design are to implement the provisions of Section 2002.

A2001—Method 1

Notation

L = length of clear span

L_1 = length of clear span in the direction normal to L

g = ratio of span between lines of inflection to L in the direction of span L, when span L only is loaded

g_1 = ratio of span between lines of inflection to L_1 in the direction of span L_1, when span L_1, only is loaded

r = gL / g_1L_1

w = total uniform load per sq ft

W = total uniform load between opposite supports on slab strip of any width or total slab load on beam when considered as one-way construction

x = ratio of distance from support to any section of slab or beam, to span L or L_1

B = bending moment coefficient for one-way construction

C = factor modifying bending moments prescribed for one-way construction for use in proportioning the slabs and beams in the direction of L of slabs supported on four sides

C_s = ratio of the shear at any section of a slab strip distant xL from the support to the total load W on the strip in direction of L

C_b = ratio of the shear at any section of a beam distant xL from the support to the total load W on the beam in the direction of L

W_1, C_1, C_{s1}, C_{b1}, are corresponding values of W, C, C_s, C_b, for slab strip or beam in direction of L_1.

(a) *Lines of inflection for determination of r* — The lines of inflection shall be determined by elastic analysis of the continuous structure in each direction, when only the span under consideration is loaded.

When the span L or L_1 is at least 2/3 and at most 3/2 of the adjacent continuous span or spans, the values of g or g_1 may be taken as 0.87 for exterior spans and 0.76 for interior spans (see Fig. 1).

For spans discontinuous at both ends, g or g_1 shall be taken as unity.

(b) *Bending moments and shear* — Bending moments shall be determined in each direction with the coefficients prescribed for one-way construction in Chapter 9 and modified by factor C or C_1 from Tables 1 or 2.

		In L direction	In L_1 direction
	Slab strip	$M = CBWL$	$M_1 = C_1 BW_1 L_1$
Bending moment	Beam	$M = (1-C)BWL$	$M_1 = (1-C_1)BW_1 L_1$

When the coefficients prescribed in Section 904(c) are used, the average value of Cw or $C_1 w$ for the two spans adjacent to a support shall be

METHOD I—TABLE I—SLABS

		$C.$ — $C_{.1}$					C / C_1
Upper figure = C				Values of x			
r	$r_1 = \dfrac{1}{r}$	0.0	0.1	0.2	0.3	0.4	
0.00		0.50	0.40	0.30	0.20	0.10	1.00
	∞	0.00	0.00	0.00	0.00	0.00	0.00
0.50		0.44	0.36	0.27	0.18	0.09	0.89
	2.00	0.06	0.03	0.02	0.00	0.00	0.06
0.55		0.43	0.33	0.23	0.15	0.07	0.79
	1.82	0.07	0.04	0.02	0.01	0.00	0.08
0.60		0.41	0.30	0.20	0.12	0.05	0.70
	1.67	0·09	0.05	0.03	0.01	0.00	0.10
0.65		0.39	0.28	0.18	0.10	0.04	0.64
	1.54	0.11	0.06	0.03	0.01	0.00	0.13
0.70		0.37	0.26	0.16	0.09	0.03	0.58
	1.43	0.13	0.08	0.04	0.01	0.00	0.15
0.80		0.33	0.22	0.13	0.07	0.02	0.48
	1.25	0.17	0.10	0.06	0.02	0.00	0.21
0.90		0.29	0.19	0.11	0.05	0.01	0.40
	1.11	0.21	0.13	0.07	0.03	0.01	0.27
1.00		0.25	0.16	0.09	0.04	0.01	0.33
	1.00	0.25	0.16	0.09	0.04	0.01	0.33
1.10		0.21	0.13	0.07	0.03	0.01	0.28
	0.91	0.29	0.19	0.11	0.05	0.01	0.39
1.20		0.18	0.11	0.06	0.02	0.00	0.23
	0.83	0.32	0.21	0.13	0.06	0.02	0.45
1.30		0.16	0.10	0.05	0.02	0.00	0.19
	0.77	0.34	0.23	0.14	0.07	0.03	0.51
1.40		0.13	0.08	0.04	0.02	0.00	0.16
	0.71	0.37	0.25	0.16	0.09	0.03	0.57
1.50		0.11	0.07	0.04	0.01	0.00	0.14
	0.67	0.39	0.27	0.17	0.10	0.04	0.61
1.60		0.10	0.06	0.03	0.01	0.00	0.12
	0.63	0.40	0.29	0.19	0.11	0.05	0.66
1.80		0.07	0.04	0.02	0.01	0.00	0.08
	0.55	0.43	0.33	0.23	0.15	0.07	0.79
2.00		0.06	0.03	0.02	0.00	0.00	0.06
	0.50	0.44	0.36	0.27	0.18	0.09	0.89
∞		0.00	0.00	0.00	0.00	0.00	0.00
	0.00	0.50	0.40	0.30	0.20	0.10	1.00

(Upper figure = C, C; Lower figure = $C_{.1}$, C_1)

used in determining the negative bending moment at the face of the support.

The shear at any section distant xL or xL_1 from supports shall be determined by modifying the total load on the slab strip or beam by the factors C_s, C_{s1}, C_b, or C_{b1} taken from Tables 1 or 2.

		In L direction	In L_1 direction
Shear	Slab strip	$V = C_s W$	$V_1 = C_{s1} W_1$
	Beam	$V = C_b W$	$V_1 = C_{b1} W_1$

METHOD I —TABLE 2—BEAMS

r	$r_1 = \dfrac{1}{r}$	0.0	0.1	0.2	0.3	0.4	$\dfrac{1-C}{1-C_1}$
0.00	∞	0.00 / 0.50	0.00 / 0.40	0.00 / 0.30	0.00 / 0.20	0.00 / 0.10	0.00 / 1.00
0.50	2.00	0.06 / 0.44	0.04 / 0.37	0.03 / 0.28	0.02 / 0.20	0.01 / 0.10	0.11 / 0.94
0.55	1.82	0.07 / 0.43	0.07 / 0.36	0.07 / 0.28	0.05 / 0.19	0.03 / 0.10	0.21 / 0.92
0.60	1.67	0.09 / 0.41	0.10 / 0.35	0.10 / 0.27	0.08 / 0.19	0.05 / 0.10	0.30 / 0.90
0.65	1.54	0.11 / 0.39	0.12 / 0.34	0.12 / 0.27	0.10 / 0.19	0.06 / 0.10	0.36 / 0.87
0.70	1.43	0.13 / 0.37	0.14 / 0.32	0.14 / 0.26	0.11 / 0.19	0.07 / 0.10	0.42 / 0.85
0.80	1.25	0.17 / 0.33	0.18 / 0.30	0.17 / 0.24	0.13 / 0.18	0.08 / 0.10	0.52 / 0.79
0.90	1.11	0.21 / 0.29	0.21 / 0.27	0.19 / 0.23	0.15 / 0.17	0.09 / 0.09	0.60 / 0.73
1.00	1.00	0.25 / 0.25	0.24 / 0.24	0.21 / 0.21	0.16 / 0.16	0.09 / 0.09	0.67 / 0.67
1.10	0.91	0.29 / 0.21	0.27 / 0.21	0.23 / 0.19	0.17 / 0.15	0.09 / 0.09	0.72 / 0.61
1.20	0.83	0.32 / 0.18	0.29 / 0.19	0.24 / 0.17	0.18 / 0.14	0.10 / 0.08	0.77 / 0.55
1.30	0.77	0.34 / 0.16	0.30 / 0.17	0.25 / 0.16	0.18 / 0.13	0.10 / 0.07	0.81 / 0.49
1.40	0.71	0.37 / 0.13	0.32 / 0.15	0.26 / 0.14	0.18 / 0.11	0.10 / 0.07	0.84 / 0.43
1.50	0.67	0.39 / 0.11	0.33 / 0.13	0.26 / 0.13	0.19 / 0.10	0.10 / 0.06	0.86 / 0.39
1.60	0.63	0.40 / 0.10	0.34 / 0.11	0.27 / 0.11	0.19 / 0.09	0.10 / 0.05	0.88 / 0.34
1.80	0.55	0.43 / 0.07	0.36 / 0.07	0.28 / 0.07	0.19 / 0.05	0.10 / 0.03	0.92 / 0.21
2.00	0.50	0.44 / 0.06	0.37 / 0.04	0.28 / 0.03	0.20 / 0.02	0.10 / 0.01	0.94 / 0.11
∞	0.00	0.50 / 0.00	0.40 / 0.00	0.30 / 0.00	0.20 / 0.00	0.10 / 0.00	1.00 / 0.00

Upper figure = C_b, Lower figure = C_{b1}. Values of x.

(c) *Arrangement of reinforcement*

1. In any panel, the area of reinforcement per unit width in the long direction shall be at least one-third that provided in the short direction.

2. The area of positive moment reinforcement adjacent to a continuous edge only and for a width not exceeding one-fourth of the shorter dimension of the panel may be reduced 25 percent.

3. At a noncontinuous edge the area of negative moment reinforcement per unit width shall be at least one-half of that required for maximum positive moment.

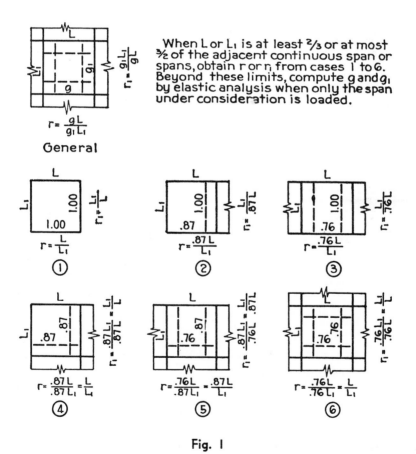

Fig. 1

A2002—Method 2

Notation

C = moment coefficient for two-way slabs as given in Table 1

m = ratio of short span to long span for two-way slabs

S = length of short span for two-way slabs. The span shall be considered as the center-to-center distance between supports or the clear span plus twice the thickness of slab, whichever value is the smaller.

w = total uniform load per sq ft

(a) *Limitations* — These recommendations are intended to apply to slabs (solid or ribbed), isolated or continuous, supported on all four sides by walls or beams, in either case built monolithically with the slabs.

A two-way slab shall be considered as consisting of strips in each direction as follows:

METHOD 2—TABLE I—MOMENT COEFFICIENTS

Moments	Short span						Long span, all values of m
	Values of m						
	1.0	0.9	0.8	0.7	0.6	0.5 and less	
Case 1—Interior panels Negative moment at—							
Continuous edge	0.033	0.040	0.048	0.055	0.063	0.083	0.033
Discontinuous edge	—	—	—	—	—	—	—
Positive moment at midspan	0.025	0.030	0.036	0.041	0.047	0.062	0.025
Case 2—One edge discontinuous Negative moment at—							
Continuous edge	0.041	0.048	0.055	0.062	0.069	0.085	0.041
Discontinuous edge	0.021	0.024	0.027	0.031	0.035	0.042	0.021
Positive moment at midspan	0.031	0.036	0.041	0.047	0.052	0.064	0.031
Case 3—Two edges discontinuous Negative moment at—							
Continuous edge	0.049	0.057	0.064	0.071	0.078	0.090	0.049
Discontinuous edge	0.025	0.028	0.032	0.036	0.039	0.045	0.025
Positive moment at midspan	0.037	0.043	0.048	0.054	0.059	0.068	0.037
Case 4—Three edges discontinuous Negative moment at—							
Continuous edge	0.058	0.066	0.074	0.082	0.090	0.098	0.058
Discontinuous edge	0.029	0.033	0.037	0.041	0.045	0.049	0.029
Positive moment at midspan	0.044	0.050	0.056	0.062	0.068	0.074	0.044
Case 5—Four edges discontinuous Negative moment at—							
Continuous edge	—	—	—	—	—	—	—
Discontinuous edge	0.033	0.038	0.043	0.047	0.053	0.055	0.033
Positive moment at midspan	0.050	0.057	0.064	0.072	0.080	0.083	0.050

A middle strip one-half panel in width, symmetrical about panel center line and extending through the panel in the direction in which moments are considered.

A column strip one-half panel in width, occupying the two quarter-panel areas outside the middle strip.

Where the ratio of short to long span is less than 0.5, the middle strip in the short direction shall be considered as having a width equal to the difference between the long and short span, the remaining area representing the two column strips.

The critical sections for moment calculations are referred to as principal design sections and are located as follows:

For negative moment, along the edges of the panel at the faces of the supporting beams.

For positive moment, along the center lines of the panels.

(b) *Bending moments* — The bending moments for the middle strips shall be computed from the formula

$$M = CwS^2$$

The average moments per foot of width in the column strip shall be two-thirds of the corresponding moments in the middle strip. In determining the spacing of the reinforcement in the column strip, the moment may be assumed to vary from a maximum at the edge of the middle strip to a minimum at the edge of the panel.

Where the negative moment on one side of a support is less than 80 percent of that on the other side, two-thirds of the difference shall be distributed in proportion to the relative stiffnesses of the slabs.

(c) *Shear* — The shear stresses in the slab may be computed on the assumption that the load is distributed to the supports in accordance with (d).

(d) *Supporting beams* — The loads on the supporting beams for a two-way rectangular panel may be assumed as the load within the tributary areas of the panel bounded by the intersection of 45-deg lines from the corners with the median line of the panel parallel to the long side.

The bending moments may be determined approximately by using an equivalent uniform load per lineal foot of beam for each panel supported as follows:

$$\text{For the short span:} \quad \frac{wS}{3}$$

$$\text{For the long span:} \quad \frac{wS}{3} \cdot \frac{(3 - m^2)}{2}$$

A2003—Method 3

Notation

A = length of clear span in short direction

B = length of clear span in long direction

C = moment coefficients for two-way slabs as given in Tables 1, 2, and 3. Coefficients have identifying indexes, such as $C_{A\ neg}$, $C_{B\ neg}$, $C_{A\ DL}$, $C_{B\ DL}$, $C_{A\ LL}$, $C_{B\ LL}$.

m = ratio of short span to long span for two-way slabs

w = uniform load per sq ft. For negative moments and shears, w is the total dead load plus live load for use in Table 1. For positive moments, w is to be separated into dead and live loads for use in Tables 2 and 3.

w_A, w_B = percentages of load w in A and B directions according to Table 4. These shall be used for computations of shear and for loadings on supports.

(a) *Limitations* — A two-way slab shall be considered as consisting of strips in each direction as follows:

A middle strip one-half panel in width, symmetrical about panel center line and extending through the panel in the direction in which moments are considered.

A column strip one-half panel in width, occupying the two quarter-panel areas outside the middle strip.

Where the ratio of short to long span is less than 0.5, the slab shall be considered as a one-way slab and is to be designed in accordance with Chapter 9 except that negative reinforcement, as required for a ratio of 0.5, shall be provided along the short edge.

At discontinuous edges, a negative moment one-third ($\frac{1}{3}$) of the postive moment is to be used.

Critical sections for moment calculations are located as follows:

For negative moment along the edges of the panel at the faces of the supports.

For positive moment, along the center lines of the panels.

(b) *Bending moments* — The bending moments for the middle strips shall be computed by the use of Tables 1, 2, and 3 from:

$$M_A = CwA^2 \quad \text{and} \quad M_B = CwB^2$$

The bending moments in the column strips shall be gradually reduced from the full value M_A and M_B from the edge of the middle strip to one-third ($\frac{1}{3}$) of these values at the edge of the panel.

Where the negative moment on one side of a support is less than 80 percent of that on the other side, the difference shall be distributed in proportion to the relative stiffnesses of the slabs.

(c) *Shear* — The shear stresses in the slab may be computed on the assumption that the load is distributed to the supports in accordance with Table 4.

(d) *Supporting beams* — The loads on the supporting beams for a two-way rectangular panel shall be computed using Table 4 for the percentages of loads in "A" and "B" directions. In no case shall the load on the beam along the short edge be less than that of an area

METHOD 3—TABLE 1—COEFFICIENTS FOR NEGATIVE MOMENTS IN SLABS*

$$M_{A\,neg} = C_{A\,neg} \times w \times A^2$$
$$M_{B\,neg} = C_{B\,neg} \times w \times B^2$$

where w = total uniform dead plus live load

Ratio $m = \dfrac{A}{B}$		Case 1	Case 2	Case 3	Case 4	Case 5	Case 6	Case 7	Case 8	Case 9
1.00	$C_{A\,neg}$		0.045		0.050	0.075	0.071		0.033	0.061
	$C_{B\,neg}$		0.045	0.076	0.050			0.071	0.061	0.033
0.95	$C_{A\,neg}$		0.050		0.055	0.079	0.075		0.038	0.065
	$C_{B\,neg}$		0.041	0.072	0.045			0.067	0.056	0.029
0.90	$C_{A\,neg}$		0.055		0.060	0.080	0.079		0.043	0.068
	$C_{B\,neg}$		0.037	0.070	0.040			0.062	0.052	0.025
0.85	$C_{A\,neg}$		0.060		0.066	0.082	0.083		0.049	0.072
	$C_{B\,neg}$		0.031	0.065	0.034			0.057	0.046	0.021
0.80	$C_{A\,neg}$		0.065		0.071	0.083	0.086		0.055	0.075
	$C_{B\,neg}$		0.027	0.061	0.029			0.051	0.041	0.017
0.75	$C_{A\,neg}$		0.069		0.076	0.085	0.088		0.061	0.078
	$C_{B\,neg}$		0.022	0.056	0.024			0.044	0.036	0.014
0.70	$C_{A\,neg}$		0.074		0.081	0.086	0.091		0.068	0.081
	$C_{B\,neg}$		0.017	0.050	0.019			0.038	0.029	0.011
0.65	$C_{A\,neg}$		0.077		0.085	0.087	0.093		0.074	0.083
	$C_{B\,neg}$		0.014	0.043	0.015			0.031	0.024	0.008
0.60	$C_{A\,neg}$		0.081		0.089	0.088	0.095		0.080	0.085
	$C_{B\,neg}$		0.010	0.035	0.011			0.024	0.018	0.006
0.55	$C_{A\,neg}$		0.084		0.092	0.089	0.096		0.085	0.086
	$C_{B\,neg}$		0.007	0.028	0.008			0.019	0.014	0.005
0.50	$C_{A\,neg}$		0.086		0.094	0.090	0.097		0.089	0.088
	$C_{B\,neg}$		0.006	0.022	0.006			0.014	0.010	0.003

*A cross-hatched edge indicates that the slab continues across or is fixed at the support; an unmarked edge indicates a support at which torsional resistance is negligible.

bounded by the intersection of 45-deg lines from the corners. The equivalent uniformly distributed load per linear foot on this short beam is

$$\frac{wA}{3}$$

METHOD 3—TABLE 2—COEFFICIENTS FOR DEAD LOAD POSITIVE MOMENTS IN SLABS*

$$M_{A\ pos\ DL} = C_{A\ DL} \times w \times A^2$$
$$M_{B\ pos\ DL} = C_{B\ DL} \times w \times B^2$$

where w = total uniform dead load

Ratio $m = \dfrac{A}{B}$		Case 1	Case 2	Case 3	Case 4	Case 5	Case 6	Case 7	Case 8	Case 9
1.00	$C_{A\ DL}$	0.036	0.018	0.018	0.027	0.027	0.033	0.027	0.020	0.023
	$C_{B\ DL}$	0.036	0.018	0.027	0.027	0.018	0.027	0.033	0.023	0.020
0.95	$C_{A\ DL}$	0.040	0.020	0.021	0.030	0.028	0.036	0.031	0.022	0.024
	$C_{B\ DL}$	0.033	0.016	0.025	0.024	0.015	0.024	0.031	0.021	0.017
0.90	$C_{A\ DL}$	0.045	0.022	0.025	0.033	0.029	0.039	0.035	0.025	0.026
	$C_{B\ DL}$	0.029	0.014	0.024	0.022	0.013	0.021	0.028	0.019	0.015
0.85	$C_{A\ DL}$	0.050	0.024	0.029	0.036	0.031	0.042	0.040	0.029	0.028
	$C_{B\ DL}$	0.026	0.012	0.022	0.019	0.011	0.017	0.025	0.017	0.013
0.80	$C_{A\ DL}$	0.056	0.026	0.034	0.039	0.032	0.045	0.045	0.032	0.029
	$C_{B\ DL}$	0.023	0.011	0.020	0.016	0.009	0.015	0.022	0.015	0.010
0.75	$C_{A\ DL}$	0.061	0.028	0.040	0.043	0.033	0.048	0.051	0.036	0.031
	$C_{B\ DL}$	0.019	0.009	0.018	0.013	0.007	0.012	0.020	0.013	0.007
0.70	$C_{A\ DL}$	0.068	0.030	0.046	0.046	0.035	0.051	0.058	0.040	0.033
	$C_{B\ DL}$	0.016	0.007	0.016	0.011	0.005	0.009	0.017	0.011	0.006
0.65	$C_{A\ DL}$	0.074	0.032	0.054	0.050	0.036	0.054	0.065	0.044	0.034
	$C_{B\ DL}$	0.013	0.006	0.014	0.009	0.004	0.007	0.014	0.009	0.005
0.60	$C_{A\ DL}$	0.081	0.034	0.062	0.053	0.037	0.056	0.073	0.048	0.036
	$C_{B\ DL}$	0.010	0.004	0.011	0.007	0.003	0.006	0.012	0.007	0.004
0.55	$C_{A\ DL}$	0.088	0.035	0.071	0.056	0.038	0.058	0.081	0.052	0.037
	$C_{B\ DL}$	0.008	0.003	0.009	0.005	0.002	0.004	0.009	0.005	0.003
0.50	$C_{A\ DL}$	0.095	0.037	0.080	0.059	0.039	0.061	0.089	0.056	0.038
	$C_{B\ DL}$	0.006	0.002	0.007	0.004	0.001	0.003	0.007	0.004	0.002

*A cross-hatched edge indicates that the slab continues across or is fixed at the support; an unmarked edge indicates a support at which torsional resistance is negligible.

METHOD 3—TABLE 3—COEFFICIENTS FOR LIVE LOAD POSITIVE MOMENTS IN SLABS*

$$M_{A\ pos\ LL} = C_{A\ LL} \times w \times A^2$$
$$M_{B\ pos\ LL} = C_{B\ LL} \times w \times B^2$$

where w = total uniform live load

Ratio $m = \dfrac{A}{B}$		Case 1	Case 2	Case 3	Case 4	Case 5	Case 6	Case 7	Case 8	Case 9
1.00	$C_{A\ LL}$	0.036	0.027	0.027	0.032	0.032	0.035	0.032	0.028	0.030
	$C_{B\ LL}$	0.036	0.027	0.032	0.032	0.027	0.032	0.035	0.030	0.028
0.95	$C_{A\ LL}$	0.040	0.030	0.031	0.035	0.034	0.038	0.036	0.031	0.032
	$C_{B\ LL}$	0.033	0.025	0.029	0.029	0.024	0.029	0.032	0.027	0.025
0.90	$C_{A\ LL}$	0.045	0.034	0.035	0.039	0.037	0.042	0.040	0.035	0.036
	$C_{B\ LL}$	0.029	0.022	0.027	0.026	0.021	0.025	0.029	0.024	0.022
0.85	$C_{A\ LL}$	0.050	0.037	0.040	0.043	0.041	0.046	0.045	0.040	0.039
	$C_{B\ LL}$	0.026	0.019	0.024	0.023	0.019	0.022	0.026	0.022	0.020
0.80	$C_{A\ LL}$	0.056	0.041	0.045	0.048	0.044	0.051	0.051	0.044	0.042
	$C_{B\ LL}$	0.023	0.017	0.022	0.020	0.016	0.019	0.023	0.019	0.017
0.75	$C_{A\ LL}$	0.061	0.045	0.051	0.052	0.047	0.055	0.056	0.049	0.046
	$C_{B\ LL}$	0.019	0.014	0.019	0.016	0.013	0.016	0.020	0.016	0.013
0.70	$C_{A\ LL}$	0.068	0.049	0.057	0.057	0.051	0.060	0.063	0.054	0.050
	$C_{B\ LL}$	0.016	0.012	0.016	0.014	0.011	0.013	0.017	0.014	0.011
0.65	$C_{A\ LL}$	0.074	0.053	0.064	0.062	0.055	0.064	0.070	0.059	0.054
	$C_{B\ LL}$	0.013	0.010	0.014	0.011	0.009	0.010	0.014	0.011	0.009
0.60	$C_{A'LL}$	0.081	0.058	0.071	0.067	0.059	0.068	0.077	0.065	0.059
	$C_{B\ LL}$	0.010	0.007	0.011	0.009	0.007	0.008	0.011	0.009	0.007
0.55	$C_{A\ LL}$	0.088	0.062	0.080	0.072	0.063	0.073	0.085	0.070	0.063
	$C_{B\ LL}$	0.008	0.006	0.009	0.007	0.005	0.006	0.009	0.007	0.006
0.50	$C_{A\ LL}$	0.095	0.066	0.088	0.077	0.067	0.078	0.092	0.076	0.067
	$C_{B\ LL}$	0.006	0.004	0.007	0.005	0.004	0.005	0.007	0.005	0.004

*A cross-hatched edge indicates that the slab continues across or is fixed at the support; an unmarked edge indicates a support at which torsional resistance is negligible.

METHOD 3—TABLE 4—RATIO OF LOAD w IN A and B DIRECTIONS FOR SHEAR IN SLAB AND LOAD ON SUPPORTS*

Ratio $m = \dfrac{A}{B}$		Case 1	Case 2	Case 3	Case 4	Case 5	Case 6	Case 7	Case 8	Case 9
1.00	W_A	0.50	0.50	0.17	0.50	0.83	0.71	0.29	0.33	0.67
	W_B	0.50	0.50	0.83	0.50	0.17	0.29	0.71	0.67	0.33
0.95	W_A	0.55	0.55	0.20	0.55	0.86	0.75	0.33	0.38	0.71
	W_B	0.45	0.45	0.80	0.45	0.14	0.25	0.67	0.62	0.29
0.90	W_A	0.60	0.60	0.23	0.60	0.88	0.79	0.38	0.43	0.75
	W_B	0.40	0.40	0.77	0.40	0.12	0.21	0.62	0.57	0.25
0.85	W_A	0.66	0.66	0.28	0.66	0.90	0.83	0.43	0.49	0.79
	W_B	0.34	0.34	0.72	0.34	0.10	0.17	0.57	0.51	0.21
0.80	W_A	0.71	0.71	0.33	0.71	0.92	0.86	0.49	0.55	0.83
	W_B	0.29	0.29	0.67	0.29	0.08	0.14	0.51	0.45	0.17
0.75	W_A	0.76	0.76	0.39	0.76	0.94	0.88	0.56	0.61	0.86
	W_B	0.24	0.24	0.61	0.24	0.06	0.12	0.44	0.39	0.14
0.70	W_A	0.81	0.81	0.45	0.81	0.95	0.91	0.62	0.68	0.89
	W_B	0.19	0.19	0.55	0.19	0.05	0.09	0.38	0.32	0.11
0.65	W_A	0.85	0.85	0.53	0.85	0.96	0.93	0.69	0.74	0.92
	W_B	0.15	0.15	0.47	0.15	0.04	0.07	0.31	0.26	0.08
0.60	W_A	0.89	0.89	0.61	0.89	0.97	0.95	0.76	0.80	0.94
	W_B	0.11	0.11	0.39	0.11	0.03	0.05	0.24	0.20	0.06
0.55	W_A	0.92	0.92	0.69	0.92	0.98	0.96	0.81	0.85	0.95
	W_B	0.08	0.08	0.31	0.08	0.02	0.04	0.19	0.15	0.05
0.50	W_A	0.94	0.94	0.76	0.94	0.99	0.97	0.86	0.89	0.97
	W_B	0.06	0.06	0.24	0.06	0.01	0.03	0.14	0.11	0.03

*A cross-hatched edge indicates that the slab continues across or is fixed at the support; an unmarked edge indicates a support at which torsional resistance is negligible.

METRIC EQUIVALENTS

The following is not part of this standard, but metric equivalents of all the dimensional values in this code and metric conversions of non-homogeneous equations are given below for the convenience of users.

Note that concrete strengths are based on standard 6 x 12-in. (15 x 30-cm) cylinders and steel strengths upon the minimum specified yield strength.

METRIC EQUIVALENTS OF DIMENSIONAL UNITS

Length

English	Metric
1 in.	2.54 cm
0.01 in.	0.25 mm
0.015 in.	0.38 mm
0.04 in.	1.02 mm
¼ in.	6.35 mm
⅜ in.	9.52 mm
½ in.	1.27 cm
¾ in.	1.90 cm
1⅜ in.	3.49 cm
1½ in.	3.81 cm
2 in.	5.08 cm
2½ in.	6.35 cm
3 in.	7.62 cm
3½ in.	8.89 cm
4 in.	10.16 cm
5 in.	12.70 cm
6 in.	15.24 cm
8 in.	20.32 cm
10 in.	25.40 cm
12 in.	30.5 cm
18 in.	45.7 cm
20 in.	50.8 cm
24 in.	61.0 cm
30 in.	76.2 cm
1 ft	0.3048 m
3 ft	0.914 m
10 ft	3.05 m
12 ft	3.66 m
12 ft 6 in.	3.81 m
125 ft	38.1 m

Weight*

1 lb per cu ft	0.016 t per cu m
70 lb per cu ft	1.121 t per cu m
90 lb per cu ft	1.442 t per cu m
145 lb per cu ft	2.323 t per cu m
155 lb per cu ft	2.482 t per cu m

*t = 1000 kg

Stress (pressure)

English	Metric
1 psi	0.07031 kg per sq cm
150 psi	10.5 kg per sq cm
200 psi	14.1 kg per sq cm
350 psi	24.6 kg per sq cm
500 psi	35.2 kg per sq cm
2,500 psi	176 kg per sq cm
3,000 psi	211 kg per sq cm
3,500 psi	246 kg per sq cm
4,000 psi	281 kg per sq cm
5,000 psi	352 kg per sq cm
10,000 psi	703 kg per sq cm
16,000 psi	1,125 kg per sq cm
17,000 psi	1,195 kg per sq cm
18,000 psi	1,266 kg per sq cm
19,000 psi	1,336 kg per sq cm
20,000 psi	1,406 kg per sq cm
24,000 psi	1,687 kg per sq cm
30,000 psi	2,109 kg per sq cm
33,000 psi	2,320 kg per sq cm
40,000 psi	2,812 kg per sq cm
50,000 psi	3,516 kg per sq cm
60,000 psi	4,219 kg per sq cm
75,000 psi	5,273 kg per sq cm
87,000 psi	6,117 kg per sq cm
145,000 psi	10,195 kg per sq cm
29,000,000 psi	2,039,000 kg per sq cm

Temperature

40 F	4 C
50 F	10 C
100 F	38 C
150 F	65 C

Cylinder

6 x 12 in.   15 x 30 cm

Shear and tension

$\sqrt{f_c'}$ psi $= 0.265 \sqrt{f_c'}$ kg per sq cm

Moment of inertia

1 in.$^4 = 41.62$ cm^4

Wire size

#10 Wire	3.43 mm diameter
#4 Wire	5.72 mm diameter

Bar size and area

Bar Size	Diameter, mm	Area, sq cm
#2	6.35	0.32
#3	9.52	0.71
#4	12.70	1.29
#5	15.88	2.00
#6	19.05	2.84
#7	22.22	3.87
#8	25.40	5.10
#9	28.65	6.45
#10	32.26	8.19
#11	35.81	10.06
#14S	43.00	14.52
#18S	57.33	25.81

METRIC CONVERSIONS OF NONHOMOGENEOUS EQUATIONS

Eq. (12-2):
$$v_c = 0.265 \sqrt{f_c'} + 91.4 \; \frac{p_w V d}{M}$$

Eq. (12-4):
$$v_c = 0.464 \sqrt{f_c'} \, (1 + 0.057 \, N/A_g)$$

Eq. (12-10):
$$v_c = 0.15 \, F_{sp} \sqrt{f_c'} + 91.4 \; \frac{p_w V d}{M}$$

Eq. (14-5):
$$f_r' = 1195 - 0.0342 \; \frac{h^2}{K_c^2}$$

Eq. (16-2)
$$P_b = 0.85 \, k_1 \, \frac{f_c'}{f_y} \, \frac{6117}{6117 + f_y}$$

Eq. (16-4):
$$(p - p') \geqq 0.85 \, k_1 \, \frac{f_c'}{f_y} \frac{d'}{d} \, \frac{6117}{6117 - f_y}$$

Eq. (17-2):
$$v_c = \phi \left(0.504 \sqrt{f_c'} + \frac{176 \; p_w V d}{M} \right)$$

Eq. (17-9):
$$v_c = \phi \left(0.28 \, F_{sp} \sqrt{f_c'} + 176 \frac{p_w V d}{M} \right)$$

Eq. (21-1): $I_c = \dfrac{0.083 \, t^3 H}{0.5 + \dfrac{w_D}{w_L}}$ (t in cm; H in cm; I_c in cm^4; w_D and w_L in kg per sq m)

Eq. (21-4):
$$t_1 = 0.106L \left(1 - \frac{2c}{3L} \right) \sqrt{\frac{w'}{f_c'/141}} + 3.81$$

Eq. (21-5):
$$t_2 = 0.091L \left(1 - \frac{2c}{3L} \right) \sqrt{\frac{w'}{f_c'/141}} + 2.54$$

L in m, w' in kg per sq m, f_c' in kg per sq cm, t in cm

Eq. (26-12):
$$V_{ci} = 0.159 b'd \sqrt{f_c'} + \frac{M_{cr}}{\frac{M}{V} - \frac{d}{2}} + V_d$$

but not less than $0.45\ b'd \sqrt{f_c'}$

where $M_{cr} = \dfrac{I}{y}\ (1.59 \sqrt{f_c'} + f_{pe} - f_d)$

Eq. (26-13): $V_{cw} = b'd\ (0.93 \sqrt{f_c'} + 0.3\ f_{pc}) + V_p$

Eq. (26-13A):

$$V_{cw} = b'd\ \left[\ 0.5\ F_{sp} \sqrt{f_c'} + f_{pc}\left(\ 0.2 + \frac{F_{sp}}{17.8}\ \right)\right]\ + V_p$$

METRIC EQUIVALENTS OF LIMITING VALUES MENTIONED IN TEXT

Sec. 909(c): $pf_y \le 500\ \text{psi} \le 35.2\ \text{kg per sq cm}$

Sec. 1102(a): $E_c = w^{1.5}\ 4270 \sqrt{f_c'}$

Sec. 1201(c): $1.1 \sqrt{f_c'}\ \text{psi}\ = 0.292 \sqrt{f_c'}\ \text{kg per sq cm}$

Sec. 1201(d): $1.75 \sqrt{f_c'}\ \text{psi}\ = 0.464 \sqrt{f_c'}\ \text{kg per sq cm}$

Sec. 1205(b): $5 \sqrt{f_c'}\ \text{psi}\ = 1.33 \sqrt{f_c'}\ \text{kg per sq cm}$

Sec. 1206(a): $3 \sqrt{f_c'}\ \text{psi}\ = 0.795 \sqrt{f_c'}\ \text{kg per sq cm}$

Sec. 1301(c)1:

$$\frac{3.4 \sqrt{f_c'}}{D}\ \text{nor 350 psi} = \frac{2.29 \sqrt{f_c'}}{D}\ \text{nor 24.6 kg per sq cm}$$

$$\frac{4.8 \sqrt{f_c'}}{D}\ \text{nor 500 psi} = \frac{3.23 \sqrt{f_c'}}{D}\ \text{nor 35.2 kg per sq cm}$$

Sec. 1301(c)2: $2.1 \sqrt{f_c'}\ \text{psi} = 0.556 \sqrt{f_c'}\ \text{kg per sq cm}$

$3 \sqrt{f_c'}\ \text{psi} = 0.795 \sqrt{f_c'}\ \text{kg per sq cm}$

Sec. 1301(c)3:

$6.5 \sqrt{f_c'}\ \text{nor 400 psi} = 1.72 \sqrt{f_c'}\ \text{nor 28.1 kg per sq cm}$

$160\ \text{psi} = 11.24\ \text{kg per sq cm}$

Sec. 1701(c): $2 \phi \sqrt{f_c'}\ \text{psi} = 0.53\ \phi \sqrt{f_c'}\ \text{kg per sq cm}$

Sec. 1701(d): $3.5\ \phi \sqrt{f_c'}\ \text{psi} = 0.93\ \phi \sqrt{f_c'}\ \text{kg per sq cm}$

Sec. 1701(e):
$$3.5 \, \phi \sqrt{f_c'} \, (1 + 0.002 \; N/A_g) \text{ psi} =$$
$$0.93 \, \phi \sqrt{f_c'} \, (1 + 0.0284 \; N/A_g) \text{ kg per sq cm}$$

Sec. 1704(b):
$$3 \, \phi b d \sqrt{f_c'} \text{ psi} = 0.795 \, \phi \, bd \sqrt{f_c'} \text{ kg per sq cm}$$

Sec. 1705(b):
$$10\phi\sqrt{f_c'} \text{ psi} = 2.65\phi\sqrt{f_c'} \text{ kg per sq cm}$$

Sec. 1707(c):
$$4\phi\sqrt{f_c'} \text{ psi} = 1.06\phi\sqrt{f_c'} \text{ kg per sq cm}$$
$$6\phi\sqrt{f_c'} \text{ psi} = 1.59\phi\sqrt{f_c'} \text{ kg per sq cm}$$

Sec. 1708(b):
$$F_{sp} = 4 \; \frac{\text{psi}}{\sqrt{\text{psi}}} = 1.06 \; \frac{\text{kg per sq cm}}{\sqrt{\text{kg per sq cm}}}$$

Sec. 1801(c)1:

$$\frac{6.7\sqrt{f_c'}}{D} \text{ nor 560 psi} = \frac{4.51\sqrt{f_c'}}{D} \text{ nor 39.4 kg per sq cm}$$

$$\frac{9.5\sqrt{f_c'}}{D} \text{ nor 800 psi} = \frac{6.39\sqrt{f_c'}}{D} \text{ nor 56.2 kg per sq cm}$$

Sec. 1801(c)2:
$$4.2\sqrt{f_c'} \text{ psi} = 1.11 \sqrt{f_c'} \text{ kg per sq cm}$$
$$6 \sqrt{f_c'} \text{ psi} = 1.59 \sqrt{f_c'} \text{ kg per sq cm}$$

Sec. 1801(c)3: $13\sqrt{f_c'}$ nor 800 psi = $3.44\sqrt{f_c'}$ nor 56.2 kg per sq cm

Sec. 1900:
$$\frac{d \, (87,000)}{87,000 + f_y} \text{ in.} = \frac{d \, (6117)}{6117 + f_y} \text{ cm}$$

Sec. 2307(b):
$$1.6 \sqrt{f_c'} \text{ psi} = 0.424 \sqrt{f_c'} \text{ kg per sq cm}$$
$$3.2 \sqrt{f_c'} \text{ psi} = 0.848 \sqrt{f_c'} \text{ kg per sq cm}$$

Sec. 2605(a)2:
$$3 \sqrt{f_{ci}'} \text{ psi} = 0.795 \sqrt{f_{ci}'} \text{ kg per sq cm}$$

Sec. 2605(b):
$$6 \sqrt{f_c'} \text{ psi} = 1.59 \sqrt{f_c'} \text{ kg per sq cm}$$

Sec. 2609(c):
$$7.5 \sqrt{f_c'} \text{ psi} = 1.99 \sqrt{f_c'} \text{ kg per sq cm}$$

Sec. 2619(c):
$$5\tfrac{1}{2} \text{ gal. per sack} = 0.49 \text{ kg per kg}$$

The units above are in the technical (MKS) system. To convert to the Système International, use the following equations:

$$1 \text{ kilogram (kg)} \times 0.0102 = 1 \text{ Newton (N)}$$
$$1 \text{ kilogram (kg)} \times 1.02 = 1 \text{ decanewton (da N)}$$
$$1 \text{ kg per sq sm} \times 0.0102 = 1 \text{ bar}$$

TABLE 1002(a)—ALLOWABLE STRESSES IN CONCRETE (METRIC)

Description		Allowable stresses, kg per sq cm				
		For any strength of concrete in accordance with Section 502	For strength of concrete shown below			
			$f_c' =$ 176 kg per sq cm	$f_c' =$ 211 kg per sq cm	$f_c' =$ 281 kg per sq cm	$f_c' =$ 352 kg per sq cm
Modulus of elasticity ratio: n		$\dfrac{2,039,000}{w^{1.5}4\ 270\sqrt{f_c'}}$				
For concrete weighing 2.323 t per cu m (see Section 1102)	n	$\stackrel{\backsim}{}\dfrac{478}{w^{1.5}\sqrt{f_c'}}$	10	9	8	7
Flexure: f_c						
Extreme fiber stress in compression	f_c	$0.45f_c'$	79	94.8	126.5	158.2
Extreme fiber stress in tension in plain concrete footings and walls	f_c	$0.424\sqrt{f_c'}$	5.63	6.16	7.11	7.95
Shear: v (as a measure of diagonal tension at a distance d from the face of the support)						
Beams with no web reinforcement*	v_c	$0.292\sqrt{f_c'}$	3.87*	4.24*	4.89*	5.49*
Joists with no web reinforcement	v_c	$0.318\sqrt{f_c'}$	4 22	4.62	5.33	5.96
Members with vertical or inclined web reinforcement or properly combined bent bars and vertical stirrups	v	$1.325\sqrt{f_c'}$	17.6	19.3	22.2	24.9
Slabs and footings (peripheral shear, Section 1207) *	v_c	$0.530\sqrt{f_c'}$	7.03*	7.73*	8.84*	9.92*
Bearing: f_c						
On full area		$0.25f_c'$	44	52.7	70.3	88.0
On one-third area or less†		$0.375f_c'$	66	79.1	105.5	132.0

*For shear values for lightweight aggregate concrete see Section 1208.
†This increase shall be permitted only when the least distance between the edges of the loaded and unloaded areas is a minimum of one-fourth of the parallel side dimension of the loaded area. The allowable bearing stress on a reasonably concentric area greater than one-third but less than the full area shall be interpolated between the values given.

INDEX

Items applying to ultimate strength design only are indicated by **bold face** page numbers (**1234**). Items applying to working stress design only are indicated by *italic* page numbers (*1234*). Items of a more general nature are indicated by page numbers in normal weight type (1234).